Advances in
THE STUDY OF BEHAVIOR
VOLUME 4

Contributors to This Volume

R. J. ANDREW

KLAUS IMMELMANN

ELIANE NOIROT

T. E. ROWELL

SARA J. SHETTLEWORTH

Advances in
THE STUDY OF
BEHAVIOR

Edited by

Daniel S. Lehrman
Institute of Animal Behavior
Rutgers University
Newark, New Jersey

Robert A. Hinde
Sub-Department of Animal Behaviour
Cambridge University
Cambridge, England

Evelyn Shaw
California Academy of Sciences
Golden Gate Park
San Francisco, California

——————————— **VOLUME 4** ———————————

ACADEMIC PRESS   New York and London, 1972

591.51
A 244
v. 4

ACADEMIC PRESS, INC.
111 Fifth Avenue, New York, New York 10003

United Kingdom Edition published by
ACADEMIC PRESS, INC. (LONDON) LTD.
24/28 Oval Road, London NW1

LIBRARY OF CONGRESS CATALOG CARD NUMBER: 64-8031

PRINTED IN THE UNITED STATES OF AMERICA

The publishers regret to announce the untimely death of

Professor Daniel S. Lehrman

as this volume was in the final stages of preparation.

Contents

Constraints on Learning
SARA J. SHETTLEWORTH

Female Reproduction Cycles and Social Behavior in Primates
T. E. ROWELL

The Onset of Maternal Behavior in Rats, Hamsters,
and Mice: A Selective Review
ELIANE NOIROT

Sexual and Other Long-Term Aspects of Imprinting in
Birds and Other Species
KLAUS IMMELMANN

Recognition Processes and Behavior, with Special Reference
to Effects of Testosterone on Persistence
R. J. ANDREW

List of Contributors

R. J. ANDREW, *Ethology and Neurophysiology Group, School of Biological Sciences, University of Sussex, Brighton, Sussex, England*

KLAUS IMMELMANN, *Zoologisches Institut der Technischen Universität, Braunschweig, Germany*

ELIANE NOIROT, *Institut de Biometrie Humaine et d'Orientation Professionnelle, Université d'Aix-Marseille, Marseille, France*

T. E. ROWELL, *Zoology Department, University of California, Berkeley, California*

SARA J. SHETTLEWORTH, *Department of Psychology, University of Toronto, Toronto, Canada*

Contents of Previous Volumes

Constraints on Learning

SARA J. SHETTLEWORTH

DEPARTMENT OF PSYCHOLOGY
UNIVERSITY OF TORONTO
TORONTO, CANADA

I. INTRODUCTION

When Willard Stanton Small reported one of the first studies of rats learning mazes, he pointed out that he chose the maze because of its similarity to the rat's natural environment. It seemed to him that

> . . . the experiments must conform to the psychobiological character of an animal if sane results are to be obtained. . . . The difficulty of two tasks . . . may be identical, yet the problem involved in the one may be so different from that in the other, so remote from the animal's experience and life habits as to be absolutely outside his capabilities. (Small, 1901, p. 206)

1

A few years later, Asa A. Schaeffer used a similar notion to account for the fact that frogs could learn to avoid touching unpalatable hairy caterpillars in a few trials, while they took up to a hundred trials to learn a maze.

It is . . . highly advantageous to frogs to learn rapidly to avoid disagreeable foods . . . (but) there could be little advantage in the ability to learn rapidly to thread a simple labyrinth. From the standpoint of natural history, such a capacity could hardly be considered as having life and death value; it would be merely an ornamental psychic quality. (Schaeffer, 1911, p. 326)

Until very recently such views have had little systematic place in the study of learning by psychologists. Rather, their work has been directed toward discovering general properties of learning which, it has been assumed, may be revealed equally well by using any species and any combination of stimulus, response, and reinforcer. Experimental findings have tended to bear out this assumption. For example, Pavlov's (1927) dogs could be conditioned to salivate to any of a wide variety of visual, auditory, and tactile stimuli, and, in instrumental learning experiments, members of a variety of species do perform similarly on schedules of intermittent reinforcement (Skinner, 1956). Thus, in contrast to the passages by Small and Schaeffer, we find statements that animals can learn virtually anything, like this one from a recent article on the use of operant conditioning methods to assess motivation.

We arbitrarily choose almost any act from the animal's repertoire and reinforce it with food, water, or whatever else the animal will work to obtain. Although typically we teach a rat to press a bar or a pigeon to peck a key to obtain a pellet of food, we can readily train either to dance around the cage if we so choose. We usually use a light to signal the delivery of a pellet but we can use a tone or a buzzer or any other stimulus the animal can detect . . . . The same act can be used for any reinforcement . . . . In effect, in any operant situation, the stimulus, the response, and the reinforcement are completely arbitrary and interchangeable. No one of them bears any biologically built-in fixed connection to the others. (Teitelbaum, 1966, pp. 566–567)

A number of similar statements about classical and operant conditioning are quoted by Seligman (1970) and by Garcia *et al.* (1972). Others can be found in Reynolds (1968), Kimble (1961), and many other books on animal learning.

Because the assumption that the elements of a learning situation are arbitrary and interchangeable vastly simplifies the search for general properties of learning and because on the whole experimental results have not contradicted it, there has appeared to be little need to consider how learning may be constrained. Nevertheless, there is some reason to think that there are important limitations on what and how animals learn. To begin with, as ethologists have often pointed out (e.g., Tinbergen, 1951; Lorenz, 1965) behavior may be as species-characteristic as any feature of morphology or physiology. This clearly must be true of learning ability as well. Generally members of each species have certain well-defined requirements for individual learning—for example, in learning to recognize mate, young, or territory, or in acquiring skills necessary for food-finding or nest-building. It seems likely that the members of a given species would be adapted to do these kinds of learning especially efficiently and would not be as well adapted to learn other things. Learning also necessarily takes place within the context of an animal's pre-existing tendencies to behave in certain ways in certain circumstances, and this species-specific behavioral organization might be expected to influence behavior in learning experiments.

Quite independently of such a priori biological considerations, empirical suggestions that there are serious constraints on the generality of the accepted "laws of learning" have recently begun to accumulate. Significantly, many of them arise from studies using species other than the traditional rat, pigeon, and monkey, reinforcers other than the traditional food, water, and escape from electric shock, or responses other than bar-pressing and key-pecking. Taken together, these findings constitute clear evidence that arbitrary combinations of stimulus, response, and reinforcer are not all equivalent. In this paper we shall review many of these experiments and discuss what kinds of constraints on learning they imply.

There have already been some attempts to deal with experimental suggestions that generalizations derived from the behavior of rats, pigeons, and a few other vertebrates in a relatively small number of situations may be limited in their applicability. One of the earliest and best-publicized was Breland and Breland's (1961, 1966) description of the results of their attempts to train such unconventional laboratory subjects as pigs, hens, and raccoons. Instead of taking the form most efficient for obtaining the reward, the behavior of these animals often "drifted" toward another behavior more or less appropriate to some aspect of the situation they were placed in. For example, a pig being trained to drop a coin from its mouth into a piggy bank began to root it around and toss it into the air instead of placing it directly into the slot. Needless to say, this sequence greatly increased the delay of reward. Apparently something about the conditioning situation was more important than the reinforcement contingency, even for a hungry pig. In fact, in some cases making the animals hungrier only increased their tendency to display such apparently counterproductive behavior. The Brelands did suggest a framework within which an animal's behavior in learning situations could be related to its overall behavioral organization, but unfortunately their work appears to have inspired little experimentation, perhaps because their accounts were largely anecdotal.

Furthermore, their generalizations appear to be based more on hypotheses about their subjects' behavior in nature than on systematic observation.

Other discussions of constraints on learning, like those of Bolles (1970) for the restrictions on possible avoidance responses and of Garcia and others (Garcia and Ervin, 1968; Revusky and Garcia, 1970; Garcia *et al.*, 1972) for poison-avoidance learning, are quite plausible for the areas they were designed to cover, but they do not always go far enough. The principles of shock-avoidance learning and acquired aversions to noxious foods are probably not isolated exceptions to the generally accepted "laws of learning." Rather, as Rozin and Kalat (1971) also conclude, they suggest that in all areas the contributions of an animal's behavioral and associative predispositions may have to be taken into account. What seems to be needed is not simply a catalog of exceptions to *the* laws of learning but rather an approach which accepts a multiplicity of principles.

Seligman (1970) has attempted a broader synthesis of the experimental demonstrations of constraints on learning by suggesting that differential ease of learning different things represents different degrees of associative "preparedness." However, the "preparedness dimension" is merely an operational classification of learning tasks. It substitutes one oversimplification (that animals are more or less "prepared" to learn things and that "prepared" behaviors are acquired and extinguished differently from "unprepared" or "contraprepared" ones) for another (that the laws of learning are the same for all arbitrarily selected elements). This obscures the fact that apparent differences in learning difficulty may be brought about by a number of different mechanisms, not all of which are specifically associative. Another type of synthesis is represented by Staddon and Simmelhag's (1971) stimulating discussion of parallels between learning and natural selection.

This paper is mainly concerned with analyzing the kinds of constraints on learning that have appeared with increasing frequency in recent studies of animal learning by psychologists. The fact that some learning, like song-learning and imprinting, may tend to occur at only one period of an animal's life has only been touched on, and undoubtedly other kinds of constraints on learning have also been neglected. Many examples of learning limited to one period of development have been discussed elsewhere and their similarities to other kinds of learning noted (e.g., Bateson, 1966). At least some of these cases may involve changes in the same mechanisms responsible for more permanent constraints on learning.

We begin by considering how behavior in traditional learning situations may be influenced by the nature of the stimulus, the response, or the reinforcer and then discuss how further constraints on learning may arise out of the relationship between pairs of these elements. Although most of the experiments demonstrating constraints on learning have not provided a thorough analysis of their mechanisms, this classification does emphasize that learning may be constrained in a number of different ways.

A complementary approach to constraints on learning is to ask whether what and how animals learn is related in a nonarbitrary way to what would be adaptive in natural conditions. The concluding sections, on learning in the wild and species differences, illustrate this approach to constraints on learning, while they also enlarge on the themes stated in earlier sections.

II. The External Stimulus

The range of stimuli that can come to control an animal's behavior is obviously limited by what its sensory systems can respond to differentially. In addition, it is possible that some of the stimuli an animal can perceive do not have access to learning mechanisms. A particularly clear example of this is provided by studies of discrimination learning in the octopus, *Octopus vulgaris* (Wells, 1964). The octopus responds to the weights of objects by adjusting its tentacles appropriately to support an object lowered into its tank on a string. But it cannot be trained to accept an object of one weight and reject one of another, although it readily learns to discriminate shape in a similar task. Considerable evidence suggests that this is because information about the location of parts of the animal's body is not available centrally.

Not all the stimuli that do acquire control of behavior do so equally quickly. For example, rats learn faster to suppress bar-pressing in the presence of a tone signaling shock when the tone is 80 dB than when it is 50 dB (Kamin, 1969). The finding that stimulus salience affects speed of acquisition is incorporated into a recent quantitative model of classical conditioning (Rescorla and Wagner, 1972) in which each stimulus has its own learning rate parameter so that associative strength increases at different rates for different stimuli even when they are paired with the same US. Two-stage, or attentional, theories of operant discrimination learning (e.g., Mackintosh, 1965; Trabasso and Bower, 1968) incorporate the finding that animals may learn discriminations on some stimulus dimensions faster than those on others by assuming that an animal must attend to a stimulus dimension before it can learn to respond differentially to values along it and that it cannot attend to all stimulus dimensions at once. The dimension an animal is most likely to attend to, and thus the one along which it will most readily learn a discrimination, can be manipulated by training. In experimentally naïve animals it is determined by a species-specific attending hierarchy (Baron, 1965). Pigeons, for example, apparently attend most readily to the color of the response key, less readily to the tilt of a line projected on it, and may need special training to attend to auditory dimensions (Westbrook and Miles, 1970). However, attentional accounts seem to imply that once an animal is attending to a given dimension it can learn a discrimination with stimuli along that dimension as readily as it can learn a discrimination with stimuli along any other dimension it might attend to.

Both attentional theories and the kind of model proposed by Rescorla and Wagner can also be used to account for the fact that behavior is typically controlled by only some aspects of a complex stimulus. For example, if a pigeon reinforced for pecking at a red disk with a white vertical line and not reinforced for pecking a green disk with a horizontal line is tested with lines of various orientations and colored keys without lines, its pecking is influenced very little by the tilt of the lines but a great deal by the colors. However, its pecking can be controlled by the tilt of the lines if the reinforced and unreinforced stimuli are distinguished only by line tilt or if it originally has training with lines alone (Johnson and Cumming, 1968). This kind of finding can be interpreted to mean that naïve birds fail to attend to line tilt when the more strongly attended-to color dimension is also present and relevant to the discrimination.

Both the associative strength and the attentional accounts of differential ease of learning discriminations imply that the relative difficulty of different discriminations is the same regardless of the response, the reinforcer, or the internal state of the animal. In the quantitative associative-strength model this assumption is embodied in the constancy of the learning rate parameter for a given CS regardless of the US with which it is paired. Different US's may also have different learning rate parameters, but these do not interact with the parameters for CS's. This means that if, for example, a given species acquires a conditioned response faster to a 70-dB tone than to a 50-dB buzzer with a shock US, it will also acquire a CR faster to the tone than to the 50-dB buzzer when food is the US. Equivalently, in the attentional approach the attending hierarchy is implied to be fixed for a given species regardless of its internal state. It can be assessed equally well by using any response and any reinforcer. Although there is some experimental evidence that the simple notion of a fixed attending hierarchy is inadequate (Gilbert, 1969), there appear to have been no experiments explicitly testing whether what element of a compound stimulus controls a given response varies with the animal's motivational state and/or with the reinforcer.

In contrast to the assumption that the response, the reinforcer, and the animal's internal state do not affect the controlling element of a given compound stimulus is some ethologists' treatment of selectivity of stimulus control. It admits of the possibility that one aspect of a stimulus may control behavior in one situation, while when the animal is in a different internal state some other aspect of the same object may have the dominant influence on behavior. Unfortunately, well-documented examples of this important phenomenon are few, probably because in most cases the relevant stimulus objects change from one situation to another. However, Baerends (1958) reports that when herring gulls, *Larus argentatus*, retrieve eggs to incubate them, they are influenced by their color and speckling more than by their shape, while when they are taking the eggs from other gulls' nests for food, they are influenced by shape more than by color and speckling. The feeding responses of the grayling butterfly, *Eumenis semele*, are markedly influenced by color, while sexual pursuit is not (Tinbergen, 1951). Impekoven (1969) studied the reactions of cold or hungry black-headed gull chicks, *Larus ridibundus*, to standard models and reports some differences in the releasing value of various models as a function of these states, although these may have been partly due to differences in activity.

This specificity in how external stimuli act as unconditioned causal factors for behavior suggests that external stimuli which come to control behavior through experience might also show some specificity. Unconditioned (cf. Tinbergen, 1951; Hinde, 1970) and conditioned causal factors for behavior share the property of commonly being only one aspect of a complex stimulus. They might also share the property of being specific to a response or a motivational state. For example, some initially neutral stimuli might come to control only certain classes of responses, or what dimension is predominantly attended to might vary with the animal's motivational state.

This notion is reasonable from a functional point of view. Animals may be predisposed to learn things that it is important to them to learn in natural conditions especially well, while, as Small suggested in 1901, they may not learn other apparently equally easy tasks at all if these have no place in their lives in nature. There is considerable evidence for this notion from field observations. For example, herring gulls appear to have reasonably good vision, they do learn some things, and their eggs vary considerably in appearance, but they do not recognize their own eggs, as shown by the fact that they readily attempt to incubate a variety of model eggs (Tinbergen, 1953). On the other hand, guillemots, *Uria aalge*, which do not build nests but lay in close groups, do recognize their own eggs (Tschanz, 1959). Similarly, noddy terns, *Anous stolidus*, which nest where exchange of chicks is unlikely, do not recognize their own young and even accept sooty tern chicks, while sooty terns, *Sterna fuscata,* which nest in dense colonies in the sand, do recognize their own chicks and attack strangers (Lashley, 1915). The fact that some passerine birds learn only certain of the songs they hear is another example of stimulus specificity in learning.

Such examples show that there may be species differences in the readiness with which similar stimuli acquire control of behavior under similar conditions and thus that there may be predispositions to learn certain things and not others. Unfortunately most of these cases have not been analyzed in sufficient detail to determine, for example, whether the animals actually could discriminate the stimuli toward which they were not reacting differentially or exactly why they were failing to perform differently toward them. However, some experiments on the sun-compass orientation of birds do show that some stimuli, or aspects of stimuli, which are irrelevant to behavior in natural conditions may be learned about only with great difficulty even though they are clearly reacted to differentially. It appears from these experiments that, although pigeons and starlings can orient by means of the sun by compensating for its apparent movement through the sky — which necessarily means that they discriminate the sun's position as well as the time of day — they cannot be trained to disregard their tendency to compensate for changes in the sun's position with time and go at a constant angle to the sun regardless of the time of day. For example, Kramer (1952) trained starlings, *Sturnus vulgaris,* to approach one of four, six, or twelve feeders in an outdoor walled arena where they had a view of the sun but of no landmarks or in an indoor arena with an artificial sun. The ring of feeders and the surrounding wall were rotated periodically and independently so that the only cue consistently available to the birds was the position of the feeders relative to the sun. When starlings were trained to approach a feeder in a fixed compass direction at the same time each day, in tests at other times of day they tended to go to the feeder in the compass direction they were trained to, although of course it was in a different position relative to the sun. In contrast, one starling could be trained only with great difficulty to go to a feeder at a constant angle to the sun and not compensate for time. Similarly, Matthews (1952) found that pigeons trained to go at the same angle to the sun regardless of the time of day learned very slowly and never reached a high level of accuracy, although, like the starlings, they readily learned to use the sun for orienting in the same compass direction at any time of day. However, pigeons did learn to choose a feeder at a constant angle to the sun at all times of day if it was designated with a white card, and a few birds were transferred to using the sun's angle alone by having the card gradually made smaller.

Similar results on transfer from an easy to a difficult discrimination have been found in more conventional studies of operant discrimination learning (e.g., Terrace, 1963). Learning a difficult discrimination may be facilitated if training is given on an easy discrimination first and the easy cues are then faded out to leave only the originally difficult ones. Thus, this particular example of a predisposition to learn might be accounted for in terms that are already familiar. However, it is significant that here the discrimination that was difficult to train involved using the sun in an unnatural way: objects in the environment like feeding locations do not usually move so as to maintain a constant angle to the sun. Furthermore, at some level the birds must have been "noticing" the angle of the feeder to the sun, since it was the only cue they could orient by. These considerations suggest that something other than attional mechanisms may be involved here. In later sections, we shall see clear evidence for specifically associative predispositions to learn certain things and not others.

III. Differences among Reinforcers

Many studies have been concerned with determining whether this or that event is a reinforcer for a particular species (e.g., Hogan, 1961; King and Weisman, 1964; Thompson, 1963, 1964, 1969; Stevenson, 1967, 1969), but most have been confined to discovering whether the event in question changes the probability of a response on which its presentation is contingent. Very few of them have also determined the effects of presenting the reinforcer on an intermittent schedule, varying the delay between the response and presentation of the reinforcer, varying its magnitude, or the like. This is reasonable in view of the assumption that all reinforcers act in the same way. But the few studies that have tested this notion directly have produced a small amount of evidence suggesting that different reinforcers may act in different ways, even if they support acquisition in a way similar to food, water, or escape from electric shock.

A number of problems are inherent in any attempt to compare the effects of different reinforcers. Some of their complexities are explored in Hearst's (1969) discussion of whether there are fundamental differences between stimulus generalization gradients of approach and avoidance. On the basis of considerable experimental evidence, he concludes that there are no such differences. Gradients of any steepness can be obtained with either approach or avoidance behavior by manipulating aspects of the experimental situation like the level of extinction and the reinforcement schedule.

Similarly, in comparing different reinforcers it is particularly important to separate effects due to differences in the quality of reinforcers from effects which may as well be due to quantitative differences — for example, to one reinforcer producing the same effects as might be produced by a small magnitude of another. The problems in doing so are illustrated by Stevenson's (1967, 1969) experiments on whether short bursts of adult chaffinch song are reinforcing for male chaffinches' perching responses. Song did appear to be a reinforcer for autumn-caught, testosterone-injected male chaffinches, *Fringilla coelebs,* when compared to white noise of the same loudness, but its effect on the birds' behavior was far from overwhelming. In most cases song presentation affected only some relative measures of perching behavior and not the absolute number of times the birds alighted on the perch that produced song. This is not just because perching behavior is difficult to condition, since food reinforcement had a large effect on perching in an otherwise identical experiment. However, it is questionable whether the perching response is suitable for reinforcement with song. The notion that hearing normal adult chaffinch song may be reinforcing for young male chaffinches just learning to sing the song themselves is based partly on the notion that chaffinches learn to sing by gradually approximating their vocalizations to normal chaffinch song (Stevenson, 1969). Experiments with deafened birds show that they do need to have feedback from their own vocal efforts to develop song normally. This suggests that hearing normal adult chaffinch song would be reinforcing for a young male chaffinch just learning to sing. But this view of song-learning does not suggest that hearing normal adult song would necessarily reinforce a behavior other than vocalization. Furthermore, the function of song at other periods of the lives of chaffinches of both sexes suggests that it might have other reinforcing or even punishing effects.

In interpreting the differences in the reinforcing effects of food and song, Stevenson emphasizes the differences in the effects of food- and song-deprivation. Only when chaffinches were severely deprived of food did hopping onto the perch which operated the feeder come to dominate their behavior; deprivation of song, on the other hand, seemed to have no effect on the birds' behavior in the experimental situation, although song deprivation might not have been complete if the birds were singing themselves. Since Stevenson does not report that slightly food-deprived chaffinches performed for food any differently from the way chaffinches performed for song, one is forced to conclude, as she does, that song is equivalent to weak food reinforcement, at least for the perching response. This also seems to be true of the sight of another rooster as a reinforcer for fighting cocks in Thompson's (1964) comparisons of this social reinforcer with water and food. However, conclusions from both these sets of experiments are necessarily limited by the fact that they compared only one amount of the "species-specific reinforcer" with one amount of another. The weak reinforcer hypothesis implies that the effects of a given amount of the weak reinforcer on several measures of learning are equivalent to those of some small amount of food or water, or to those of food or water for nearly satiated animals.

As the preceding discussion suggests, a single difference in acquisition rates, asymptotic performance levels, extinction rates, or the like with different reinforcers does not necessarily imply any more than a difference in their strengths. However, if one reinforcer is stronger than another, it might be expected to have a greater effect on several measures of behavior. This assumption is implicit in the early controversy over whether intracranial electrical stimulation (ICS) is the same as more traditional reinforcers (review in Milner, 1970). With some electrode placements rats bar-press for ICS at high rates but extinguish almost immediately and do not work for it on high ratios. More recently this discrepancy has been resolved in terms of aspects of brain stimulation other than its reinforcing value, but the fact that it was regarded as a problem implies the assumption that a given reinforcer should appear to be equally strong relative to other reinforcers however its effects are measured. This notion suggests that we can discover whether two reinforcers differ qualitatively or simply quantitatively by comparing their effects on several aspects of behavior. However, this is complicated by the fact that even variations in the parameters of a single reinforcer do not always have consistent effects (Steiner, 1968). In theory this problem can be eliminated by comparing the effects of varying the parameters of one reinforcer with the effects of varying the parameters of another, using several measures of reinforcement strength (cf. Steiner, 1968). This is essentially the same as the method of systematic variation suggested by Bitterman (1965) for comparing the learning abilities of different species. Here we are comparing functional relationships (for example, the relative effects of increasing deprivation on acquisition, extinction, and ratio performance) across reinforcers rather than across species. However, as we shall discuss in a later section, differences in such relationships may be due to differences in the behaviors elicited by the reinforcers or facilitated by different motivational states as well as to differences in reinforcing effect per se. Furthermore, different theoretical accounts of how various parameters of reinforcement affect behavior—for example, whether they act through learning or incentive (cf. Bolles, 1967; Steiner, 1968)—will naturally influence the interpretation of such differences.

A single illustration of what it might mean to say that different reinforcers act differently is provided by Hogan's (1967; Hogan et al., 1970) comparisons of the effects of reinforcing male *Betta splendens* with food or with the opportunity to display at a mirror. In Hogan's first experiments (1967), the fishes' initial rates of acquisition of alley-swimming were similar for food and display, but the asymptotic rate of swimming for display was lower and more variable than the rate for food. Also, swimming for display extinguished almost as soon as the reinforcement was withdrawn, whereas the food-reinforced swimming showed the gradual decline typical of extinction. However, various aspects of the fishes' behavior, such as the fact that they sometimes swam for display faster than they ever swam for food, suggest that display is not simply a weak reinforcer but rather that food and display depend on different mechanisms for their effects.

Stronger evidence for this conclusion comes from the experiments of Hogan *et al.* (1970) in which male *Bettas* were reinforced with either food or display on various fixed ratios for swimming through a short tunnel. As in the previous experiments, the fish lived in the experimental tanks, and sessions lasted for the 12 daily hours of light. On ratios that were increased gradually from one response to six for each food reinforcement, the fish showed the behavior usually found on fixed ratio schedules, increasing their total number of responses per session roughly in proportion to the response requirement and thus obtaining a constant amount of food daily. For display reinforcement, on the other hand, the

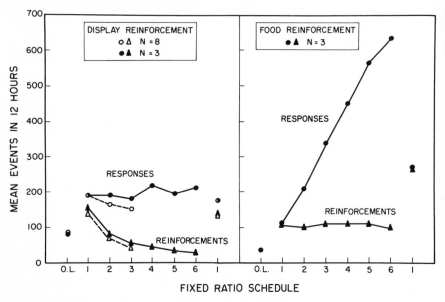

Fig. 1. Mean response rates of groups of male *Betta splendens* reinforced for swimming through a tunnel with food or the opportunity to display at their mirror image on various fixed ratio schedules. O.L. = operant level. From Hogan *et al.* (1970). Copyright (1970) by the Americal Psychological Association and reproduced by permission.

number of responses was roughly constant across all the ratios used, while the number of reinforcements declined (Fig. 1). Furthermore, varying the duration of mirror presentation between 5 and 40 seconds had no effect on responding for display when reinforcement was given for each response, while at least research with other fish (e.g., Rozin and Mayer, 1961) suggests that manipulating the magnitude of food reinforcement would affect the rate of response. Of course this comparison rests on equating increased duration of mirror presentation with increased amount of food reinforcement. The adequacy of a model fish presented for a constant period of time might be a more appropriate analog to magnitude of food reinforcement.

Now, it is possible that close observation of the behavior of the fish in Hogan's experiments would reveal that basic differences in the behavior of hungry fish and fish that have just displayed, or in the behaviors elicited by food and display, were responsible for the differences in reinforcing effect, but the results are also compatible with food and display being basically different kinds of reinforcers. Observations of fish responding for food and display as well as further experiments using different responses are necessary to confirm that the differences are due to differences in reinforcer per se. However, it is tempting to conclude that the differences between food and display with ratio reinforcement represent basic differences between regulatory systems, designed to maintain homeostasis by increasing effort to obtain a constant amount of some variable such as food, and systems that do not maintain some internal state necessary for survival (cf. also Stevenson, 1969; Oatley, 1970). Clearly, there is need for further detailed comparisons between such reinforcers as food, water, and thermal stimuli, and those like the opportunity to perform aggressive or sexual behavior which are not apparently homeostatic. Such studies will need to compare effects of the different reinforcers in a number of situations where the reinforced response, the degree of deprivation, and the schedule and magnitude of reinforcement are varied.

Although much more work is needed with "species-specific" reinforcers like song and display, differences are even beginning to appear between the traditional reinforcers of food and water for rats. Macdonald and de Toledo (in preparation) reinforced hungry or thirsty rats with food or water respectively for bar-pressing on CRF or a VI 1-minute schedule and extinguished them when they had reached asymptotic performance. The two food-reinforced groups showed the usual effect on the speed of extinction as well as the usual increase in rate at the beginning of extinction. However, although water reinforcement is commonly believed to be equivalent to food reinforcement (Seligman, 1970), the water-reinforced groups showed neither of these effects.

Similar comparisons need to be made with other schedules and other responses as well as with animals deprived simultaneously of food and water.

As a further example of differences between food and water reinforcement for rats, Logan and Spanier (1970) report that in two experiments delay of water reward for rats running down an alley produced relatively less decrement in running speed than the same delay of food reward. Again, Levy and Seward (1969) report that withholding expected food from rats produced a larger frustration effect (increase in immediately subsequent running speed) than withholding water. However, neither of these results can be interpreted unambiguously because in both cases the levels of performance for water and food differed before the experimental manipulation was made. Nevertheless, the major results of all three of these experiments suggest that withholding expected water has less effect on the behavior of rats than withholding expected food. It remains to be seen whether this represents a difference in persistence between hungry and thirsty rats or a difference in reinforcing effects per se. At present there is only scanty evidence for any differences of this latter sort among reinforcers, but this appears to be more because they have not explicitly been looked for than because they may not exist. On the view that each subsystem of behavior—for example, predator avoidance, feeding, migration—should have laws of learning peculiarly appropriate to it (cf. Rozin and Kalat, 1971), different reinforcers might well support learning in different ways.

IV. Constraints on the Response

Any operant response must first occur "for other reasons" before it can be reinforced (Skinner, 1966). The "other reasons" are generally assumed to become unimportant once reinforcement has taken effect, but a number of experiments show that this is not necessarily the case. A response may continue to be influenced by its normal causal factors even though it is at the same time under the control of operant reinforcement contingencies.

One example of this kind of constraint on responses is provided by the experiments of Black and Young (1972). They trained rats to bar-press or to drink to avoid electric shock or to obtain food. Each rat was trained with one of these reinforcers to bar-press in the presence of one stimulus and to drink (actually to consume water) in the presence of another. Although the rats could be trained to drink to avoid, the response was still partly under the control of its normal causal factors because they drank at a high rate only if they were water-deprived or if the water was sweetened. However, when either of these conditions was met, in the experimental situation the rats drank mainly in the presence of the stimulus signaling that drinking would avoid shocks. Black and Young interpret these results by suggesting that satiation still actively inhibits drinking plain water even though drinking has been brought under the control of the avoidance contingency: "Drinking water is part of the subsystem regulating water intake; when you make drinking part of a new subsystem controlling avoidance of danger, the constraints of the old one still are operative." (p. 42).

However, rats did drink water at the same rate to obtain food whether they were satiated or thirsty. This finding tends to contradict the notion that water-satiation per se inhibits drinking, but, as Black points out, the drinking and feeding systems interact in subtle ways. Experiments on the effects of preloading with water on drinking for food are needed to clarify the role of thirst in the use of drinking as an operant for food reinforcement.

Although they do not directly manipulate an independent causal factor for responding, experiments in which pigeons are trained to attack other pigeons to obtain food provide observations similar to Black and Young's. They also suggest that when a response belonging to one behavioral system is used as an operant in another, it is not controlled entirely by the reinforcement contingencies. In such experiments (e.g., Skinner, 1959; Reynolds et al., 1963; Azrin and Hutchinson, 1967), a hungry pigeon is shaped to peck another pigeon in order to get food. "Agression" is defined as a certain force exerted against the target pigeon. However, in such studies the behavior engendered by the reinforcement contingency is apparently not confined to pecks at the target animal. Rather, "cold" pecking gives way to full-blown aggression — vocalization, feather erection, wing-flapping, and the like (Skinner, 1959). Furthermore, although this behavior is clearly controlled by the food reinforcement in that it shows typical scalloping when reinforced on a fixed ratio schedule and extinguishes when food is withdrawn (Azrin and Hutchinson, 1967), it often continues into and even through periods of food presentation. This is also true in rats trained to show aggression for water reward (Ulrich et al., 1963). Some of the Brelands' (1961, 1966) findings appear similar.

Related observations were also made by Reynolds et al. (1963), who trained two pigeons to depress a bar with their breasts to obtain food. When the birds were simply reinforced with food for pressing the bar, they tended to peck at it, but when they had to attack another pigeon before they could obtain food by pressing the bar, they tended to shake the bar violently with their beaks.

Of course all these observations are difficult to interpret because, as Azrin and Hutchinson (1967) noted, the behavior of the target bird may change as it is pecked more frequently, but they do suggest that the behavior of simply pecking a conspecific may not occur readily, at least in pigeons, in the absence of a whole complex of related behaviors. This notion might be tested by using a stuffed or otherwise immobilized target bird in such an experiment.

So far we have looked at constraints on operant responses in terms of the notion that responses may be seen as being more or less tightly linked to particular sets of internal and external causal factors, with patterns like drinking near one end of a continuum and "motivationally neutral" behaviors like bar-pressing and locomotion at the other. This kind of classification parallels the familiar distinction between voluntary and involuntary behaviors (Teitelbaum, 1966; Vanderwolf, 1969, 1971; Black and Young, 1972), the involuntary behaviors being those tied to a restricted set of causal factors. However, the voluntary—involuntary distinction obviously breaks down when an "involuntary" behavior like drinking is brought under operant control. And the distinction in terms of tightness of control by normal causal factors can easily become circular. It is unlikely that observation of what internal and external conditions are correlated with the appearance of a given response in the natural flow of an animal's behavior would always show how necessary any or all of these factors are for its occurrence. Experiments attempting to bring it under control of other factors would be needed, and it is just the results of such experiments that one was trying to predict in the first place. On the basis of Vanderwolf's (1969, 1971) findings that "involuntary" behaviors like grooming and drinking are correlated with the disappearance of hippocampal theta waves in rats, Black and Young (1972) suggest that responses constrained by their normal causal factors may be identified by the absence of theta waves during their performance. This remains to be tested with responses other than drinking in rats. In any case, the absence of theta waves does not indicate what factors are necessary for performance of the response.

Another approach to limitations on the control of responses by operant reinforcement is a functional one. Many behaviors appear to have a well-defined single function; chewing, drinking, preening, and nest-building movements are examples. Others, like locomotory patterns or pecking—the sorts of responses usually chosen for operant reinforcement—can serve many functions, depending on their context. On the view that an animal's capacity for learning should be geared to the requirements for learning in nature, it would seem unlikely that behaviors in the former class could be used for anything other than their normal function—for example, that an animal could learn to preen for food or drink to avoid shock. From this point of view it is as much a problem that such things are acquired at all as it is that there are some constraints on their acquisition. Thus neither of these approaches provides an adequate account of what responses can become operants. The approach which suggests that some responses can be used as operants only if their normal causal factors are present at least has the merit of suggesting what conditions may have to be met before they can be performed for reinforcement.

Although Black and Young mention the possibility that satiated rats might increase their rate of drinking to avoid after prolonged training, their more theoretical discussion implies that drinking depends indefinitely on its normal causal factors. Some experiments reported by Konorski (1967) suggest a slightly different role for the normal causal factors of a response. Konorski and his colleagues trained cats to perform such responses as rubbing their faces, scratching their ears, or licking their anuses for food reinforcement. At first these responses were elicited by presenting appropriate stimuli like gum arabic on the face, cotton in the ear, or soap on the anus. Unlike thirst or saccharine in the experiments reported by Black, these stimuli were not required indefinitely in order for the response to be performed. For instance, in dogs and cats trained to jerk a hindleg for food reinforcement, the response initially had to be elicited by a tight band around the leg, but after reinforcement was instituted the band could gradually be loosened and finally removed altogether without disrupting behavior. This might suggest that the function of an external eliciting stimulus like the tight band is merely to raise the operant level of the response so that it can be reinforced, but the fact that the band could only be removed gradually suggests that this is not the case. The suggestion that in such cases the eliciting stimuli do not simply raise the operant level is also supported by Konorski's report that, when cats were trained to scratch an ear, the eliciting stimulus (a wad of cotton in the ear) sometimes had to be reinstated at the beginning of the first few sessions even though reinforcement had already increased the probability of response in earlier sessions.

Now, results with conventional operants suggest that reinforcement brings about a sudden complete shift in control of a response from its original causal factors to the new experimental factors. For example, Skinner (1938, pp. 67–68) describes as typical a change from operant level of bar-pressing to a maximum high rate after one or two reinforcements. However, the experiments described by Konorski show that the shift of control may be gradual. At an intermediate stage, reinforcement controls the response to some extent, in the sense of having increased its rate, for example, but the original causal factors are still necessary, although at a lower level than initially. Finally the response can be performed in the absence of its original causal factors. In contrast, Black and Young suggest that drinking in their experiments continues to depend indefinitely on the presence of the original level of water deprivation, even though its rate and the stimuli that occasion it have been modified by the avoidance contingency. This represents not a shift in control but an addition of new controlling factors to old ones. However, further experiments assessing the degree of control over various responses by original and experimental factors after various amounts of training are necessary to show whether such a distinction can be maintained empirically.

As Konorski did later, Thorndike (1911) tried to train cats to scratch or lick themselves for operant reinforcement, provided in his experiments by escape from a puzzle box. He reports that in these cats, as well as in a chick trained to preen to escape from a puzzle box, the response deteriorated during training until it was a mere vestige of the normal response. Such observations led him to conclude that an important factor in learning was "the readiness of the response to be connected with the situation" (Thorndike, 1911, p. 248). Konorski observed similar alterations in topography and suggested another plausible reason for them. Responses that are defined topographically instead of by their effect on a machine are very difficult to reinforce in a standard way. A movement may sometimes be reinforced just as it begins, and this might well make it appear to degenerate during training. Konorski provides support for this view with the report that when his cats began to perform an incomplete version of the ear-scratching movement the complete response could be reinstated by withholding reinforcement until it was performed. Further support for this notion is provided by Hogan's (1964) experiment in which pigeons were trained to preen for food reinforcement. When every preening movement was reinforced, preening tended to be very brief and incomplete and was often accompanied by excited "dancing." Hogan suggests that this is because reinforcement was sometimes given at different parts of the preening movement and because locomotion toward the feeder was adventitiously reinforced. This explanation is supported by the fact that during extinction and variable interval reinforcement, when not all preening movements were being reinforced, they became more stereotyped and more normal in appearance.

Such observations show that the deterioration in topography apparently characteristic of such responses during operant reinforcement may be explicable with traditional reinforcement principles and need have nothing to do with the special nature of the response. However, it is also possible that in some cases the deterioration in topography is due to the absence of the normal stimuli for the response. This may be the case for yawning and sneezing, which Konorski suggests are completely

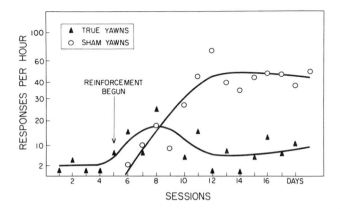

Fig. 2. Rates of true yawning and "sham yawning" (mouth opening) in a dog reinforced with food for yawning. After Konorski (1967).

refractory to operant contingencies. A dog reinforced with food for yawning, for example, did learn to open his mouth as if in a yawn but increased his "true yawning" very little (Fig. 2). Since the normal stimulus for yawning seems to be internal and not readily manipulable, it is not necessary to conclude from this that yawning is otherwise different from a response like anus-licking, which could become an operant if its normal eliciting stimulus was present at first.

In concluding this section on constraints on the conditionability of responses, it should be noted that the assumption that arbitrary responses can be controlled by arbitrary reinforcers has seldom been accepted unconditionally. Thus, Solomon (1964) suggests that "reflexive, short-latency" responses are less amenable to control by punishment or avoidance contingencies than are "nonreflexive, longer-latency" responses. Reflexes, while susceptible to classical conditioning, have until recently appeared to be refractory to operant contingencies. For example, Sheffield (1965) was unable to train dogs to inhibit salivation for food reinforcement, but Miller and Carmona (1967), using water reinforcement in a slightly different procedure, were able to train dogs to increase or to decrease their rate of salivation. Another dichotomy has been that between autonomic and skeletal responses, but recently this has been broken down by the demonstrations of Miller and his colleagues (Miller, 1969) that heart rate, stomach contractions, and the like, as well as salivation, can be operantly conditioned. Although there may well be responses that are not influenced by their consequences, this section seems to leave us with the conclusion that the frequencies of most responses can be modified by operant reinforcement contingencies. But this does not mean that there are no constraints on the conditions under which they may be acquired. Even when they can be used as operants and brought under stimulus control, some responses may continue to depend for their occurrence, in varying degrees, on the presence of the factors that normally cause them. Such dependence may limit the effectiveness of reinforcement contingencies. Furthermore, as we shall see in the next section, whether such responses can be conditioned may depend on what the reinforcer is.

So far we have dealt entirely with constraints on whether or under what conditions responses can be acquired. A further question is whether all responses that are acquired are equally susceptible to modification by such variables as the schedule of reinforcement. Hemmes (1970) reports some evidence that they may not be. She found that pigeons learn rather poorly to respond for food at a low rate (that is, on a DRL schedule) when they are pecking a key, but they do much better when the response is depressing a treadle. On the basis of this and considerable other evidence, she concludes that the DRL performance is poor with pecking because hungry pigeons cannot inhibit pecking. On the other hand, like bar-pressing in Black and Young's experiments, treadle-pressing in pigeons appears to be relatively free of such a motivational constraint.

V. The Relationship between the Response and the Reinforcer

A. Direct Effects of Reinforcers

Complementary to the notion that some behaviors can be performed as operants only when their own causal factors are present is the notion that internal and external factors restrict behavior in particular ways. Important among such factors are those necessary for reinforcers to be effective. The factors necessary to the effectiveness of a given reinforcer (for example, food deprivation, a high level of testosterone) may alter the probabilities of behaviors other than those (for example, eating, copulation) that occur when the reinforcer is presented. For example, increasing food deprivation for rats running in an alley decreases grooming, sniffing, and various exploratory behaviors (Cotton, 1953). Since different motivational states can be expected to affect behavior in adaptively different ways, the relationship between responses and reinforcers or motivational states might be expected to be a source of important constraints on learning.

In contrast to this notion is the assumption (e.g., Reynolds, 1968) that such operations as depriving an animal of food are merely technical procedures to render reinforcers effective. On this view the choice of reinforcer should not influence the relative ease of conditioning different responses. The essential equivalence of different drive states and their

associated reinforcers is also implicit in Hull's (1943) concept of generalized drive. His notions inspired many experiments on the effects of
"irrelevant" deprivation states, drive substitution and summation, and
the effects of different levels of the same drive on learning and extinction
(reviews by Kimble, 1961, and Bolles, 1967), but on the whole they provide little evidence for generalized drive. As Bolles (1967, p. 279) concludes, "It has been found that it is much more important to discover
just what responses occur in a particular situation and under a particular
set of drive conditions than anyone had supposed."

In spite of this and much other evidence (cf. Hinde, 1970) that different motivational states have qualitatively different effects on behavior,
only a few experiments have compared the effects of different motivational states and/or reinforcers on the learning of different responses.
One striking example of such an experiment is reported by Petrinovich
and Bolles (1954). They reinforced hungry or thirsty rats with the appropriate reinforcer either for always going to the same side of a T-
maze or for alternating sides. The hungry rats were superior to the
thirsty ones in the alternation task, but the thirsty rats were superior on
the position task (Fig. 3). Unfortunately, this experiment lacks hungry and
thirsty control groups reinforced no matter what they did, because
Petrinovich and Bolles conclude that their results are due not to food's
being a better reinforcer for alternation and water's being a better rein-

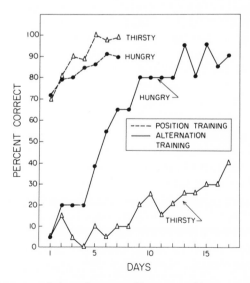

FIG. 3. Percent correct choices of groups of hungry or thirsty rats reinforced with food
or water, respectively, for always going to the same arm of a T-maze or for alternating
sides. After Petrinovich and Bolles (1954). Copyright (1954) by the American Psychological Association, and reproduced by permission.

forcer for a position habit but to alternation's being a dominant behavior of hungry rats and stereotypy's being dominant in thirsty ones. However, the results of a later experiment (Bolles and Petrinovich, 1956) suggest that the important variable in these experiments may have been not the deprivation condition but the weights of the animals. Whatever they are due to, these modes of behavior are not entirely unmodifiable. The hungry rats did reach quite a high level of performance on the position task, although the thirsty rats showed only very slight improvement in the alternation experiment. Furthermore, the results cannot simply be due to differences in the operant level of the two behaviors as a function of drive state, since in each task the initial performance levels of the hungry and thirsty rats were the same. Differences appeared only after some reinforcements had been given (see Fig. 3). Control groups simply given water or food in the apparatus are needed to show how much the emergence of this difference depends on a particular response being reinforced.

Direct effects of the reinforcer, or of the internal state necessary for its effectiveness, are particularly intrusive in experiments using electric shock. It is very difficult to train rats to press a lever to escape or avoid shock, and when they are trained to do so the response is often some variant of freezing on the bar (review by Bolles, 1970, 1971). However, rats readily learn to run or jump out of situations where they receive the same electric shocks. This difference in the conditionability of different responses has usually been regarded as a problem of operant level rather than as a theoretically important feature of avoidance learning. However, Bolles (1970), in a paper which has much the same spirit as this review in its attempt to relate learning in the laboratory to behavior in the wild, has recently suggested that understanding how aversive stimulation restricts an animal's behavior is basic to understanding escape and avoidance learning. He proposes that shock restricts an animal's behavior to its species-specific defense reactions (SSDR's). The reinforcement contingencies in escape or avoidance training suppress those SSDR's that are ineffective in the situation, while responses other than SSDR's can be brought to occur only with great difficulty.

Although Bolles' notion fits nicely with the thesis of the present discussion, at this stage designating SSDR's is still very much a post hoc affair. Close observation of many behaviors during various kinds of avoidance training could help to make this rather general notion more precise. Furthermore, recent evidence (Masterson, 1970) suggests that behaviors other than some form of flight, freezing, or aggression are not difficult to condition in an avoidance situation simply because painful stimulation inhibits them. Rats learn quite readily to press a bar in the normal way if bar-pressing opens a door through which they can run from the place where they are shocked. This result can be accounted for by the notion that actually getting out of the place where shock occurs is more reinforcing than just postponing shocks, but it also fits with Bolles' suggestion that the external situation plays a role in determining what SSDR's the animal will exhibit: if the situation allows functional escape, then active behavior, rather than freezing, will emerge.

The results of attempts to train pigeons to peck keys to avoid or escape shock also point to the conclusion that responses cannot all be equally easily conditioned for all reinforcers and that this may be because of the way in which the state necessary for the reinforcer to be effective acts directly rather than contingently on behavior. Shock avoidance must be an effective reinforcer for pigeons because they will learn to avoid by running in a shuttlebox (Macphail, 1968), but although Hoffman and Fleshler (1959) could shape pigeons to lift their heads to avoid shocks, they could not shape key-pecking. Only after laborious shaping using constantly changing shock intensities were Rachlin and Hineline (1967) able to train pigeons to avoid by pecking a key. Rachlin (1969) suggests that this is partly because the operant level of key-pecking is much lower in pigeons being shocked than in pigeons that are hungry and/or being fed in the experimental situation. However, the appeal to operant level is simply a way of saying that it is difficult to reinforce shocked pigeons for pecking because they seldom peck. But they clearly do peck sometimes, and acquisition of pecking for shock escape or avoidance reinforcement appears unduly protracted for low operant level or changing sensitivity to shock (Rachlin and Hineline, 1967) to be the only factor involved. An alternative possibility is that the motivational state induced by shock actively inhibits investigatory and feeding behaviors like pecking.

Direct, as opposed to contingent, effects of aversive stimulation may also play a role in punishment experiments. For example, Walters and Glazer (1971) punished Mongolian gerbils, *Meriones unguiculatus,* with a conditioned punisher either for digging in the sand covering the floor of the testing chamber or for assuming their alert posture. The punisher was a tone which had been established as a conditioned aversive stimulus by pairings with foot shocks while the gerbils were in a transparent shocking chamber placed in the testing area. On each day of punishment training there was a classical conditioning session with the tone, followed a few hours later by a punishment session in the sandbox with the classical conditioning apparatus removed. Punishment training was preceded by habituation sessions with the tone only. Control groups continued to receive only the tone, contingent either on digging or on alert posturing.

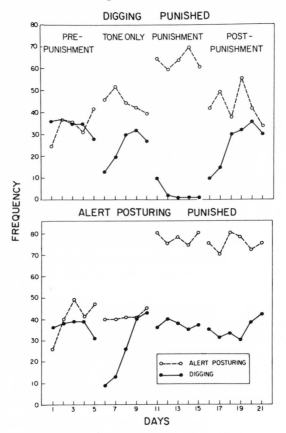

FIG. 4. Mean numbers of digging and alert posturing responses shown by groups of Mongolian gerbils punished either for digging or for alert posturing with a tone that had been established as a conditioned punisher. The tone was paired with shocks in separate sessions after the prepunishment baseline sessions and the habituation sessions with the tone only. From Walters and Glazer (1971). Copyright (1954) by the American Psychological Association and reproduced by permission.

From the point of view of this discussion, the most interesting result of this experiment was that, while the group that had the conditioned punisher presented whenever they dug quickly suppressed digging almost completely and the group punished for alert posturing continued to dig at the pre-punishment rate, *both* punished groups *increased* alert posturing greatly above pre-punishment levels (Fig. 4). This could not have been due to the tone eliciting alert posturing, since the group punished for digging had very few tone presentations once they had learned to suppress digging, while the group punished for alert posturing had the tone presented many times. This suggests that the sessions with shocks had somehow caused the whole experimental situation to elicit more alert posturing. This explanation has not been verified, since the experiment included no control groups that received tone–shock pairings but no tone presentation during the punishment sessions when digging and alert posturing were measured.

A similar direct effect of aversive stimulation may be involved in the experiments reported by Bolles and Seelbach (1964). Earlier results had suggested that whether loud noise is an effective punisher for rats depends on the response being punished. Bolles and Seelbach tested this notion by punishing three responses of rats—grooming, rearing, and approaching a hole in the test chamber wall ("window investigation")— with loud noise. In addition, they reinforced the same three responses with escape from the same loud noise. The effectiveness of the punishment and escape contingencies was assessed by comparisons with yoked control groups. Each of the three responses was affected differently: neither contingency affected grooming; both affected "window investigation" appropriately; and while the escape contingency increased rearing, punishment did not decrease it. Bolles and Seelbach suggest that their results can be accounted for by the notion that the effect of a punishment or escape contingency is partly determined by the relationship of the responses elicited by the noxious stimulus to the responses being reinforced or punished. However, they do not explain exactly how this accounts for their experimental results.

Bolles and Seelbach's suggestion, like the interpretation of Walters and Glazer's results, implies that the instances of lack of control by aversive stimuli may occur in spite of the contingencies. It attributes the lack of control neither to the response being refractory to operant control nor to the aversive stimulus not being a reinforcer but to a particular relationship between the response and the reinforcer. It implies that the responses not amenable to control by negative reinforcement might be controlled by some positive reinforcer. For example, digging in the Walters and Glazer study and grooming in the Bolles and Seelbach study might be increased in frequency by food reinforcement. However, this remains to be tested. It is also possible that they are not amenable to operant control at all or that, as in some of the examples discussed earlier, their amenability to such control is limited to special conditions.

It should be noted that some experiments on pain-elicited aggression provide reason to question the notion that a given aversive stimulus cannot both elicit and punish the same response. For example, Myer and Baenninger (1966) suppressed mouse-killing in rats that spontaneously killed mice with electric shock. However, once mouse-killing had been suppressed, shock could elicit it in the same rats. Similarly, shock-elicited "aggression" (hose-biting) in monkeys is suppressed if a shock is also contingent on elicited hose-biting (Azrin, 1970). These results imply that the behavior elicited by an aversive stimulus is not always primary in determining the effects of making that stimulus contingent on behavior.

It should also be noted that the inadequacy of contingencies alone for predicting the outcome of punishment experiments is already acknowledged. Such factors as the nature of the response being punished, the nature of the punisher, and the age, previous history, and species of the subject also have been taken into account (Solomon, 1964). However, while this situation has been treated as exceptional, the theme of the present discussion is that similar factors may interact with any reinforcement contingency, positive or negative.

B. Inhibitory Effects of Reinforcers

So far we have considered constraints on the reinforcers that can control given responses mainly in terms of the notion that responses may be directly elicited by a reinforcer or facilitated by the internal state necessary for a reinforcer to be effective. Most of these demonstrations of direct effects of reinforcers on behavior can readily be encompassed by the concepts of operant level and competing responses which are already familiar in the analysis of learning. The causal factors appropriate to the reinforcer, perhaps in interaction with some stimuli in the experimental situation, may tend to cause behavior incompatible with the response that is being reinforced, or at least incompatible with the reinforced response occurring at a high rate. On this view, differences in the ease of training pigeons to peck for food and to avoid shock, for example, can be attributed simply to different initial levels of pecking brought about by the two drive states and/or by shock tending to cause a high rate of behavior incompatible with pecking. However, the causal factors necessary for the reinforcer to be effective and those necessary for the response to be performed may be not simply incompatible but mutually inhibitory. In general it may be difficult to distinguish competitive from inhibitory relationships (but see McFarland, 1969), but in some carefully analyzed cases there is evidence for central inhibitory relationships between systems of behavior (e.g., Sevenster, 1961). The implication of this notion for learning experiments is that there may be cases in which a response dependent on the presence of its normal causal factors cannot be performed for a given reinforcer because the factors necessary for the reinforcer to be effective have an inhibitory relation to the system to which the response belongs. An experiment reported by Sevenster (1968) clearly demonstrates this kind of effect.

Sevenster trained male sticklebacks, *Gasterosteus aculeatus*, to bite a rod or swim through a ring for the opportunity to display at a sexually ripe female. The fish acquired both of these responses about equally fast, but they performed them at very different rates. They swam through the ring at about as high a rate as could be expected, given that the courting sequence initiated various other behaviors such as visiting the nest (training was done in the males' home tanks). But they bit the rod at a rather low rate with about three minutes between responses. In extinction, however, the rate of rod biting immediately rose and equalled the rate of swimming through the ring (Fig. 5).

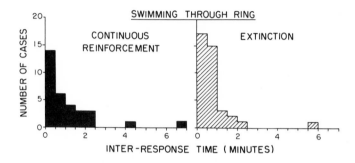

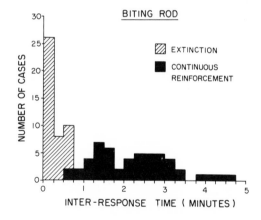

Fɪɢ. 5. Distributions of interresponse times during continuous reinforcement and extinction for male sticklebacks that were swimming through a ring or biting a rod for the opportunity to court a female. After Sevenster (1968).

Observation of the fish during training and knowledge of the normal context of biting suggested a simple and compelling explanation for the differences between the two responses. The stickleback's biting response is normally associated with aggressive motivation. Both aggressive and sexual tendencies are usually present in sexual encounters and are mutually inhibitory. Observation of the males biting the rod suggested that the interaction between sex and aggression was responsible for the long interresponse times. The male usually visited the rod quite soon after withdrawal of the female, but instead of biting it he performed zigzags (indicative of a conflict between sex and aggression) and sometimes made slow biting movements near the rod. Because the motivational significance of all the behaviors the fish displayed in the conditioning experiments had been worked out independently (e.g., Sevenster, 1961), it was possible to conclude that although the biting response had come to some extent under the control of reinforcement, it was still controlled by its normal aggressive factors. Because sexual motivation was raised by presentation of the female, aggression, and thus the biting operant, was inhibited immediately after reinforcement, even though the fish acted as if it "knew" what it had to do. The increased biting rate in extinction can be accounted for similarly by the absence of these inhibitory factors once reinforcement ceased. Swimming, on the other hand, appears to be "motivationally neutral" in the sense of having no tight relationship to any particular behavioral system. Thus it was not subject to such effects.

This interpretation suggests that if the opportunity to display aggressively to another male was made contingent on biting, the fish would bite the rod at a high rate. This did happen in a single fish trained by the time of Sevenster's published report as well as in others trained subsequently (Sevenster, personal communication, 1969). Furthermore, when the fish were biting the rod to see the female on a ratio schedule, the interresponse times following nonreinforcement were short like those in extinction, while those following reinforcement as well as those following noncontingent presentations of the female were as long as those in training with continuous reinforcement.

Although Sevenster's experiment is a unique example of the fruitfulness of applying motivational analysis to otherwise paradoxical behavior in a learning experiment, there are probably other examples of the kind of inhibitory relationship it illustrates. For example, in some animals grooming and other maintenance activities are thought to occur only when factors for all other behaviors are at a low level or are mutually inhibiting each other (Andrew, 1956; Rowell, 1961). The level of hunger or thirst necessary to make food or water effective reinforcers might actively inhibit grooming and thereby make it appear difficult to condition. This kind of effect could have contributed to the difficulty of conditioning grooming and similar responses in the experiments of Konorski and others referred to earlier. Similarly, the difficulty of conditioning pecking and bar-pressing for shock escape or avoidance may be due partly to fear inhibiting these responses. However, especially in the case of positive reinforcers, it is also possible that responses elicited by the reinforcer become classically conditioned to stimuli preceding reinforcement (for example, the manipulandum). Such classically conditioned responses might facilitate the acquisition of some operants and retard or prevent the acquisition of others. Such an effect appears in one of Hogan's (1961) experiments with *Betta splendens*. A male trained to push a rod for display reinforcement displayed at and attacked the rod. Similar effects might be partly responsible for the phenomena described by the Brelands (1961, 1966).

In conclusion then, motivational effects arising from the relationships of responses and reinforcers may limit the effectiveness of experimental contingencies of reinforcement. This can mean that whether something is a reinforcer depends on what response it is contingent on, and, conversely, that whether a response can be reinforced depends on what the reinforcer is. Such relativity of reinforcer and reinforceable response has also been suggested by Premack (1965), although on a somewhat different basis. Both his and the present notions contradict the idea that reinforcers are necessarily transsituational. However, as Meehl (1950) points out, the proposition that anything that reinforces one response will reinforce all learnable responses can be regarded as an empirical one requiring experimental proof. Meehl's arguments notwithstanding, the transsituationality of reinforcers is often taken for granted (cf. Teitelbaum, 1966; Miller and Carmona, 1967) even though the experiments described here show that response–reinforcer interactions can at least severely limit the effectiveness of reinforcement contingencies. Functional considerations also suggest that any reinforcer would not necessarily control any response. Clearly there is a need for more explicit comparisons of the effects of different reinforcers on the same response and/or the effects of one reinforcer on different responses to increase our understanding of how constraints are imposed on learning by the reinforcer–response relation as well as by the nature of particular responses or particular reinforcers per se. The present discussion also implies that it may be useful, if not essential, to accompany such experiments with an attempt to understand the role of the responses and the reinforcers under study in the normal behavioral organization of the species.

C. AUTOSHAPING

The phenomenon known as autoshaping belongs in a general way in our discussion of direct, as opposed to contingent, effects of reinforcers. In some respects it is simply a further demonstration of how causal factors relevant to the reinforcer may affect the response, in this case determining its form, but it has some unique characteristics which also place it beyond the pale of traditional conditioning principles. The basic phenomenon, as described by Brown and Jenkins (1968), is that a hungry pigeon placed in a key-pecking chamber and presented with food on an irregular schedule regardless of what it is doing will begin to peck the key within fifty trials or so, provided the key is lighted briefly before each food presentation. Appropriate control experiments have shown that the initiation of pecking depends on the contingency between the lighting of the key and the presentation of food. Pecking does not begin if the key is illuminated continuously, and it does not depend on the key's being illuminated by the same color light as that which illuminates the food tray.

Not only is autoshaping observed when there is no contingency between key-pecks and food, but pigeons even continue to peck the key when pecking specifically prevents food presentation (Williams and Williams, 1969). Such "automaintenance" is sensitive to reinforcement contingencies to some extent, however, since when the illumination of two keys signals food presentation the birds come to peck the one that does not cancel reinforcements, even though food would be presented if they made no response at all.

Now it is tempting to conclude that the apparently deterministic emergence of key-pecking, rather than some other behavior not directed toward the key, has something to do with the fact that the pigeons are hungry and/or that they are being reinforced with food. This interpretation is supported by the film of Jenkins and Arnold (1968) showing pigeons autoshaped for water reward. They, too, come to depress the key when it is lighted, but their "pecks" are clearly drinking movements of the beak and throat; this difference is not confined to autoshaped birds (Wolin, 1968). This suggestion is also supported by Breland and Breland's (1966) observations that, when animals of a number of species were trained to manipulate an object in order to get food, the object (whose presentation, like that of the key light in the autoshaping experiments, always precedes food) began to elicit food-related behaviors. These observations fail to account for the directed quality of the autoshaped pecks, but they do suggest that it is not unique to pigeons. Bobwhite quail (Gardner, 1969), monkeys (Sidman and Fletcher, 1968), and various fish (Squier, 1969) have also been autoshaped. In all these cases the patterns which emerged can be seen as similar to those involved in collecting or eating the food reinforcer.

All these findings suggest that an invariable result of presenting an animal with a signal followed by food or water is the emergence of food- or water-related behaviors directed toward the signal if it is localized. (An interesting question, then, is what happens if the signal is not localizable.) The autoshaping procedure is identical to one of classical conditioning except that the autoshaped animals are free to move about.

This notion suggests that autoshaping can be seen as classical conditioning of feeding responses to the key or whatever other stimulus precedes food, but it still fails to account for why the behavior is directed as it is. It does raise the question, however, whether dogs in a salivary conditioning experiment would run over and lick the CS if they were not strapped down.

This interpretation suggests that autoshaped pecking should not be obtained in an escape or avoidance paradigm. However, Rachlin (1969) has reported that some pigeons spontaneously begin to peck a key which is lighted just before the termination of a train of shocks. In order for this behavior to appear, however, it was necessary for the key to have a hemispherical covering projecting out into the chamber, and this resulted in some birds hitting the key with their wings as they moved about upon being shocked. Some of these birds learned to depress the key by wing-flapping instead of by key-pecking. The proportion of birds learning to peck decreased when the projection on the key was removed. On the other hand, it also decreased when the key was illuminated continuously, just as in the autoshaping experiments with food. However, only a few pigeons were run in each condition, and even those that did begin pecking did so very erratically, even when pecking was continuously reinforced with escape from shock. Also, whereas Brown and Jenkins observed their birds orienting toward the key on several trials before their first peck, Rachlin observed his pigeons only at the moment of reinforcement and did not see any orienting behavior.

In view of these peculiarities and of the other problems surrounding key-pecking as an avoidance response, perhaps the only possible conclusion is that further study of this phenomenon is needed. It might be noted, however, that wild rats also display behavior that could be described as autoshaping: if a novel object like a rubber ball is introduced into the cage of a wild or half-wild rat, *Rattus norvegicus,* immediately before it is shocked, the rat will attack the novel object and will do so in preference to attacking a similar object that has been present in its cage for some time (Galef, 1970). If the novel object were a lever or a lighted key, the rats might be said to be exhibiting autoshaped escape or avoidance responses. Therefore, it might be asked whether the pigeons' behavior in Rachlin's experiments is a similar case of shock-elicited aggression by finding, for example, whether replacing the key light by a more salient stimulus and having it appear just before the onset of shock makes pecking emerge sooner and makes it more likely to be maintained. New information about autoshaping is accumulating at a rapid rate, however. It seems likely that the next few years will see considerable elucidation of this phenomenon, possibly along entirely different lines from those discussed here.

VI. The Relationship between the Stimulus and the Response

A. Direct Effects of Stimuli

External stimuli used in learning experiments can be unconditioned causal factors for behavior just as can internal states and reinforcing stimuli. However, in considerations of how external stimuli gain control of behavior, those that are not initially "neutral" are generally implicitly or explicitly excluded. This seems to be mainly because the responses elicited by such stimuli may compete with the response to be conditioned and thereby make it difficult to assess the effects of reinforcement. However, Pavlov (1927) reports that under some conditions strong noxious stimuli like electric shock or pricks to the dog's skin could become conditioned stimuli for salivation. There has been little other work on whether there are any limits on the extent to which causal factors for one response can be made causal factors for another or on whether conditioning with stimuli that are not initially neutral has any unusual properties.

Just as the internal state produced by the reinforcer or the internal state necessary for the reinforcer's effectiveness may cause specific responses, so an internal state may interact with apparently neutral external stimuli to alter behavior. In learning experiments such an effect is known as pseudoconditioning or sensitization. It is particularly common in experiments with electric shock. For example, Myers (1962, 1964) found that rats learned two different avoidance tasks faster with a buzzer as a warning stimulus than with a light or a tone, but they also performed the response at a high level in the presence of the buzzer when they simply received shocks unpaired with the buzzer. Similarly, when they are signals for shock some frequencies of white noise pulses produce faster acquisition of conditioned suppression of bar-pressing in rats than do others, and this apparently reflects how much the various sounds cause shocked rats to freeze (de Toledo, 1971). Because such effects are commonly taken into account in assessing the effects of experimental contingencies (review in Kling and Stevenson, 1970), we shall not consider them further here, except to note, as have Bolles (1970) and Garcia et al. (1972), that the concern not to confuse pseudoconditioning, sensitization, and the like with true conditioning can obscure the fact that in nature these processes may be as important as true conditioning in bringing about adaptive behavior.

B. Associative Predispositions:
Specificity of Stimulus to Response

The effects of stimuli on responses reviewed in the preceding section, as well as most of the interactions between responses and reinforcers and constraints on the conditionability of responses discussed in previous sections, are motivational in nature rather than specifically associative. Such factors as the eliciting properties of drive states or reinforcers or the dependence of responses on their normal causal factors may limit the effectiveness of contingencies of reinforcement, but they are not constraints on learning per se. The effects of such motivational factors in learning experiments can probably be accounted for in terms of the kind of causal analysis familiar from the study of other aspects of behavior. On the other hand, some constraints on the control of behavior by external stimuli appear to be specifically associative in nature. In some cases, one class of stimuli selectively gains control of behavior in one situation, while a class of stimuli that has little or no control in the first situation selectively controls behavior in another. Stimuli may be specific to responses or to reinforcers.

To demonstrate that the external stimuli which can become causal factors for responses depend on the response, it is necessary to use one reinforcer and the same few stimuli while varying the response to be conditioned. Konorski and his colleagues are responsible for perhaps the only set of experiments in which this has been done. Dobrzecka et al. (1966) trained dogs on two operant discrimination tasks with similar compound discriminative stimuli but different responses. In one task, dogs were trained to place the left foreleg on the feeder when a metronome sounded from in front of them and to place the right foreleg on the feeder when a buzzer sounded from behind. When they were performing very accurately they were tested with the metronome behind and the buzzer in front. Most dogs responded primarily to the position of the sounds regardless of their quality (for example, they placed the left foreleg whether the buzzer or the metronome was in front). In contrast, when dogs were trained to move a foreleg in response to a metronome in front and not to move in response to a buzzer behind, similar tests revealed that they were responding primarily on the basis of the quality of the sounds and ignoring their position (Fig. 6). In this experiment similar results were obtained with tones of different frequencies. Further experiments showed that dogs learned the left–right differentiation only very slowly with qualitative cues alone, while they took many trials to learn the go–no go differentiation when only directional cues were available. Konorski (1967) reports that Lawicka has found similar results with monkeys.

Konorski's view (1964, 1967) of these findings is that cases of little or no learning are due to the absence of predisposing connections between the centers involved in the task. Results like these, which do not involve a simple attentional factor, probably do have some such anatomical basis, but at this stage of knowledge about the anatomical basis

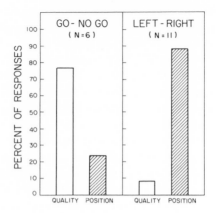

Fig. 6. Responding on test trials for two groups of dogs trained on a left–right or a go–no go discrimination with the same stimuli, which differed in both quality and position. They were trained with a metronome in front and a buzzer behind and tested with the buzzer in front and the metronome behind. The figure shows the percent of responses that were according to the position of the signal, front or back, and the percent according to quality, buzzer or metronome. For example, a dog trained to respond to the buzzer behind and not to the metronome in front would be counted as giving a position response if he responded when the metronome was behind him or if he failed to respond when the buzzer was in front. Data from Dobrzecka *et al.* (1966).

of learning it is questionable whether anatomical speculation can predict new constraints on learning. Furthermore, while these experiments do demonstrate a constraint on the stimuli that can control a given response, the phenomenon needs further analysis. For example, does the propensity of directionally differentiated responses to be controlled by directionally differentiated stimuli extend to other stimulus modalities (such as visual and tactile), reinforcers other than food, and responses other than paw-placing? Do the directionally differentiated responses have to be responses of different limbs, or would the location of discriminative stimuli also selectively control differentially oriented responses of the same limb like placing the paw to the left and placing it to the right? Experiments designed to answer these questions would clarify the nature of the constraint on learning demonstrated by Dobrzecka *et al.*

VII. SPECIFICITY OF STIMULUS TO REINFORCER

Animals may have predispositions to associate specific stimuli with specific reinforcers as well as with specific responses. Such stimulus–reinforcer specificity can be revealed in experiments where the same stimuli are paired with different reinforcers while the response is kept constant. Here we discuss two examples of this kind of constraint on learning. Both of them also illustrate how animals may be specialized to learn especially easily about the relationships among events which are most likely to obtain in natural conditions.

A. ASSOCIATIVE PREDISPOSITIONS IN POISON-AVOIDANCE LEARNING

The most thoroughly studied and best-known example of constraints on the stimuli which can be associated with a given reinforcer arises in the poison-avoidance behavior of rats. A number of experiments by Garcia and others (reviews by Garcia and Ervin, 1968; Garcia et al., 1972; Revusky and Garcia, 1970; Rozin and Kalat, 1971) have shown that, if a rat eats something that makes him sick, or if he is made sick some time after eating by injections of apomorphine or lithium chloride or by x-irradiation, he later avoids foods with the same taste but neither those with the same appearance nor those accompanied by a distinctive sound which was on when he ate the poisoned food. In contrast, if the rat is shocked immediately upon eating he later avoids foods accompanied by the same exteroceptive stimuli but not those with the same taste. Presentation of the tastes and the exteroceptive stimuli to shocked and poisoned rats have not always been strictly equated in such experiments, but a growing number of experiments clearly show that rats have the ability to associate the taste of a substance with sickness experienced some hours after eating and that this ability does not extend to other aspects of the substance like its temperature, its texture, or features of the dish from which it was eaten (reviews by Rozin and Kalat, 1971). Since rats cannot vomit and therefore presumably do not experience aftertastes, the delay must be bridged centrally. This interpretation is given especially strong support by the fact that rats come to reject selectively a substance in one concentration but not in another if ingestion of one concentration is followed by sickness (Rozin, 1969a).

Such experiments demonstrate quite clearly that the rat's learning ability is adapted to the fact that illness or well-being normally is caused by something ingested, that it normally occurs some time after ingesting the thing that causes it, and that foods can be reliably distinguished by their tastes. Where they were eaten and what they looked like are less reliable cues to their identity. In contrast, causal relationships among exteroceptive events are normally immediate. The adaptation of learning mechanisms to this kind of causation is reflected in the considerable decrements in learning when the delay between an exteroceptive stimulus and a reinforcer like food or shock is more than seconds or fractions of seconds.

Not only does poison-avoidance learning take place over longer stimulus–reinforcer intervals than most learning involving purely exteroceptive stimuli, it also appears to violate the "law" that the stimulus temporally most contiguous with the reinforcer will be associated with it most strongly. The novelty of a gustatory CS may be more important than its contiguity with sickness: rats poisoned after eating some of a new and some of a familiar food later selectively reject the new food, regardless of whether they eat it first or second on the training day (Revusky and Bedarf, 1967). Some novel tastes are more readily associated with the effects of poisoning than others, although these differences could be due partly to differences in the similarity of the tastes to the flavor of the rat's usual food (Kalat and Rozin, 1970).

The behavior of rats toward novel foods is also nicely adapted to facilitate learning whether they are poisonous or beneficial. Rats encountering a new food typically take only a small amount and wait some time before taking more (Shorten, 1954; Rozin, 1969b). Since young rats follow adults in the colony and eat what they are eating, even when other foods are available (Galef and Clark, 1971), they will display this neophobic reaction toward any other, possibly poisonous, food and thereby be likely to learn very quickly about its nutritional value. Thus the rat's specialized ability to associate tastes with sickness or well-being is part of a whole system of behavior which allows it to select beneficial foods and avoid poisonous ones.

Faster learning with unfamiliar than with familiar stimuli is not peculiar to poison-avoidance learning, however. The observation that novel stimuli acquire control of behavior more readily than ones to which the subject has been repeatedly exposed was first made by Pavlov (1927), who called the phenomenon latent inhibition. It has more recently been observed in a variety of classical and operant conditioning situations (e.g., Shettleworth, 1972a; review by Siegel, 1972). It is clearly an adaptive mode of behavior. If something new and biologically significant happens to an animal (the reinforcer), another novel stimulus is more likely than an old familiar stimulus to have had something to do with it. In displaying latent inhibition animals display a behavioral adaptation to this fact about the world (cf. Oatley, 1970).

The ability to associate the taste of a food with sickness following its ingestion by several hours is probably not confined to rats, although it may be especially well developed in wild rats because of selective pressure from man. However, there is some evidence that species differ in the stimuli they use to identify poisoned foods. Wilcoxon et al. (1971) gave rats and bobwhite quail, Colinus virginianus, sickness-inducing injections 30 minutes after they had drunk the same sour blue solution. In subsequent tests with liquids that were only sour or only blue, the rats rejected only the sour liquid, but the quail rejected both blue and sour liquids.

These results clearly show that the quail can learn something that rats cannot, but it is impossible to make any useful statements about the relative abilities of rats and quail to associate tastes with sickness, since, among other things, the particular tastes involved, as well as the visual stimuli, may have been more discriminable or salient for one species than for the other. In such comparative experiments it is difficult to separate sensory and associative abilities without testing members of the species under consideration in several situations.

B. A SPECIALIZED LEARNING ABILITY IN THE RECOGNITION
   OF UNPALATABLE OBJECTS

Another adaptively specialized learning ability which probably represents a predisposition to associate certain stimuli with certain reinforcers arises in animals' learning to avoid attempting to consume unpalatable substances. Members of a wide variety of species seem to associate the appearance of a potential food object with its taste very readily (Cott, 1940). The ability of insectivorous predators to do so plays a role in mimicry systems: insects that are unpalatable to their predators tend to be distinctively colored and patterned, and, because the predators learn to avoid them on this basis, some palatable insects have evolved similar patterns (Cott, 1940; Rettenmeyer, 1970). Some young animals also seem to rely at least partly on visual–taste associations in learning what to eat and drink. Domestic chicks, *Gallus gallus,* provide one example: right after hatching they peck indiscriminately at all small objects and they do not recognize water. However, within a few days they come to peck predominately at food, they avoid pecking at their own feces and other objects that elicit rejection, and they recognize water. Of course, mother hens may have some role in directing them to food and water, but they can learn by themselves what to eat and drink, and normally visual cues would be the only basis on which they could do so. The question arises, then, whether they have a specialized ability to take advantage of the natural relationship between how things look and how they taste, as opposed to some arbitrary and normally irrelevant relationship like that between sounds that might accompany water or food and their tastes. The following experiments directed to this problem (Shettleworth, 1972b) illustrate how such a question, arising from functional considerations, can be tackled.

In a series of experiments similar to those that Brower and others (e.g., Brower, 1958; Brower *et al.,* 1960) have used to investigate mimicry, Shettleworth trained young domestic chicks on successive discriminations between plain, palatable water and water made "unpalatable" with quinine or with a mild shock which the chicks received through the beak when they touched it. The "unpalatable" water was distinguished from the palatable water by the presence or absence of several visual and auditory cues. The rates at which the chicks learned to avoid touching it were compared for the various cues.

There were large differences in learning with the different discriminative stimuli: when either the color of the water or the flashing of the light illuminating the testing chamber was the discriminative stimulus, chicks learned within a few trials to avoid touching the unpalatable water while they continued to drink the palatable water readily. With either a clicking sound or a loud interrupted tone, they did not appear to learn at all, although when they received a rather strong shock for drinking, they did show some signs of learning with the clicks. As might be expected from these results, when the presence or absence of a compound of the flashing light and clicks signaled the presence of shock for drinking, they learned very quickly and their behavior was completely controlled by the presence or absence of the flashing light (Fig. 7).

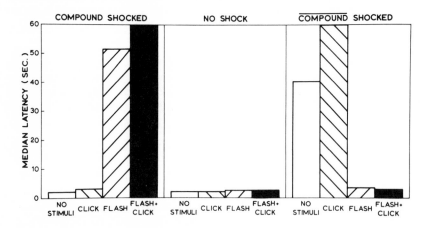

FIG. 7. Median latencies to touch the water on test trials for three groups of domestic chicks shocked for drinking in the presence of a compound of a flashing light and a clicking sound, not shocked at all, or shocked for drinking in the absence of the compound stimulus. During the test session the compound, the no-stimulus condition, the flashing light, and the clicks alone were presented to each bird. From Shettleworth (1970).

These differences between visual and auditory stimuli were not due to the chicks' being unable to hear the sounds. On their initial presentations both the clicks and the tone caused a significant increase in the chicks' latency to drink. The tone even had a much larger effect than either of the visual stimuli. Under some conditions the unconditioned reaction to the sounds persisted for a number of trials and was finally replaced by complete absence of differential behavior in the presence and absence of sound. This indicates that the failure to learn with the sounds was probably not due to too rapid habituation to them.

The poor learning with sounds also does not appear to be due to their not being localized in the water, since the flashing light, which supported rapid learning, was also diffuse. A visual stimulus explicitly removed from the water — the presence or absence of colored stripes on the tray beside the water dish — supported better discrimination learning than the sounds, although not as good as that with the other two visual stimuli. However, the unconditioned effects of the stripes showed that the chicks noticed them. Thus the location of visual stimuli with respect to the water appears to have some effect on how rapidly chicks associate them with immediate consequences of drinking. However, moving the speaker from the ceiling to just behind the water dish did not increase the effectiveness of sounds.

All this evidence strongly suggests that chicks do have a predisposition to associate visual but not auditory stimuli with immediate aversive consequences of drinking. But it is also possible that chicks do not learn about the more or less arbitrary sounds used in these experiments in any situation. This possibility was examined by using both the clicking sound and the flashing light in a second conditioning paradigm. Chicks of the same ages as before were simply placed in the same apparatus and given a series of Pavlovian fear conditioning trials in which the flashing light or the clicks came on for 20 seconds and was immediately followed by a brief foot shock. Control groups had a stimulus and shocks unpaired in a mixed order. The experimental chicks clearly associated the clicks and shock: within a few trials they began to run around, jump, and shrill call whenever the sound came on. The controls displayed similar behavior for the first few trials, but later they did not change their behavior at all when the sound came on. With the flashing light as the CS, on the other hand, the changes in the chicks' behavior were much less dramatic, and on the whole the experimentals and controls did not differ significantly. Furthermore, the behavior of chicks trained in this procedure with the compound of flashing light and clicks was controlled primarily by the sound, as tests with the flashing light or the clicks alone showed (Fig. 8). Therefore it seems possible to conclude that domestic chicks do have a specific predisposition to associate visual stimuli with immediate consequences of drinking. It may also be that they selectively associate sound with a painful stimulus like shock to the feet, but this probably needs further testing in a second fear-conditioning situation.

Although these experiments were done to investigate the possible non-arbitrariness of the stimuli chicks can associate with the consequences of drinking, they also demonstrate that to some extent domestic chicks can acquire associations between elements that are arbitrarily related with respect to natural contingencies. Changes in illumination throughout the whole environment would seem to be as unnatural a cue

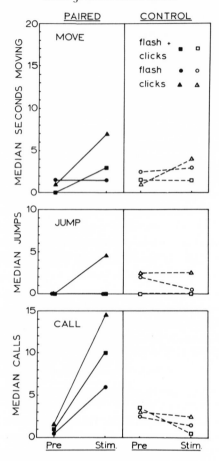

FIG. 8. Behavior during a test session of domestic chicks which had had Pavlovian conditioning in which the compound of flashing light and clicking sound signaled a brief foot shock. The figure shows the median number of jumps, calls, and seconds moving during the 20 seconds preceding stimulus presentation and during the 20 seconds of the stimulus on trials with the compound stimulus and on trials with each of its elements separately for the group that had had the compound paired with shock and for a control group that had had the compound explicitly unpaired with shocks. From Shettleworth (1970).

to the palatability of water as sounds, yet in the drinking experiments chicks learned relatively rapidly with the flashing light while they learned very little if at all with the sounds. Similarly, whether the aversive consequence of drinking was a bad taste or the "unnatural" stimulus of shock through the beak made no difference to what stimuli acquired control of the chicks' drinking. These aspects of the results emphasize that, although considering the normal function of various kinds of learning may generate predictions that might never be considered otherwise, saying that animals can only learn things that would be relevant in nature is as much an oversimplification as saying that they can learn anything.

Although Shettleworth's results clearly demonstrate that what stimuli come to control behavior may depend on the situation in which they are used, it is still necessary to analyze which of the many differences between the two conditioning paradigms are responsible for the differences in stimulus control between them. The specificity of the rat's poison-avoidance learning to taste has been interpreted as suggesting that rats have some neural circuitry specialized so that only memories of tastes are accessible to information about gastrointestinal states. The fact that in Shettleworth's experiments beak shock and bad tastes had effects similar to each other suggests that chicks may be built to associate visual stimuli with stimuli from the beak. But the results of experiments giving chicks foot shocks rather than beak shocks for drinking are more compatible with specificity of visual control to the response of drinking.

Unlike the experiments of Garcia and others on poison-avoidance behavior, Shettleworth's experiments rely on comparing results from two vastly different experimental paradigms. Any or all of the differences between them could be responsible for the differences in stimulus control. However, what is known about most of these differences (for example, that in duration and temporal relationship of the stimuli and shocks) cannot account for the reversal in the relative potency of visual and auditory stimuli from one of these paradigms to the other. The interpretation of these results in terms of chicks having an adaptively specialized associative ability is very compelling on functional grounds. These problems are raised simply to emphasize that it may take considerable experimental analysis before something apparently as straightforward as a specialized ability to learn is understood or even demonstrated. There are many examples of animals learning obviously adaptive things very quickly (e.g., Eibl-Eibesfeldt, 1970, Chapter 13). However, much more than such observations is needed before it can be concluded that any animal has a specialized ability to learn only certain things.

VIII. Learning in the Wild

To say that the behavior of animals in learning experiments cannot be understood independently of what and how they learn in the wild is to imply that psychological accounts of learning should at least consider the role of learning in the wild. We must begin to ask how far the principles of learning developed for relatively few species in laboratory situations can encompass the learning that animals do in natural conditions. It also seems that what constraints there are on learning would constrain behavior to develop in species-typical ways. Therefore examples of the role of experience in the natural development and modification of behavior might provide particularly rich material for research into the nature of constraints on learning.

The aim of presenting the following few examples of learning in the wild (see Thorpe, 1956, and Eibl-Eibesfeldt, 1970, for further examples) is not primarily to demonstrate that all such learning can be reduced to classical or operant conditioning. Indeed, quite the opposite is intended. Nevertheless, approaching learning in the wild in terms of conventional learning principles can be useful, even if only to show where they fall short. However, it will become apparent in the course of this discussion that much learning in the wild does exemplify the kinds of learning that have been analyzed in the laboratory, even though it has not always been approached in this way. Our first example, the analysis of the development and organization of movement patterns, illustrates both the applicability of conventional learning principles to learning in the wild and some of the new problems such an analysis raises.

A. THE FORM AND ORGANIZATION OF MOVEMENT PATTERNS

Movement patterns may take the form they have in mature, experienced individuals through shaping or trial-and-error learning. For example, some finches apparently perfect their skill in husking seeds through operant reinforcement. Nestling chaffinches mandibulate seeds of various sizes and gradually begin to husk them. They husk those with the thinnest coverings earliest and only later learn to open those like sunflower seeds which must be held in a special position in the bill to be cracked. The fact that finch species with relatively large bills can husk large tough seeds most efficiently while those with small bills can obtain food most efficiently from small seeds appears to account in part for the different food preferences of different finch species living in the same area (Kear, 1962).

The way squirrels learn to crack nuts is similar in some respects. Red squirrels, *Sciurus vulgaris,* open hazelnuts by gnawing one or two lengthwise furrows in their shells and then cracking them by inserting their teeth into the furrows. Inexperienced squirrels pick up hazelnuts and gnaw furrows all over them until they crack, but gradually they reduce the number of furrows and orient them lengthwise along the grooves in the nutshell (Eibl-Eibesfeldt, 1967). This is not simply due to improvement of the squirrel's coordination with age because it happens in squirrels not given nuts until they are several months old. The most efficient movements may be selected by operant reinforcement because they result in the kernel of the nut being obtained most quickly. However, things are not that simple. Eibl-Eibesfeldt reports that some inexperienced squirrels given nutshells with the kernels removed also continued to open them and became more efficient at doing so, which means that the improvement is not brought about solely by food reinforcement. But the kernels must have some reinforcing value, because experienced squirrels learned to choose nuts with kernels over those with the kernels removed.

Eibl-Eibesfeldt emphasizes that on their first encounter with nuts his squirrels showed all the nut-cracking movements of experienced squirrels. In the course of experience the unsuccessful movements dropped out and only the furrowing which was oriented most efficiently remained. However, movements can also change in form through experience. For example, the first time young domestic chicks encounter water, they peck at it as they would peck at any shiny object. Pecking brings water into the beak, which elicits head-raising and swallowing. This experience brings about an immediate and dramatic change in the chick's behavior. Whereas it may initially have encountered water in the course of exploratory pecking, it now pecks repeatedly at the water and the water container. This usually brings more water into its beak. If it is then deprived of water, it will approach water when it is offered again, but it still obtains water largely by pecking movements followed by head-raising and swallowing. Only over the course of several days and some hundreds of drinks does the chick begin to display a smooth coordinated scooping movement accompanied by swallowing movements while the beak is submerged. This change is not merely a function of age, since the drinking responses of chicks tube-fed water for the first four days develop similarly to those of chicks given water from the day of hatching (Shettleworth, unpublished observations, 1968). The behavior of chicks taking their first drinks suggests that water (or performing the movements of head-raising and swallowing elicited by it) is positively reinforcing for them, so it may be that the scooping and swallowing pattern develops because it yields more water per drink, but, as in the case of the squirrels' nut-cracking, some of the changes might be independent of experience.

In the foregoing cases, all members of a species develop nearly identical movements. The question arises whether this occurs because the environmental circumstances are similar for all species members or because they have a common predisposition to acquire a particular pattern. Demonstrations that physically abnormal individuals develop idiosyncratic forms of a movement suggest that the common experience of most species members can be important in shaping the species-typical form. For example, birds with grossly abnormal bills may be fat and healthy even though they obviously could not feed themselves normally (Pomeroy, 1962). Some of these individuals have been observed scraping up food with their beaks held sideways on the ground. Others, like hens whose upper mandibles have been clipped, obtain food with abnormal scooping movements.

Similarly, Eibl-Eibesfeldt (1967) reports that one of his squirrels succeeded in opening hazelnuts by gnawing a circular furrow at one end. This animal apparently never switched to the more common method of gnawing a lengthwise furrow and then splitting the shell. The fact that most squirrels do develop the lengthwise furrowing method seems to be due to the way the structure of the nut guides their movements. This could be studied more directly by seeing how squirrels learn to open nuts of different shapes, textures, and hardnesses. They are probably not constrained to use a single method regardless of the structure of the nuts they encounter. Both Eibl-Eibesfeldt's observations and those of Pomeroy suggest that the lack of variation in normal individuals occurs because there is normally so little variation in the effectors and in the external stimulus situation rather than because the species-typical patterns are developed and maintained independently of reinforcement. But factors such as those discussed in the section on response–reinforcer interactions still could constrain the movements animals can learn to obtain various reinforcers.

However, some notions about development imply that some of the motivational constraints on learning are absent in very young animals. Kruijt (1964) and Hogan (1971) suggest that behavior early in development consists of more or less causally independent elements not yet organized into systems of responses with common causal factors. This implies that constraints on learning like those due to interactions between the causal factors for the response and the causal factors for the effectiveness of the reinforcer might not be operative in very young animals. It is an open question whether this also means that, in contrast to the case in adult animals, arbitrarily chosen responses could come to have arbitrarily chosen causal factors.

Operant reinforcement could have some role during development in organizing responses into systems with common causal factors. In some cases it does have a role, but not always the one that might be expected. For example, whereas Kruijt (1964) found that the sexual and aggressive behavior of the Burmese red jungle fowl, *Gallus gallus spadiceus,* gradually became organized during the course of normal social experience, Hogan (1971) found that, in contrast, this bird's feeding behavior was already organized at hatching. Ground scratching and pecking, the two movements that would function to obtain food, tended to occur together in jungle fowl chicks a few days old. However, under the conditions of Hogan's experiments where ground scratching had no function because food was freely available and did not need to be uncovered, ground scratching lost its correlation with pecking as the birds grew older. Hogan suggests that if ground scratching had functioned to obtain food it would have remained correlated with pecking and food deprivation. Thus, in this case, reinforcement apparently functions not to bring about a new organization of responses but to maintain a pre-existing one.

The notion that behaviors shown by young animals prior to experience of their function may not be maintained without reinforcement was referred to by William James (1890) as the transitoriness of instincts: "*Most instincts are implanted for the sake of giving rise to habits*" (p. 402; italics in original). He thought that if such behaviors could not fulfill their function at the proper time they would fade away, but if they did function they would be transformed into habits. The only evidence he gives for this notion is from Spalding's observations that domestic chicks only imprint at a certain age, but it is interesting to note that he also expresses the belief that the behavior of a squirrel described by a Dr. H. D. Schmidt in 1875 would obey the law of transitoriness of instincts. Schmidt observed a young squirrel carry out all the movements of digging a hole and burying a nut on a smooth blanket. Precisely similar observations are cited by Eibl-Eibesfeldt (1967) as evidence that adaptive behavior may occur without prior experience of the situation in which it functions. Such observations certainly illustrate this point, but it is also worth asking whether behavior like the squirrel's digging and burying would continue indefinitely if it never fulfilled its normal function. At least the orientation of the digging movements can be influenced by their consequences, because Eibl-Eibesfeldt reports that when inexperienced squirrels did not cover the nut effectively at first, they continued covering until they were successful, and the orientation of their covering movements improved with experience. But this does not necessarily mean that the tendency of the behavior to occur at all in the presence of nuts could be modified by its consequences. As we have seen in a previous section, it is not always possible to predict whether a given response can be modified by a specific reinforcer. Even if such responses as digging and burying in squirrels and ground scratching in jungle fowl are reinforced by their normal consequences, it is a separate question whether they are susceptible to control by other reinforcers. For example, if ground scratching is reinforced by uncovering food or by the opportunity to eat, could it also be reinforced by the opportunity to drink or to engage in sexual behavior? Preliminary results of current experiments by Miranski and Hogan suggest that young jungle fowl learn to ground-scratch only for food reinforcement, although they learn to peck a key for either water or food.

Another question we have encountered before arises again in considering how movement patterns become organized during normal development; this is the question of what events are reinforcing. It seems quite likely that some complex sequences of behavior are maintained by the act that normally brings them to an end. For example, in female canaries gathering and carrying nesting material may be reinforced by the opportunity to perform nest-building movements with it in the nest cup (Hinde, 1958; Hinde and Stevenson, 1969). This is suggested by the observation that birds never given nesting material develop bizarre habits such as plucking out their own feathers that allow them to obtain material with which to perform building movements. On the other hand, early in the nesting season when hormonal factors for nesting are at a low level, inexperienced females gather and carry nesting material without building. Thus the apparently straightforward analysis in terms of operant conditioning is probably as inadequate for this behavior as it is for the nut-cracking behavior of squirrels.

B. LEARNING AND ECOLOGY: MIMICRY SYSTEMS

An example of learning in the wild that can apparently be wholly described in terms of known principles of learning is that involved in avoidance of unpalatable prey. Numerous caged and wild predators have been shown to learn — in many cases after only a few trials — to avoid attacking unpalatable insects and palatable insects that mimic their appearance (reviews by Cott, 1940, and Rettenmeyer, 1970). This learning may be part of a whole system of Batesian mimicry involving the unpalatability of the models, the resemblance of the mimics to the models, and the relative abundance of models and mimics as well as the learning abilities of their predators. Although the factors contributing to this kind of learning have not been studied within model-mimic systems to a great extent, the experiments that have been done show that all the usual parameters of instrumental learning play a role in it and thereby may affect the evolution of such diverse phenomena as the resemblance of unrelated species to each other and the times of year at which prey species emerge.

For example, starlings fed on various proportions of colored quinine-flavored mealworms and visually identical palatable "mimics" refuse the most prey when the proportion of models is largest (Brower, 1960). In an analogous way, pigeons punished with electric shock for various proportions of their pecks peck less the higher the percentage of shocked responses (Azrin *et al.*, 1963; Azrin and Holz, 1966; for a general review of factors in punishment see Solomon, 1964). Food deprivation may decrease the effectiveness of experience with distasteful prey in depressing the tendency to eat it (Sexton *et al.*, 1966), and the presence of alternative prey probably increases the effectiveness of experience with models

(Holling, 1963). Similarly, rats and other mammals increase their intake of an unpalatable food as their deprivation is increased (Miller, 1957; Mrosovsky, 1964), and punishment of a food-reinforced response with electric shock is more effective if an alternative reinforced response is available (Azrin and Holz, 1966). Having learned to reject prey of a given appearance, predators generalize their rejection to similar-appearing mimics, the more so the more similar they are to the models (Sexton, 1959; Duncan and Sheppard, 1965). Analogous results have been obtained in a variety of operant conditioning situations using both positive and negative reinforcement (e.g., Hoffman, 1969). Duncan and Sheppard also found that chicks generalize more, the stronger the electric shock paired with the model. This observation also has parallels in the psychological literature. And, finally, some birds learn to reject novel prey on sight more readily than they learn to reject those resembling familiar palatable prey (Brower, 1958; Shettleworth, 1972a), a futher example of the fact that new associations are formed more readily to a novel stimulus than to a familiar one (see p. 36).

That predators can learn to reject unpalatable prey on sight after very few experiences suggests that they have a special predisposition to associate what something looks like with how it tastes. The fact that unpalatable insects are often brightly colored and patterned and that their mimics evolve similar patterns suggests that indeed their main predators are especially likely to use the appearance of prey as a cue to its edibility. Experiments like those with the chicks already described (pp. 38–41) could be used to discover whether this is so. However, some predators do not use the appearance of their prey exclusively. The prey's behavior, its habitat, and the sounds it makes may also be important (Rettenmeyer, 1970). Different species probably differ in the stimulus dimensions they use to identify their prey, and it would be surprising if the prey did not vary similarly in how they advertise or conceal themselves. Thus, while the prey of diurnal birds may sport warning colors, some arctiid and ctenucid moths that are unpalatable to bats broadcast high-frequency warning sounds when stimulated by a bat's ultrasound. Bats avoid these sounds (Dunning and Roeder, 1965). These moths even have auditory mimics (Dunning, 1968). This suggests, then, that although many animals may be predisposed to associate certain stimuli especially readily with some immediate or delayed consequence of eating, those stimuli vary with the species.

C. SPECIFIC SEARCHING IMAGES

The formation of specific searching images is a kind of learning in the wild similar in many ways to that involved in avoiding unpalatable prey, but it has been suggested to represent a special type of learning. The behavior taken as evidence that an animal has a searching image for a particular kind of prey has two essential characteristics. First, the selection of prey is not what would be expected if prey were taken as they were encountered by chance: prey new in the environment are ignored at first and then suddenly preyed on intensively (de Ruiter, 1952; Tinbergen, 1960). Second, predation is selective: the predator tends to take one kind of prey at a time and ignore other potential prey (Beukema, 1968). This kind of behavior has been attributed to the predator's learning to attend to, or search for, a particular kind of prey. This use of the term attention contrasts with its use in attentional theories of discrimination learning (e.g., Mackintosh, 1965). Such theories assume that attention is to particular stimulus dimensions like brightness or shape. Differential responding to stimuli within a given dimension is achieved by differential reinforcement along that dimension. It does not imply that positive and negative stimuli are differentially attended to. Whether or not one feels that the concept of attention is helpful in understanding discrimination learning in general, the behavior displayed in many of the experiments on specific searching images does not appear to be basically different from conventional operant discrimination learning, and thus, not to call for a different use of the term attention (see also Dawkins, 1971a).

Certainly the behavior indicative of a searching image can be acquired very quickly. For example, the jays in De Ruiter's experiment began to peck at the sticks in their cages, which they had formerly come to ignore, as soon as they had discovered and eaten a single stick caterpillar. However, as we have seen, learning may take place this quickly in a variety of other situations. Most of the ones described here are, like this one, examples of rapid association of the appearance of an object with its edibility. This simply provides more evidence that many animals may have a special ability to associate what something looks like with whether it is good to eat, but it is not evidence that searching image behavior represents a special kind of learning.

There is slightly more evidence that the second and more essential feature of searching image behavior—the predator's selectivity—represents a special kind of learning. Evidence for this characteristic of prey selection can be obtained only from experiments where a predator is confronted simultaneously with two or more kinds of prey known to be acceptable to it. There have been a few experiments like this. Beukema (1968) found that sticklebacks ignored the red worms they had formerly accepted and appeared to be searching for white worms when they had eaten one of the preferred white worms. But this implies no more than a preference for one kind of food over another. That the sticklebacks did not attack and eat the red worms does not imply that they suddenly did not see them. A similar problem arises in many of the experiments of Croze (1970) in which he presented variously colored mussel shells hiding meat to wild or tame carrion crows, *Corvus corone*. In most cases, the crows had only one type of shell available at a time, and the fact that they turned over only these or objects of closely similar appearance should not be surprising. They had had ample opportunity to extinguish their responses to inedible objects in the experimental area like pebbles and sticks. In fact, Croze reports that the crows would sometimes stop to eat some natural prey they encountered on their search for his artificial prey, so they could not have been attending to the experimental prey to the exclusion of all else. Similarly, when both cockle and mussel shells were presented, the crows turned over some of both, although they tended to prefer those that had been rewarded most recently. Again, these facts parallel findings in operant discrimination learning. None of them necessarily implies that the predators did not notice objects that they did not attempt to eat.

However, the results of Croze's "trimorphism" experiment do seem to require something like the searching image concept. In this experiment crows sometimes encountered mussel shells of one color and at other times equal numbers of red, yellow, and black shells in the same place and in the same overall density. They turned significantly fewer shells in the trimorphic population than in the monomorphic populations. Since the crows had previously learned to eat meat from under shells of all three colors, this suggests that indeed they were not searching for or attending to all three colors at once. But if this were the case, they might also be expected to take shells in runs of one color at a time. This did not happen. However, domestic chicks pecking at a mixture of orange and green grains do tend to take several grains of one color and several of another (Dawkins, 1971b).

Croze also compares specific searching image behavior to other kinds of learning, in particular to acquisition of perceptual sets and to matching-to-sample, a situation in which an animal is reinforced for choosing an object like one it has previously been shown. He points out that the situation in which searching image behavior is demonstrated differs from matching-to-sample experiments in that in experiments like his the samples are reinforced rather than simply displayed to the subjects. But this difference in procedure makes the specific searching image situation little different from a simultaneous discrimination training procedure except that in the natural setting the animal is presumably discriminating food objects from among many more alternative stimuli than are ever present in a discrimination experiment in the laboratory.

In conclusion, then, many of the observations which have been interpreted in terms of specific searching images seem to be examples of operant discrimination learning and not to entail any special mechanisms. However, situations in which the predator has two or more equally familiar and acceptable prey objects available at once have yielded observations without parallels in other situations. They might repay further study.

D. LATENT LEARNING AND ORIENTATION

In contrast to the examples described so far, much learning in the wild apparently occurs entirely by mechanisms other than those of classical or operant conditioning. Many observations and experiments show that an animal's behavior at one stage of its life may depend on its having been exposed to certain external stimuli at an earlier time, in the absence of anything that might be called a reinforcer and without performance of the responses which are later affected. Song learning and the learning that determines which species an individual's sexual responses are directed to are examples (reviews in Hinde, 1969; Klinghammer, 1967). One example of this sort of learning displayed by many different kinds of animals is the learning involved in homing. Although latent learning, the learning of a maze without reinforcement, once had considerable interest for psychologists (Kimble, 1961), accounts of this phenomenon have paid little or no attention to examples of this kind of learning in the wild.

One example of apparent "latent learning" is provided by the homing of honeybees (von Frisch, 1953) and of digger wasps. These wasps locate their nests by using nearby landmarks. By inspecting the area around the nest, they learn how to orient approach to the nest on the next return with prey (Fig. 9). They immediately detect when the landmarks have changed, as for example when a pinecone falls near the nest entrance or an experimenter places something there, and change their behavior appropriately on the basis of a short orientation flight before flying away from the nest (Tinbergen, 1958; van Iersel and van den Assem, 1964). The first time a wasp returns to its nest and finds new landmarks, it is clearly disoriented and will make an orientation flight upon leaving the nest. The next time it returns, it seldom appears disoriented. This suggests that new stimuli can completely replace old ones in controlling the wasp's homing after one exposure.

An equally fascinating although less well-analyzed example of the learning of topographies occurs in the gobiid fish, *Bathygobius soporator* (Aronson, 1951). This fish lives near tropical shores. At low tide, individuals may be trapped in tide pools isolated from the sea. If it is disturbed, such a fish may jump out of its pool, and it nearly always lands in a neighboring pool rather than on the intervening rocks (Fig. 10).

Fig. 9. A digger wasp, *Philanthus triangulum,* makes a locality study before leaving the nest when new landmarks have been placed around it. One wasp persistently chose a transposed circle of pinecones over the true nest entrance during a test conducted one hour after it had made a single six-second study of the artificial landmarks. From Tinbergen (1951).

Accurate orientation must depend on experience in the area, since fish moved into a given pool from some distance away did not tend to land in other pools when they jumped. They were probably not using the sun to orient by because they jumped as accurately on cloudy as on sunny days. When Aronson (1956) introduced some of these gobies into a laboratory tank with artificial tide pools, they failed to jump accurately from one pool to another at first, but they did jump accurately when they were again trapped in the pools after they had had 12 hours of "high tide" when they could swim freely over them. Unfortunately, Aronson does not report whether the fish engaged in any special behavior like swimming unusually close to the substrate during the 12-hour learning period which might be necessary to learning the topography of the tank. For more recent experiments on factors influencing ease of learning, and on the cues used by the fish, see Aronson, 1971.

Learning of a similar kind is probably involved in much migration and homing behavior. Even if all species members respond to the same stimuli, learning may be involved. For example, migrating indigo buntings, *Passerina cyanea,* orient by the circumpolar constellations, but planetarium experiments with skies rotating around an arbitrary axis

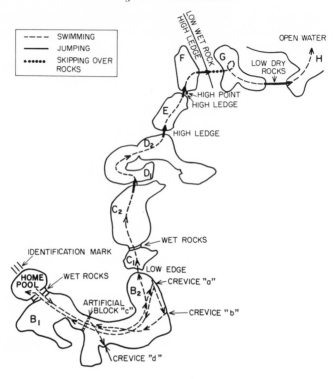

FIG. 10. Path taken by one *Bathygobius soporator* in moving from the home pool to open water. The fish was about 4 cm long; the longest jumps were over 30 cm long. After Aronson (1951).

show that they use whatever constellation happens to be at the pole during a period early in their lives (Emlen, 1970). In any case where individual species members must react to cues peculiar to them, as in finding their own mates, parents, or homes, some individual learning is required, and in many cases it seems to be accomplished without reinforcement of specific responses.

Examples of such learning suggest that different functional categories of behavior (e.g., migration, feeding, individual and species recognition) are modified by experience in adaptively different ways. The models of classical and instrumental conditioning are probably not appropriate to at least some aspects of imprinting, song-learning, homing, and the like. Rather, as Rozin and Kalat (1971) conclude from their more extensive discussion of this point, we might profitably begin to look for and compare different mechanisms of learning in different subsystems of behavior. Even where conventional psychological models seem appropriate to "new" sorts of learning, detailed comparisons are needed. For example, poison-avoidance learning fits the classical conditioning paradigm with the simple exception that conditioning still occurs with the unconditioned response of sickness hours after the taste CS. But more detailed comparisons being carried out by Rozin and Kalat are revealing further differences. For example, the blocking effect of a previously conditioned stimulus on conditioning to an added stimulus element apparently is not found in taste-aversion learning (Rozin and Kalat, 1971).

IX. SPECIES DIFFERENCES

In one sense no special new evidence is needed to show that animals have adaptive predispositions for learning. The very fact that they tend to repeat actions with outcomes that promote survival and tend to refrain from repeating actions with outcomes that are detrimental to survival — that is, that positive and negative reinforcement work — is in itself an adaptive predisposition for learning (Lorenz, 1965). However, while such a generalized predisposition may be common to all species that learn at all, some predispositions to learn may be species-specific. Demonstrations that members of different species learn quite different things in similar situations provide some of the most compelling evidence for constraints on learning.

Most examples of species differences in what is learned in similar situations come from field observations rather than from laboratory conditioning experiments. Differences in whether various sea birds learn to recognize their own eggs or chicks have already been described (pp. 7–8). Whether one of these birds learns to recognize its own egg or chick appears to be related to whether the circumstances in which it nests make it necessary for it to do so. Whether a bird recognizes its own chick is probably also related to whether the chick learns to recognize its own parents: if the chick learns to recognize its parents at an early age or if it tends to stay in the nest (for example, in altricial species or cliff-nesters), the parent would probably not need to learn to recognize it.

Species differences in the role of experience in determining what song a bird will sing and what species it will mate with have been extensively documented. In some cases the adaptive significance of these differences is still obscure, but in others it is quite obvious. For example, the young of a bird that lays its eggs in other birds' nests clearly must be able to mate with birds of its own species rather than birds of the species that raised it. Therefore it cannot depend on experience of its foster parents to select a mate. Nonparasitic altricial species, on the other hand, can and do depend on early experience of the parent bird to select mates. However, the extent to which this experience affects them, as shown by fostering experiments, varies greatly with the species and may even vary with sex within a species. Furthermore, some species that parasitize several different species and lay eggs resembling those of their hosts learn characteristics of their foster parents that enable them to select hosts of the appropriate species (review by Klinghammer, 1967).

Species differences in the role of experience in the development of song by birds have also been extensively described (reviews in Hinde, 1969; Marler, 1970). Some birds need never hear the song of their species to sing it at the appropriate time, while others must hear their species-typical song at a certain time in their lives to sing it properly when they mature. There are many intermediate cases. Those species whose singing is influenced by hearing song vary in the specificity of the song they must hear: some species will imitate virtually any song they hear during a critical period; others, like the white-crowned sparrow, *Zonotrichia leucophrys*, must hear the song of their species. White-crowned sparrows exposed to the very similar song of white-throated sparrows, *Zonotrichia albicollis*, later display the same disorganized vocal behavior as white-crowned sparrows that have never heard song at all (Marler, 1970).

Clearly, then, there are large, and in some cases obviously adaptive, species differences in various kinds of learning by birds. Species differences have also appeared in a variety of laboratory learning studies on mammals. For example, if rats are given the opportunity to hoard food pellets into their cages from a chamber connected to the cage by an upward-sloping tunnel, they always carry the pellets down to their cages (Licklider and Licklider, 1950). But if golden hamsters, *Mesocricetus auratus*, are tested in a similar apparatus, many of them soon learn to stand in the chamber with the pellets and roll them down toward their cages (Waddell, 1951). Even strains within the same species may vary in their response to the same kind of experience (review by Levine, 1962). For instance, the same early handling affects the behavior of two subspecies of deermice, *Peromyscus maniculatus gracilis* and *P.m. bairdii*, on exploration and avoidance tasks in opposite ways (King and Eleftheriou, 1959). It may be possible, however, to account for differences like these in terms of a single unifying concept. Opposite effects of prior immersion in water on hoarding in two strains of mice can be accounted for by an interaction of the treatment with their differing initial levels of emotionality together with the notion that hoarding is an index of emotionality (Manosevitz, 1965).

This analysis of Manosevitz's findings is but one illustration of the fact that conclusions about species differences in learning ability cannot usually be drawn unambiguously from species differences in performance on a single learning task. Bitterman (1965) has pointed out some of the difficulties involved. For example, poorer performance in a given situation by one species than by another may always be due to the reinforcer's being weaker for the animals that learned poorly or to differences in the overall effects of deprivation states on the behavior of the species involved (see also Mrosovsky, 1964). The species differences in learning observed in the field, like those described above, could be due to differences in sensory ability, attention, or motivation rather than to predispositions to learn or not to learn certain things. Motivational and preceptual differences may be as important in bringing about adaptive species differences in learning as specifically associative mechanisms, but it is important to discover which ones are operating in any particular case.

In contrast to the approach that emphasizes adaptive species differences in what animals learn in the wild is the emphasis of some comparative psychologists on the similarities in how very widely differing species learn various discrimination tasks. For example, Mackintosh's (1964) comparison of discrimination learning in octopus, *Octopus vulgaris*, and rat leads to the remarkable conclusion that there are

... no grounds for drawing rigid distinctions between the learning processes of rat and octopus: neither species attends equally to all features of the stimulus input; both show the phenomenon of transfer along a continuum; both learn reversals faster than earlier reversals in a series; both learn a nonreversal shift faster after prior overtraining. (Mackintosh, 1964, p. 133)

A considerable number of experiments have been devoted to comparing the behavior of animals from different classes on successive discrimination reversals and probability learning. It is still debatable whether the differences among rats, birds, and fish on these tasks represent two qualitatively different types of performance or differing degrees of efficiency at the same type of performance (Bitterman, 1965; Mackintosh, 1969; Bitterman and Mackintosh, 1969), but it is even more debatable what phylogenetic meaning such differences could have.

Historically, one purpose of comparative psychology has been to trace "the evolution of intelligence" by means of phylogenetic comparisons of learning ability (review by Bitterman, 1965), and indeed the differences among the relatively few species tested in reversal and probability learning are remarkably orderly. However, attempting to trace the evolution of intelligence seems to assume that animals have a generalized ability to learn rather than specialized abilities to learn only certain things. Yet if learning ability were measured by the amount of exposure needed to home by new landmarks, the digger wasps that homed correctly after a single short orientation flight (van Iersel and van den Assem, 1964) would come out very high on the scale. So might the gobies studied by Aronson (see pp. 50–51). Of course, we have no evidence about how well these particular species learn other things, but experiments with other species certainly cast considerable doubt on the notion that animals have a general ability to learn that can equally well be revealed in any situation. For example, bullfrogs, *Rana catesbeiana*, like some other frogs and toads, have been reported to learn conventional laboratory tasks like shock avoidance very slowly, if at all, but they learn quite readily to approach the area of the tank where they will be fed at the appropriate time of day, and they can change their behavior appropriately after a few experiences if food is given at a new place or at a new time (van Bergeijk, 1967). Leopard frogs, *Rana pipiens*, do not learn to avoid shock in a shuttlebox at all (Boice, 1970), but they develop and retain reliable feeding hierarchies (Boice and Witter, 1969).

While these considerations suggest that a ranking of species based on their performance in a few anthropocentrically defined tests of "intelligence" has limited meaning, a second use of such comparative studies is less questionable. The performance of different species on reversal and probability learning tasks can be used simply as a way to test detailed theories of discrimination learning. At least one such theory seems to be able to encompass these differences in terms of differences in how well attention to the relevant dimension of a discrimination can be maintained in the face of inconsistent reinforcement (Mackintosh, 1969).

A related use of comparative studies, one which the approach of the present paper implies may be especially important, is to test ideas about the adaptive significance of various aspects of behavior. For instance, Petrinovich and Bolles (see pp. 21–22) suggest that the stereotypy found in thirsty rats and the variability in hungry rats represent adaptive modes of behavior for a niche where water tends to stay in the same place while—for the omnivorous rat—food can be found in different places. As Petrinovich and Bolles point out, observations of rats in the wild are needed to verify this notion, but their suggestion does imply that animals that are likely to find water in different places or those with more restricted diets that always find their food in the same place might behave differently from rats under thirst and hunger. Breland and Breland (1966) suggest many similar hypotheses about the relationship between ecology and what and how animals learn and describe a number of observations on different species which support them.

One experimental attempt to relate behavior in a standard learning situation to different species' behavior in the wild has been made by Boice (1970) using four species of frogs and toads. He found that two species which were relatively active hunters, *Rana clamitans* and *Bufo woodhousei*, learned to avoid shock in a one-way shuttlebox, while two relatively passive species, *Rana pipiens* and the fossorial toad *Scaphiopus hammondi*, did not learn at all (Fig. 11). Boice emphasizes the differences in activity between the species that learned and those that did not.

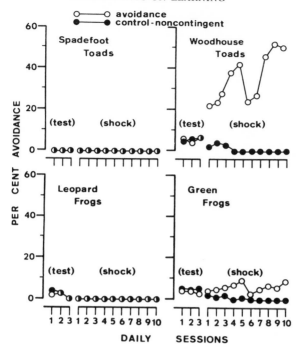

FIG. 11. Percent of twenty daily shuttlebox trials on which jumping occurred for groups of frogs and toads of four different species. Spontaneous jumping to the CS consisting of raising of the barrier dividing the shuttlebox was measured in the test sessions, and then some animals had shock avoidance training while the control groups had noncontingent shocks in the shuttlebox to assess pseudoconditioned jumping to the CS. From Boice (1970). Copyright (1970) by the American Psychological Association, and reproduced by permission.

The species that did learn showed the most unconditioned or pseudo-conditioned jumping in the testing situation, so it seems possible that the species differences he found are simply differences in activity per se — that is, in the operant level of the to-be-conditioned response. How-ever, it is also possible that species that are active hunters would have evolved a greater ability to learn to avoid danger than a species like the spadefoot toad, *Scaphiopus hammondi,* which spends much of its life in hibernation. It might be possible to test these two interpretations of Boice's findings by training members of the same four species on an avoidance task not requiring gross active movement. Certainly this study illustrates how species differences in behavior in a learning situa-tion can begin to be related to species differences in ecology in a mean-ingful way. Any speculations about such relationships — speculations that are all too easy to make — ultimately need to be tested by means of such cross-species comparisons.

X. CONCLUSIONS

On the whole, "laws of learning" are statements of qualitative relationships between independent and dependent variables. Generalizations about the effect on responding of changing magnitude, frequency, or delay of reinforcement, or reinforcing a response in the presence of a stimulus but not in its absence, are examples. To the extent that such "laws" are about stimuli, responses, and reinforcers in general, they imply that all combinations of these elements are equivalent. Of course this simplicity is really just apparent, because only stimuli the animal can perceive, responses it can make, and reinforcers appropriate for it are included. The opportunity to display to a male fighting fish is presumably not among the reinforcers for chaffinches. Constraints beyond these are also acknowledged. For example, not all the responses in an animal's repertoire are held to be susceptible to manipulation by operant reinforcement. But once such constraints on stimuli, responses, and reinforcers are known for a particular species, they implicitly apply equally to all combinations of these elements. However, the evidence reviewed in this paper shows that further constraints on learning also need to be considered. These are motivational or associative factors peculiar to certain stimuli, responses, or reinforcers or arising out of the relationship of any two, or even three, of them. Cases where they are strongly in evidence, like those reviewed here, are not exceptions to traditional learning principles so much as evidence for further factors in learning requiring systematic study in their own right. Many of the examples reviewed here suggest that it may be especially important to take such factors into account in attempts to generalize traditional learning principles to new responses, reinforcers, or species.

By way of summary, the main constraints on learning proposed in this review are listed here.

1. The relative salience or effectiveness of external stimuli may vary with the animal's motivational state (Section II).

2. The effects of variations in parameters of reinforcement—e.g., magnitude, delay, or schedule—may depend on the reinforcer. Different reinforcers may act in different ways (Section III).

3. Some responses may be performed as operants only if at the same time their own normal causal factors are present (Section IV).

4. The ease with which a response can be brought under the control of reinforcement contingencies may depend on how tightly it is linked to its own normal causal factors and the relationship of these factors to the internal state necessary for the reinforcer to be effective. Such interactions may result in different responses being affected differently by the same reinforcer or one response being affected differently by different reinforcers (Section V).

5. Some external stimuli may acquire control of certain responses especially readily while they do not control other equally conditionable responses at all (Section VI).

6. Some external stimuli may be especially easily associated with certain unconditioned stimuli while they are not associated with others at all (Section VII).

7. The ways in which learning occurs may reflect the causal relationships among environmental events in the natural situation where the learning occurs. Consideration of the function of learning in its natural context may predict what and how a particular species will learn (Sections II, VIII, IX).

All these generalizations simply state what factors may affect learning and how they may affect it. Unlike generalizations that apply to all stimuli, responses, reinforcers, and species, they do not predict whether or in what degree any particular factor will be effective for particular combinations of these elements. Furthermore, they should not be taken to imply that generalizations can be made from one species to another on the basis of identity of stimulus, response, or reinforcer. The fact that rats can drink to avoid shock only when they are thirsty does not mean that domestic chicks, or even other mammals, can use drinking as an operant under the same circumstances. Similarly, the fact that rats selectively associate tastes with sickness over long delays does not necessarily mean that other species use tastes in the same way. Bobwhite quail, for example, associate visual stimuli with illness (Wilcoxon *et al.*, 1971). That is to say, while it seems to be possible to delineate certain kinds of constraints on learning, it is probably not possible to predict where they will operate by translating directly from one case to another. However, as research in this area progresses, it may well become possible to characterize the contraints on learning and the cases in which they occur much more explicitly.

In some respects this situation parallels that which arises in the study of the role of learning in singing and mate selection by birds. The effects of experience on both song-learning and mate selection have been studied in a large number of bird species, and comparison of the generalizations that emerge in these areas with those that seem to be possible for classical and instrumental conditioning suggests that the "laws" of song-learning or learning in mate selection might serve as a model for generalizations about other kinds of learning.

For example, how much a bird's auditory experience affects the song it develops varies greatly across even closely related species. It is therefore not possible to draw a general conclusion like "birds need experience of song Y between ages n and $n + k$ in order to sing their species-typical song at the appropriate time." However, the factors that affect song-learning can be delineated, even though the importance of each factor varies among species. For example, it can be concluded that a bird's singing may be most influenced by auditory input at a certain stage of its life cycle. It may also be affected by only certain kinds of sounds. This selectivity may be such that a bird learns only certain kinds of songs, only its species-typical song, or only the song of a bird with which it has a social bond, or its singing may not be influenced at all by what it has heard. Similar generalizations can be made about how the bird's own vocalizations develop into adult song. For example, auditory feedback from the bird's own vocalizations may be important, but its role varies with the species and with the age of the bird.

Generalizations that can be made about the effect of experience on mate selection by birds have a similar character. Klinghammer (1967) concludes his review of the role of experience in mate selection by altricial birds as follows:

. . . several factors emerge that all affect, singly or interacting in various degrees, the choice of sexual partner in the sexually mature bird.

The amount of a bird's exposure to its own versus another species is important, so is early versus later exposure in the life of the bird. It matters in some species whether siblings are present when the bird is raised away from its natural parents, while in others it does not. The same holds for the free-choice test. Finally, releasers for sexual behavior for example postures and calls, innate or acquired, undoubtedly have an effect on choice of mate, although analysis of these factors was made in only a few instances.

. . . At the level of organization that we have examined, that is, the overt behavior patterns of courting and mating birds, there is no *one* way in which the final choice of mate is achieved. (pp. 39–40)

Some of the experiments reviewed here suggest that not only statements about constraints on learning but also the traditional "laws of learning" are similar in character. For example, if poison-avoidance learning is taken as a case of classical conditioning, the fact that it takes place with CS–US intervals of several hours is a clear counterexample to the generalization that conditioning is weak or nonexistent with CS–US intervals much longer than 0.5 second. However, it is still true, even in poison-avoidance learning, that increasing the CS–US interval decreases the degree of learning (Revusky, 1968), although the variation is in hours rather than in seconds. Indeed, it seems unlikely from a functional point of view that increasing the delay of reinforcement would ever be completely without effect. It is hard to imagine any function for associating events separated by months or years. On the other hand, functional considerations, the experiments of Seligman *et al.* (1970), and earlier research on shock avoidance suggest that there may well be cases in which the operations of extinction have little or no effect on behavior. Thus the general "law of extinction" may be, "discontinuing reinforcement *may* decrease the probability or rate of the response."

On the whole, the kinds of constraints on learning suggested here are added factors in classical and/or operant conditioning overlaid on the variables already known to be important. They are factors limiting what stimuli control what responses, what reinforcers control what responses, and the like. Within these limitations, or in combination with them, the factors traditionally considered in learning experiments are assumed to operate in their usual ways. However, the notion that behavior should be modified in ways that are adaptive in natural conditions suggests that there may also be important differences in mechanisms of learning (cf. Rozin and Kalat, 1971). For example, although poison-avoidance learning superficially fits a classical conditioning paradigm, Rozin and Kalat (1971) suggest that detailed study may reveal basically different principles. Even if it should not, there are already many examples of the modification of behavior by experience that do not fit conventional learning paradigms at all. For instance, some aspects of song-learning and the learning involved in migration and homing do not seem appropriately considered in classical or operant conditioning terms. However, detailed study of such examples of learning and comparison with other types of learning, like that which has already been attempted for imprinting (e.g., Bateson, 1966), would appear to be a legitimate concern of the psychology of animal learning.

In conclusion, this paper has made many suggestions for future investigation of the constraints on learning. There is a great need for more research explicitly designed to question the assumption that all stimuli, responses, and reinforcers are equivalent. But cataloging examples of constraints on learning is only a beginning. It is necessary to analyze their mechanisms. The examples described in this paper represent only a start in this direction. Notions about the ways learning is constrained need considerable refinement and testing. To do this fully it will probably be necessary to relate the behavior of animals in learning situations to their normal behavioral organization and to the function of their behavior in the wild. Comparative studies could be especially useful here, as could the attitudes and methods usually identified with ethologists' approach to animal behavior. Attempts to apply notions from laboratory studies of learning to the study of the development and modification of behavior in natural conditions may also lead to insight into the nature and function of constraints on learning. Such analyses should also lead to a more thorough understanding of the many examples of learning which have been observed in the field, and they may even uncover yet unrecognized kinds of learning.

Acknowledgments
The development of the ideas and examples in this paper has been influenced by discussions with many people, but most especially by many discussions with Jerry A. Hogan, Glenn E. Macdonald, and Nicholas Mrosovsky over the past several years. I am very

grateful for their many and varied contributions to the preparation of this paper. I should also like to thank Leyla de Toledo and Oded Frenkel for helpful comments on the manuscript and Mrs. Margaret Koehnke for typing it. Preparation of this paper was supported by a Research Fellowship from the Ontario Mental Health Foundation and by Grant APA 116 from the National Research Council of Canada to G. E. Macdonald.

References

Andrew, R. J. 1956. Normal and irrelevant toilet behaviour in *Emberiza* spp. *Anim. Behav.* **4**, 85–91.

Aronson, L. R. 1951. Orientation and jumping behavior in the gobiid fish, *Bathygobius soporator. Amer. Mus. Novit.* No. 1486.

Aronson, L. R. 1956. Further studies on orientation and jumping behavior in the goby fish, *Bathygobius soporator. Anat. Rec.* **125**, 606.

Aronson, L. R. 1971. Further studies on orientation and jumping behavior in the gobiid fish, *Bathygobius soporator. Ann. N. Y. Acad. Sci.* **188**, 378–392.

Azrin, N. H. 1970. Punishment of elicited aggression. *J. Exp. Anal. Behav.* **14**, 7–10.

Azrin, N. H., and Holz, W. C. 1966. Punishment. *In* "Operant Behavior: Areas of Research and Application" (W. K. Honig, ed.), pp. 380–447. Appleton, New York.

Azrin, N. H., and Hutchinson, R. R. 1967. Conditioning of the aggressive behavior of pigeons by a fixed-interval schedule of reinforcement. *J. Exp. Anal. Behav.* **10**, 395–402.

Azrin, N. H., Holz, W. C., and Hake, D. F. 1963. Fixed-ratio punishment. *J. Exp. Anal. Behav.* **6**, 141–148.

Baerends, G. P. 1958. The contribution of ethology to the study of the causation of behaviour. *Acta Physiol. Pharmacol. Néerl.* **7**, 466–499.

Baron, M. R. 1965. The stimulus, stimulus control, and stimulus generalization. *In* "Stimulus Generalization" (D. I. Mostofsky, ed.), pp. 62–71. Stanford Univ. Press, Stanford, California.

Bateson, P. P. G. 1966. The characteristics and context of imprinting. *Biol. Rev.* **41**, 177–220.

Beukema, J. J. 1968. Predation by the three-spined stickleback (*Gasterosteus aculeatus* L.): the influence of hunger and experience. *Behaviour* **31**, 1–126.

Bitterman, M. E. 1965. Phyletic differences in learning. *Amer. Psychol.* **20**, 396–410.

Bitterman, M. E., and Mackintosh, N. J. 1969. Habit-reversal and probability learning: rats, birds, and fish. *In* "Animal Discrimination Learning" (R. M. Gilbert and N. S. Sutherland, eds.), pp. 163–185. Academic Press, New York.

Black, A. H., and Young, G. A. 1972. Constraints on the operant conditioning of drinking. *In* "Reinforcement: Behavioral Analyses" (R. M. Gilbert and J. R. Millenson, eds.), pp. 35–50. Academic Press, New York.

Boice, R. 1970. Avoidance learning in active and passive frogs and toads. *J. Comp. Physiol. Psychol.* **70**, 154–156.

Boice, R., and Witter, D. W. 1969. Hierarchical feeding behaviour in the leopard frog (*Rana pipiens*). *Anim. Behav.* **17**, 474–479.

Bolles, R. C. 1967. "Theory of Motivation." Harper, New York.

Bolles, R. C. 1970. Species-specific defense reactions and avoidance learning. *Psychol. Rev.* **77**, 32–48.

Bolles, R. C. 1971. Species-specific defense reactions. *In* "Aversive Conditioning and Learning" (F. R. Brush, ed.), pp. 183–233. Academic Press, New York.

Bolles, R. C., and Petrinovich, L. 1956. Body weight changes and behavioral attributes. *J. Comp. Physiol. Psychol.* **49**, 177–180.

Bolles, R. C., and Seelbach, S. E. 1964. Punishing and reinforcing effects of noise onset and termination for different responses. *J. Comp. Physiol. Psychol.* **58**, 127–131.

Breland, K., and Breland, M. 1961. The misbehavior of organisms. *Amer. Psychol.* **16**, 681–684.

Breland, K., and Breland, M. 1966. "Animal Behavior." Macmillan, New York.

Brower, J. van Z. 1958. Experimental studies of mimicry in some North American butterflies. III. *Danaus gilippus berenice* and *Limenitis archippus floridensis. Evolution* **12**, 273–285.

Brower, J. van Z. 1960. Experimental studies of mimicry. IV. The reactions of starlings to different proportions of models and mimics. *Amer. Natur.* **94**, 271–282.

Brower, L. P., Brower, J. van Z., and Westcott, P. W. 1960. Experimental studies of mimicry. 5. The reactions of toads (*Bufo terrestris*) to bumblebees (*Bombus americanorum*) and their robberfly mimics (*Mallophora bomboides*) with a discussion of aggressive mimicry. *Amer. Natur.* **96**, 343–355.

Brown, P. L., and Jenkins, H. M. 1968. Auto-shaping of the pigeon's key-peck. *J. Exp. Anal. Behav.* **11**, 1–8.

Cott, H. B. 1940. "Adaptive Coloration in Animals." Methuen, London.

Cotton, J. W. 1953. Running time as a function of amount of food deprivation. *J. Exp. Psychol.* **46**, 188–198.

Croze, H. 1970. Searching image in carrion crows. *Z. Tierpsychol. Suppl.* **5**, pp. 1–85.

Dawkins, M. 1971a. Perceptual changes in chicks: another look at the 'search image' concept. *Anim. Behav.* **19**, 566–574.

Dawkins, M. 1971b. Shifts of 'attention' in chicks during feeding. *Anim. Behav.* **19**, 575–582.

De Ruiter, L. 1952. Some experiments on the camouflage of stick insects. *Behaviour* **4**, 222–232.

de Toledo, L. 1971. Changes in heart rate during conditioned suppression in rats as a function of US intensity and type of CS. *J. Comp. Physiol. Psychol.* **77**, 528–538.

Dobrzecka, C., Szwejkowska, G., and Konorski, J. 1966. Qualitative versus directional cues in two forms of differentiation. *Science* **153**, 87–89.

Duncan, C. J., and Sheppard, P. M. 1965. Sensory discrimination and its role in the evolution of Batesian mimicry. *Behaviour* **24**, 269–282.

Dunning, D. C. 1968. Warning sounds of moths. *Z. Tierpsychol.* **25**, 129–138.

Dunning, D. C., and Roeder, K. D. 1965. Moth sounds and the insect-catching behavior of bats. *Science* **147**, 173–174.

Eibl-Eibesfeldt, I. 1967. Concepts of ethology and their significance in the study of human behavior. *In* "Early Behavior: Comparative and Developmental Approaches" (H. W. Stevenson, E. H. Hess, and H. L. Rheingold, eds.), pp. 127–146. Wiley, New York.

Eibl-Eibesfeldt, I. 1970. "Ethology: The Biology of Behavior." Holt, New York.

Emlen, S. T. 1970. Celestial rotation: its importance in the development of migratory orientation. *Science* **170**, 1198–1201.

Galef, B. G. 1970. Target novelty elicits and directs shock-elicited aggression in wild rats. *J. Comp. Physiol. Psychol.* **71**, 87–91.

Galef, B. G., and Clark, M. M. 1971. Social factors in the poison avoidance and feeding behavior of wild and domestic rat pups. *J. Comp. Physiol. Psychol.* **75**, 341–357.

Garcia, J., and Ervin, F. R. 1968. Gustatory-visual and teleceptor-cutaneous conditioning—adaptation in internal and external milieus. *Commun. Behav. Biol.* Part A **1**, 389–415.

Garcia, J., McGowan, B. K., and Green, K. F. 1972. Sensory quality and integration: constraints on conditioning. *In* "Classical Conditioning II" (A. H. Black and W. F. Prokasy, eds.), pp. 3–27. Appleton, New York.

Gardner, W. M. 1969. Auto-shaping in bobwhite quail. *J. Exp. Anal. Behav.* **12**, 279–281.

Gilbert, R. M. 1969. Discrimination learning? *In* "Animal Discrimination Learning" (R. M. Gilbert and N. S. Sutherland, eds.), pp. 455–489. Academic Press, New York.

Hearst, E. 1969. Aversive conditioning and stimulus control. *In* "Punishment and Aversive

Behavior" (B. A. Campbell and R. M. Church, eds.), pp. 235–277. Appleton, New York.

Hemmes, N. S. 1970. DRL efficiency depends upon the operant. Paper presented at meetings of the Psychonomic Society, San Antonio, Texas.

Hinde, R. A. 1958. The nest-building behaviour of domesticated canaries. *Proc. Zool. Soc. London* **131,** 1–48.

Hinde, R. A. (ed.) 1969. "Bird Vocalizations." Cambridge Univ. Press, London and New York.

Hinde, R. A. 1970. "Animal Behaviour." McGraw-Hill, New York.

Hinde, R. A., and Stevenson, J. G. 1969. Sequences of behavior. *Advan. Study Behav.* **2,** 267–296.

Hoffman, H. S. 1969. Stimulus factors in conditioned suppression. *In* "Punishment and Aversive Behavior" (B. A. Campbell and R. M. Church, eds.). pp. 185–234. Appleton, New York.

Hoffman, H. S., and Fleshler, M. 1959. Aversive control with the pigeon. *J. Exp. Anal. Behav.* **2,** 213–218.

Hogan, J. A. 1961. Motivational aspects of instinctive behavior in *Betta splendens.* Unpublished doctoral dissertation, Harvard University, Cambridge, Massachusetts.

Hogan, J. A. 1964. Operant control of preening in pigeons. *J. Exp. Anal. Behav.* **7,** 351–354.

Hogan, J. A. 1967. Fighting and reinforcement in the Siamese fighting fish (*Betta splendens*). *J. Comp. Physiol. Psychol.* **64,** 356–359.

Hogan, J. A. 1971. The development of a hunger system in young chicks. *Behaviour* **39,** 128–201.

Hogan, J. A., Kleist, S., and Hutchings, C. S. L. 1970. Display and food as reinforcers in the Siamese fighting fish (*Betta splendens*). *J. Comp. Physiol. Psychol.* **70,** 351–357.

Holling, C. S. 1963. Mimicry and predator behavior. *Proc. 16th Int. Congr. Zool. Washington, D.C.* Vol. 4, pp. 166–173. Natural History Press, New York.

Hull, C. L. 1943. "Principles of Behavior." Appleton, New York.

Impekoven, M. 1969. Motivationally controlled stimulus preferences in chicks of the black-headed gull (*Larus ridibundus* L.). *Anim. Behav.* **17,** 252–270.

James, W. 1890. "The Principles of Psychology." Vol. 2. Holt, New York.

Jenkins, H. M., and Arnold, L. 1968. "Autoshaping of Pigeons with Food and Water Reinforcement." Film. McMaster University, Hamilton, Ontario.

Johnson, D. F., and Cumming, W. W. 1968. Some determiners of attention. *J. Exp. Anal. Behav.* **11,** 156–166.

Kalat, J. W., and Rozin, P. 1970. "Salience": a factor which can override temporal contiguity in taste-aversion learning. *J. Comp. Physiol. Psychol.* **71,** 192–197.

Kamin, L. J. 1969. Predictability, surprise, attention, and conditioning. *In* "Punishment and Aversive Behavior" (B. A. Campbell and R. M. Church, eds.), pp. 279–296. Appleton, New York.

Kear, J. 1962. Food selection in finches with special reference to interspecific differences. *Proc. Zool. Soc. London* **138,** 163–204.

Kimble, G. A. 1961. "Hilgard and Marquis' Conditioning and Learning." Appleton, New York.

King, J. A., and Eleftheriou, B. E. 1959. Effects of early handling upon adult behavior in two subspecies of deermice, *Peromyscus maniculatus. J. Comp. Physiol. Psychol.* **52,** 82–88.

King, J. A., and Weisman, R. G. 1964. Sand-digging contingent upon bar-pressing in deermice (*Peromyscus*). *Anim. Behav.* **12,** 446–450.

Kling, J. W., and Stevenson, J. G. 1970. Habituation and extinction. *In* "Short-Term Changes in Neural Activity and Behaviour" (G. Horn and R. A. Hinde, eds.), pp. 41–61. Cambridge Univ. Press, London and New York.

Klinghammer, E. 1967. Factors influencing choice of mate in altricial birds. *In* "Early Behavior: Comparative and Developmental Approaches" (H. W. Stevenson, E. H. Hess, and H. L. Rheingold, eds.), pp. 1–42. Wiley, New York.

Konorski, J. 1964. Some problems concerning the mechanism of instrumental conditioning. *Acta Biol. Exp., Vars.* **24,** 59–72.

Konorski, J. 1967. "Integrative Activity of the Brain." Univ. of Chicago Press, Chicago, Illinois.

Kramer, G. 1952. Experiments on bird orientation. *Ibis* **94,** 265–285.

Kruijt, J. P. 1964. Ontogeny of social behaviour in the Burmese red jungle fowl (*Gallus gallus spadiceus*) Bonnaterre. *Behaviour Suppl.* **12,** 1–201.

Lashley, K. S. 1915. Notes on the nesting activities of the noddy and sooty terns. *Publ. Carnegie Inst.* **7,** 61–83.

Levine, S. 1962. The effects of infantile experience on adult behavior. *In* "Experimental Foundations of Clinical Psychology" (A. J. Bachrach, ed.), pp. 139–169. Basic Books, New York.

Levy, N., and Seward, J. P. 1969. Frustration and homogeneity of rewards in the double runway. *J. Exp. Psychol.* **81,** 460–463.

Licklider, L. C., and Licklider, J. C. R. 1950. Observations on the hoarding behavior of rats. *J. Comp. Physiol. Psychol.* **43,** 129–134.

Logan, F. A., and Spanier, D. 1970. Relative effect of delay of food and water reward. *J. Comp. Physiol. Psychol.* **72,** 102–104.

Lorenz, K. 1965. "Evolution and Modification of Behavior." Univ. of Chicago Press, Chicago, Illinois.

Macdonald, G. E., and de Toledo, L. in preparation. Partial reinforcement effects and type of reward.

Mackintosh, N. J. 1964. Discrimination learning in the octopus. *Anim. Behav. Suppl.* **1,** 129–134.

Mackintosh, N. J. 1965. Selective attention in animal discrimination learning. *Psychol. Bull.* **64,** 124–150.

Mackintosh, N. J. 1969. Comparative studies of reversal and probability learning: rats, birds, and fish. *In* "Animal Discrimination Learning" (R. M. Gilbert and N. S. Sutherland, eds.), pp. 137–162. Academic Press, New York.

Macphail, E. 1968. Avoidance responding in pigeons. *J. Exp. Anal. Behav.* **11,** 629–632.

Manosevitz, M. 1965. Genotype, fear, and hoarding. *J. Comp. Physiol. Psychol.* **60,** 412–416.

Marler, P. 1970. A comparative approach to vocal learning: song development in white-crowned sparrows. *J. Comp. Physiol. Psychol.* **71,** Monogr. Suppl., pp. 1–25.

Masterson, F. A. 1970. Is termination of a warning signal an effective reward for the rat? *J. Comp. Physiol. Psychol.* **72,** 471–475.

Matthews, G. V. T. 1952. The relation of learning and memory to the orientation and homing of pigeons. *Behaviour* **4,** 202–221.

McFarland, D. J. 1969. Mechanisms of behavioural disinhibition. *Anim. Behav.* **17,** 238–242.

Meehl, P. E. 1950. On the circularity of the law of effect. *Psychol. Bull.* **47,** 52–75.

Miller, N. E. 1957. Experiments on motivation. *Science* **126,** 1271–1278.

Miller, N. E. 1969. Learning of visceral and glandular responses. *Science* **163,** 434–445.

Miller, N. E., and Carmona, A. 1967. Modification of a visceral response, salivation in thirsty dogs, by instrumental training with water reward. *J. Comp. Physiol. Psychol.* **63,** 1–6.

Milner, P. M. 1970. "Physiological Psychology." Holt, New York.

Mrosovsky, N. 1964. The performance of dormice and other hibernators on tests of hunger motivation. *Anim. Behav.* **12,** 454–469.

Myer, J. S., and Baenninger, R. 1966. Some effects of punishment and stress on mouse killing by rats. *J. Comp. Physiol. Psychol.* **62,** 292–297.

Myers, A. K. 1962. Effects of CS intensity and quality in avoidance conditioning. *J. Comp. Physiol. Psychol.* **55,** 57–61.

Myers, A. K. 1964. Discriminated operant avoidance learning in Wistar and G-4 rats as a function of type of warning stimulus. *J. Comp. Physiol. Psychol.* **58,** 453–455.

Oatley, K. 1970. Brain mechanisms and motivation. *Nature London* **225,** 797–801.

Pavlov, I. P. 1927. "Conditioned Reflexes" (transl. by G. V. Anrep). Oxford Univ. Press, London and New York.

Petrinovich, L., and Bolles, R. C. 1954. Deprivation states and behavioral attributes. *J. Comp. Physiol. Psychol.* **47,** 450–453.

Pomeroy, D. E. 1962. Birds with abnormal bills. *Brit. Birds* **55,** 49–72.

Premack, D. 1965. Reinforcement theory. *Neb. Symp. Motiv.* **13,** 123–180.

Rachlin, H. 1969. Autoshaping of key pecking in pigeons with negative reinforcement. *J. Exp. Anal. Behav.* **12,** 521–532.

Rachlin, H., and Hineline, P. N. 1967. Training and maintenance of key-pecking in the pigeon by negative reinforcement. *Science* **157,** 954–955.

Rescorla, R. A., and Wagner, A. R. 1972. A theory of Pavlovian conditioning: variations in the effectiveness of reinforcement and non-reinforcement. *In* "Classical Conditioning II" (A. H. Black and W. F. Prokasy, eds.), pp. 64–99. Appleton, New York.

Rettenmeyer, C. W. 1970. Insect mimicry. *Ann. Rev. Entomol.* **15,** 43–74.

Revusky, S. H. 1968. Aversion to sucrose produced by contingent X-irradiation: temporal and dosage parameters. *J. Comp. Physiol. Psychol.* **65,** 17–22.

Revusky, S., and Bedarf, E. W. 1967. Association of illness with prior ingestion of novel foods. *Science* **155,** 219–220.

Revusky, S. H., and Garcia, J. 1970. Learned associations over long delays. *In* "Psychology of Learning and Motivation," (G. Bower and J. T. Spence, eds.), Vol. 4, pp. 1–84. Academic Press, New York.

Reynolds, G. S. 1968. "A Primer of Operant Conditioning." Scott, Foresman, Glenview, Illinois.

Reynolds, G. S., Catania, A. C., and Skinner, B. F. 1963. Conditioned and unconditioned aggression in pigeons. *J. Exp. Anal. Behav.* **6,** 73–74.

Rowell, C. H. F. 1961. Displacement grooming in the chaffinch. *Anim. Behav.* **9,** 38–63.

Rozin, P. 1969a. Central or peripheral mediation of learning with long CS-US intervals in the feeding system. *J. Comp. Physiol. Psychol.* **67,** 421–429.

Rozin, P. 1969b. Adaptive food sampling patterns in vitamin deficient rats. *J. Comp. Physiol. Psychol.* **69,** 126–132.

Rozin, P., and Kalat, J. W. 1971. Specific hungers and poison avoidance as adaptive specializations of learning. *Psychol. Rev.* **78,** 459–486.

Rozin, P., and Mayer, J. 1961. Regulation of food intake in the goldfish. *Amer. J. Physiol.* **201,** 968–974.

Schaeffer, A. A. 1911. Habit formation in frogs. *J. Anim. Behav.* **1,** 309–335.

Seligman, M. E. P. 1970. On the generality of the laws of learning. *Psychol. Rev.* **77,** 406–418.

Seligman, M. E. P., Ives, C. E., Ames, H., and Mineka, S. 1970. Conditioned drinking and its failure to extinguish: avoidance, preparedness, or functional autonomy? *J. Comp. Physiol. Psychol.* **71,** 411–419.

Sevenster, P. A. 1961. A causal analysis of a displacement activity (fanning in *Gasterosteus aculeatus* L.). *Behaviour Suppl.* **9,** 1–170.

Sevenster, P. 1968. Motivation and learning in sticklebacks. *In* "The Central Nervous System and Fish Behavior" (D. Ingle, ed.), pp. 233–245. Univ. of Chicago Press, Chicago, Illinois.

Sexton, O. J. 1959. Experimental studies of artificial Batesian mimics. *Behaviour* **15**, 244–252.

Sexton, O. J., Hoger, C., and Ortleb, E. 1966. *Anolis carolinensis:* effects of feeding on reaction to aposematic prey. *Science* **153**, 1140.

Sheffield, F. D. 1965. Relation between classical conditioning and instrumental learning. *In* "Classical Conditioning" (W. F. Prokasy, ed.), pp. 302–322. Appleton, New York.

Shettleworth, S. J. 1970. The role of conditioned and reinforcing stimuli in the development of drinking behavior by domestic chicks. Unpublished doctoral dissertation, University of Toronto, Toronto, Ontario.

Shettleworth, S. J. 1972a. The role of novelty in learned avoidance of unpalatable "prey" by domestic chicks, *Gallus gallus. Anim. Behav.* **20**, 29–35.

Shettleworth, S. J. 1972b. Stimulus relevance in the control of drinking and conditioned fear responses in domestic chicks, *Gallus gallus. J. Comp. Physiol. Psychol.* **80**, in press.

Shorten, M. 1954. The reaction of the brown rat towards changes in its environment. *In* "Control of Rats and Mice" (D. Chitty, ed.), Vol. 2, pp. 307–334. Oxford Univ. Press, London and New York.

Sidman, M., and Fletcher, F. G. 1968. A demonstration of auto-shaping with monkeys. *J. Exp. Anal. Behav.* **11**, 307–309.

Siegel, S. 1972. Latent inhibition and eyelid conditioning. *In* "Classical Conditioning II." (A. H. Black and W. F. Prokasy, eds.), pp. 231–247. Appleton, New York.

Skinner, B. F. 1938. "The Behavior of Organisms." Appleton, New York.

Skinner, B. F. 1956. A case history in scientific method. *Amer. Psychol.* **11**, 221–233.

Skinner, B. F. 1959. An experimental analysis of certain emotions. *J. Exp. Anal. Behav.* **2**, 264.

Skinner, B. F. 1966. The phylogeny and ontogeny of behavior. *Science* **153**, 1205–1213.

Small, W. S. 1901. Experimental study of the mental processes of the rat. II. *Amer. J. Psychol.* **12**, 206–239.

Solomon, R. L. 1964. Punishment. *Amer. Psychol.* **19**, 239–253.

Squier, L. H. 1969. Autoshaping key responses with fish. *Psychonomic Sci.* **17**, 177–178.

Staddon, J. E. R., and Simmelhag, V. L. 1971. The "superstition" experiment: a reexamination of its implications for the principles of adaptive behavior. *Psychol. Rev.* **78**, 3–43.

Steiner, J. 1968. Positive reinforcement. *In* "Analysis of Behavioral Change" (L. Weiskrantz, ed.), pp. 4–18. Harper, New York.

Stevenson, J. G. 1967. Reinforcing effects of chaffinch song. *Anim. Behav.* **15**, 427–432.

Stevenson, J. G. 1969. Song as a reinforcer. *In* "Bird Vocalizations" (R. A. Hinde, ed.), pp. 49–60. Cambridge Univ. Press, London and New York.

Teitelbaum, P. 1966. The use of operant methods in the assessment and control of motivational states. *In* "Operant Behavior: Areas of Research and Application" (W. K. Honig, ed.), pp. 565–608. Appleton, New York.

Terrace, H. S. 1963. Errorless transfer of a discrimination across two continua. *J. Exp. Anal. Behav.* **6**, 223–232.

Thompson, T. I. 1963. Visual reinforcement in Siamese fighting fish. *Science* **141**, 55–57.

Thompson, T. I. 1964. Visual reinforcement in fighting cocks. *J. Exp. Anal. Behav.* **7**, 45–49.

Thompson, T. 1969. Conditioned avoidance of the mobbing call by chaffinches. *Anim. Behav.* **17**, 517–522.

Thorndike, E. L. 1911. "Animal Intelligence." Macmillan, New York.

Thorpe, W. H. 1956. "Learning and Instinct in Animals." Methuen, London.

Tinbergen, L. 1960. The natural control of insects in pinewoods. I. Factors influencing the intensity of predation by song birds. *Arch. Néerl. Zool.* **13,** 265–336.

Tinbergen, N. 1951. "The Study of Instinct." Oxford Univ. Press (Clarendon), London and New York.

Tinbergen, N. 1953. "The Herring Gull's World." Collins, London.

Tinbergen, N. 1958. "Curious Naturalists." Country Life, London.

Trabasso, T., and Bower, G. H. 1968. "Attention in Learning: Theory and Research." Wiley, New York.

Tschanz, B. 1959. Zur brutbiologie der trottellumme. *Behaviour* **14,** 1–100.

Ulrich, R., Johnston, M., Richardson, J., and Wolff, P. 1963. The operant conditioning of fighting behavior in rats. *Psychol. Rec.* **13,** 465–470.

van Bergeijk, W. A. 1967. Anticipatory feeding behaviour in the bullfrog (*Rana catesbeiana*). *Anim. Behav.* **15,** 231–238.

Vanderwolf, C. H. 1969. Hippocampal electrical activity and voluntary movement in the rat. *Electroenceph. Clin. Neurophysiol.* **26,** 407–418.

Vanderwolf, C. H. 1971. Limbic–diencephalic mechanisms of voluntary movement. *Psychol. Rev.* **78,** 83–113.

van Iersel, J. J. A., and van den Assem, J. 1964. Aspects of orientation in the diggerwasp *Bembix rostrata. Anim. Behav. Suppl.* **1,** 145–161.

von Frisch, K. 1953. "The Dancing Bees." Harcourt, New York.

Waddell, D. 1951. Hoarding behavior in the golden hamster. *J. Comp. Physiol. Psychol.* **44,** 383–388.

Walters. G. C., and Glazer, R. D. 1971. Punishment of instinctive behavior in the Mongolian gerbil. *J. Comp. Physiol. Psychol.* **75,** 331–340.

Wells, M. J. 1964. Learning and movement in octopuses. *Anim. Behav. Suppl.* **1,** 115–128.

Westbrook, R. F., and Miles, C. G. 1970. The effect of a fading procedure upon the acquisition of control by an overshadowed auditory feature. *J. Exp. Anal. Behav.* **13,** 179–185.

Wilcoxon, H. C., Dragoin, W. B., and Kral, P. A. 1971. Illness-induced aversions in rat and quail: relative salience of visual and gustatory cues. *Science* **171,** 826–828.

Williams, D. R., and Williams, H. 1969. Auto-maintenance in the pigeon: sustained pecking despite contingent non-reinforcement. *J. Exp. Anal. Behav.* **12,** 511–520.

Wolin, B. R. 1968. Differences in manner of pecking a key between pigeons reinforced with food and with water. *In* "Contemporary Research in Operant Behavior" (A. C. Catania, ed.), p. 286. Scott, Foresman, Glenview, Illinois.

Female Reproduction Cycles
and Social Behavior in Primates

T. E. ROWELL

ZOOLOGY DEPARTMENT
UNIVERSITY OF CALIFORNIA
BERKELEY, CALIFORNIA

"Admitting that the whole of a monkey is disgraceful yet their bottoms really are excessively disgraceful and horrible." From *12th Century Bestiary*, translated by T. H. White, Cambridge University Library, 1926.

I. SCOPE

Unfortunately it is impossible to write a review anywhere near so wide in scope as this title suggests, because there are enormous gaps in our knowledge in the area. Reasonably complete information on both physiology and behavior of reproductive cycles is available for only a handful of species, nearly all Old World monkeys, Most data are provided by the rhesus macaque, and there is good information about several other *Macaca* spp. and the baboons. Two species of the big *Cercopithecus* genus have been studied, and there are preliminary observations on the related *Erythrocebus* and *Miopithecus;* there are also only a few indications on *Presbytis* (Colobinae), though anatomical data on the less well-known Colobines suggest that they may be a very interesting and varied group in this respect. Chimpanzees have been well studied, the other apes hardly at all. Physiological data on human females are good, but with few exceptions behavioral material is expressed in psychoanalytic terms impossible to compare with information on other primates. Of the New World primates only the squirrel monkey has been intensively studied in the laboratory, and the results so far are very confusing. Field studies in South America have provided little information relevant to our topic beyond descriptions of sexual behavior. It appears (Zuckerman, 1935; Kaiser, 1947) that the physiological and histological basis of their cycles may even differ considerably from that of the Old World monkeys. With the exception of Jolly's (1966) study of two lemurs and a study of captive *Lemur catta* by Evans and Goy (1968), investigation of the prosimians is still at the basic level of establishing seasonal breeding and gestation length data (see Manley, 1966), and, since most of the species are nocturnal, it will be very difficult to gather behavioral data, especially field material.

The studies discussed in this review fall into four main types, each with inherent advantages and disadvantages. First, there are field studies. Particularly where these are of undisturbed populations, they probably provide the most reliable samples of normal behavior, where observation conditions have been good enough to make records sufficiently complete for our purpose. On the other hand, data on reproductive status are often inadequate. Studies of free-ranging but manipulated groups (for example, the Cayo Santiago rhesus colony studies) fall into this category, providing much more complete data than field studies about behavior which may theoretically be somewhat distorted. Second, there are studies of caged groups of relatively undisturbed animals. Here data on reproductive cycles can be complete, but behavior will certainly differ from that observed in the wild (Rowell, 1967b), though, it is hoped, in predictable ways. Third, there are laboratory studies on highly manipulated animals. Here reproductive status will again be completely known, and conditions under which behavior occurs can be carefully controlled, so that results are usually internally consistent; conditions are, however, so far removed from the normal life of monkeys for which their evolution has presumably fitted them, that conclusions are sometimes difficult to relate to those of more natural studies. A fourth group are those laboratory studies where not only are the conditions under which behavior takes place rigidly controlled, but so also is the endocrinal status of the animals, by castration and replacement therapy. I have included some of these studies because their authors carried them out to study behavior in reproductive cycles, but I am uneasy as to how such studies may be interpreted in this context. The ovary is a complex organ and can hardly be considered adequately replaced by a known quantity of estradiol. The physiological changes which take place during menstrual cycles, pregnancy, and lactation have been related to dynamic endocrine processes; some of the most important events occur when the output of one hormone is changing at a particular rate and in a particular direction *in relation* to similar changes in one or more other hormones. The whole system is characterized by a remarkable absence of steady states. It seems likely that behavioral events are also influenced by these dynamic processes, and where in this do we place the castrated female with steady replacement therapy of one or two hormones in constant proportion? Studies of such animals do, however, produce consistent and reproducible answers; for the behavioral zoologist they can provide valuable pointers, but they should not be accepted unreservedly as illustrating events in normal cycles without confirmation.

There is a great body of literature on the effects of gonadal and gonadotropic hormones on primates [see Young (1961) and especially Hisaw and Hisaw therein], and frequently conclusions relating them to social behavior have been drawn, but this review is limited to studies in which observations on social behavior have actually been made. The reader will find a bias in favor of studies in which relatively normal social opportunities were available to the animals. This is because all the primate species mentioned here have been evolved to live in environments that include a variety of members of their own species. To show normal behavior they need this aspect of the environment just as they need an appropriate diet and living space of structure appropriate to their skeletal and muscular adaptations. Individuals will of course survive in conditions that are inadequate in any of these respects, and it may frequently be necessary to study primates in suboptimal conditions. It is essential in that case to make reference, in assessment and in interpretation of results, to the "control" situation of normal animals in conditions as close as possible to those for which natural selection has fitted them. This would be true whether a study of, say, physical development in relation to diet or behavioral development in relation to social environment were carried out under controlled, and therefore restricted, conditions.

II. REPRODUCTIVE CYCLES: BACKGROUND

All female mammals show physiological cycles of ovarian activity, with extremely varied time relations between the stages, so that the interval between successive infertile ovulations may be anything from four days to a year in different species. Long before these cycles were studied, it was common knowledge that in most species females showed relatively brief periods of heat—the phrase "sexual receptivity" hardly conveys the intense appetitive behavior for copulation shown by most mammals in heat. In domestic animals heat was found to occur just about the time of ovulation in spontaneously ovulating animals like the cow and the white rat. The term "estrus," which had originally been used (see Heape, 1900) as a scientific synonym for heat, a behavioral term, came to be used to include all the physiological changes attending ovulation—to such an extent that Zuckerman (1932) found it necessary to remind his readers that estrus had a behavioral *as well as* a physiological meaning. This usage continued, although wider research showed that the timing of heat relative to ovulation varied even in the domestic animals, and that in some species the two events may be a long time apart: the horseshoe bat, *Rhinolophus ferrusequinus,* which is in heat in the autumn, stores sperm through the winter, and ovulates and conceives in the spring (Everett, 1961), is an extreme example. I have here reverted to the prior meaning, and "estrus" will be used as a strictly behavioral term with no histological implications. It will be seen that this distinction is particularly necessary when considering the primates.

The menstrual cycle is one of growth and breakdown of the lining of the uterus. The breakdown is accompanied by bleeding, though in some species (for example, *Cercopithecus mitis*) this is usually too slight to be seen at the vulva. Menstrual cycles have a rather constant average length of around one month in species so far described except for the squirrel monkey, which appears to have a one-week cycle (Rosenblum *et al.,* 1967). In all published data, cycle lengths vary, the samples showing a characteristic skew-normal distribution, with a scattering of extremely long cycles pulling the mean length to the right of the median and modal lengths, which are usually the same or very close (Gilman and Gilbert, 1946; Fujiwara *et al.,* 1967; Rowell and Chalmers, 1970; Hartman, 1932; Yerkes and Elder, 1936; Zuckerman, 1937; for discussion of variation in cycle length, see Section VII). The menstrual cycle is considered to begin on the first day of menstrual bleeding. There is a fairly precise timing relationship between ovulation and the onset of the next menstruation, this interval, the luteal phase of the cycle, varying by only a day or so in individual animals (Zuckerman and Parkes, 1932): variation in cycle length occurs in the preovulatory, follicular phase of the cycle. This pattern has been ascertained in the baboon and chimpanzee, whose perineal swellings make observations on the point easy, and in women. It has not been generally demonstrated, and the rhesus macaque has been reported to have as variable a luteal as follicular phase (Rossman and Bartelmez, 1946). Menstrual cycles continue throughout the adult life of the female until menopause, except during pregnancies and early lactation: there is no regular equivalent in the menstrual cycle to the prolonged anestrus in the ovarian cycle of many annual-breeding nonprimates. Menstrual cycles continue in the absence of ovulation in seasonally breeding monkeys (Hartman, 1932), and for this reason it is probably simpler to consider menstrual and ovulation cycles separately; it is usual to refer to menstrual rather than ovulation cycles when describing cycling female primates.

It is important to remember that for most adult female primates the usual conditions are pregnancy or lactation interval (a period of amenorrhea and sexual quiescence during the early weeks of her infant's life) (Zuckerman, 1931b). Where behavioral changes can be demonstrated during menstrual cycles, they must be compared in size with changes occurring in the longer reproductive cycle of receptivity–pregnancy–lactation if biologically meaningful inferences are to be drawn.

Again, although by far the greatest attention has been paid to male–female interaction in relation to reproductive cycles, females of most species interact less with males than they do with other adult females, juveniles, and infants. If reproductive cycles are shown to affect interaction with these classes of animals, the effect will be larger, on the total social pattern of a monkey group, then that of changes in male–female interaction alone. The problem of analysis of interactions between adult females with respect to cycle is particularly difficult because cycles of both animals are variable, and the cycle state of either the actor or the receiver of a behavior pattern may be the critical factor (see Section V).

Sexual Skin

Some primates, and by coincidence most of the better-known species, have areas of "sexual skin." Zuckerman *et al.* (1938) used this term for areas of skin that respond by swelling and/or heightened color to injection of estrogens in the castrated animal. These skin areas have been assumed to convey information about female reproductive state to males. There has been some confusion about their distribution, both anatomically and in time: some authors have even assumed that the swelling area includes the horny ischial callosites (e.g., Wickler, 1963). Therefore some discussion of these structures seems relevant before behavior is considered.

1. Anatomy

Some swelling of the vulva during estrus is common among mammals (cf. the bitch). "Ordinary" swellings of this type can be seen in the lemurs, and perhaps in some Colobines, though there is no behavioral information on the genus *Colobus* at present, so the association of the observed swelling of the vulva with estrous behavior is merely inferential.

In the baboon–mangabey species group, swelling is confined to the perineum. In the white-cheeked mangabey, *Cercocebus albigena*, it is even more strictly limited, involving only the vulva (see illustration in Rowell and Chalmers, 1970). Color and shape of the swelling are highly individual—a baboon is easier to recognize from her rear than from her front view. There are also regular differences between races; for example, *Papio "cynocephalus,"* the yellow baboon, has a neat, heart-shaped swelling, whereas *P. "anubis,"* the olive race, has a less clearly defined lumpy swelling. The chacma baboon, *P. porcarius,* has an enormous swelling, far larger than that of other species. The color varies from gray-purple to pale pink. There is usually a brightening of color in the last week of the life of the swelling.

In the genus *Papio* there is a large, well-defined area of naked skin over the hips. This does not swell, except in pathological cases. In *P. hamadryas* and *P. papio* it is always red; in the other species it is black and very shiny, but loses melanin and becomes vivid red during pregnancy. After birth it rapidly pales to a salmon pink over a few days, and then slowly blackens during the lactation interval [Altman, personal communication, suggests that it does not become completely repigmented in older females]. This lateral skin is not sexual skin by Zuckerman's definition. When considering possible signal function, it must be noted that its changes in appearance are much more obvious than those of the perineum except at very close range—the female baboon indicates pregnancy more clearly than receptivity.

The chimpanzee has a large, pale swelling limited to the perineum. The other apes show no more than the usual mammalian vulval enlargement when receptive.

The macaques have unusually varied sexual skin, and it is amazingly difficult to find good descriptions, so the following remarks concern only the species of which the author has personal observation. Macaques have naked or sparsely haired skin over the whole rump, but the area is not sharply defined, and sexual skin extends into the fully furred area. The best-known swelling is probably that of the adolescent female rhesus monkey. The first sign of approaching maturity is irregular swelling of the inguinal area, giving the female the appearance of having a scrotum. In its full form the swelling includes this area but is much more prominent around the dorsal surface of the tail root, and from there corrugations run down the edge of the naked area, along the edge of the thighs. The perineal area and the skin immediately surrounding it are not swollen. *Macaca nemestrina* adults have a swelling which involves the perineum, and also extends around the tail root. Swellings of other adult macaques (for example, *M. maurus, M. silenus,* and *M. sylvana*) seem to be centered on the dorsal tail root area, with larger swellings extending ventrally to the anus and laterally over the hips, but not, in my experience, including the vulva.

Mature *M. mulatta, M. fuscata, M. irus,* and *M. speciosa* show a reddening, without edema, of the rump, and also of other areas of naked skin — face, nipples, and belly — in response to estrogen. At least in *M. mulatta,* this reddening is rather unreliable during menstrual cycles, the degree to which it occurs being an individual characteristic. It also depends on the amount of sunlight the animals receive — the colony that lives out-doors at the virus research unit at Entebbe, Uganda (on the Equator), was far more vividly colored than an outdoor colony in Cambridge, England, while laboratory monkeys may be quite white-skinned. As in *Papio,* color changes during pregnancy are by far the most dramatic, all coloring areas becoming brilliant by the end of gestation and paling immediately after birth.

There is no sexual skin in the genera *Cercopithecus* and *Erythrocebus,* though some specimens of patas monkey have been observed to show vulval swellings at adolescence. In most species the perineal skin is dark gray and remains so. In *C. aethiops* the perineum is bluish and the clitoris red, a coloring similar to that of the male genitalia. Wickler (1967) states that the color brightens "during oestrus," but in a captive breeding colony this could not be confirmed. Sick and lactating females have unusually pale genitalia, and once again the most brilliant colors are seen in late pregnancy. Struhsaker (1967) also reported no change in appearance in estrous vervets in the wild. Two single-species genera close to *Cercopithecus — Allenopithecus* and *Miopithecus —* show swellings. *Miopithecus talapoin* has a diffuse swelling of the naked rump involving especially the clitoris, the underside of the tail, and the area just lateral to the tail base. The color is pale pink, and there is some reddening of the rump and nipples during pregnancy. *Theropithecus gelada* does not swell, but has naked areas of skin on the rump and chest which are bright red in the mature animal. The areas are surrounded by small white blisters, which are said to enlarge, and the red color to brighten, "before menstruation" (Pocock, 1925). Much has been made of the possible signal function of these two areas, which are said to resemble each other (Wickler, 1967). The pattern seems to be rather macaque-like; effectively all naked areas on this very shaggy animal redden, except the black face. Like the adolescent rhesus macaque, swellings reach their maximum in the late luteal phase of the cycle (Matthews, 1956).

2. Timing of Changes

The gradual development of some of the most brilliant color changes during pregnancy has already been noted. Much more attention has been centered, however, on changes in the sexual skin during the menstrual cycle. (Attention here should be paid only to descriptions of females in breeding groups, since nonbreeding zoo animals not infrequently develop permanent — possibly slightly fluctuating — and unusually large swellings.) Of sexual swellings, it may be said that all types are reduced or absent during menstruation. Swellings involving the perineum only (and those of *M. nemestrina*, which extend to the tail root) begin to increase during menstruation, reach a maximum several days before ovulation, and deflate rapidly a day or two after ovulation (e.g., Hendrickx and Kraemer, 1969). The luteal phase of these species is characterized by a flat, wrinkled perineum (though still further reduction of tissue occurs during pregnancy or other acyclic interval).

Swellings centered on the tail root, and those of talapoins, where both the tail and the clitoris swell, have a much vaguer time course: there is certainly no rapid deflation after ovulation. Observations on two adolescent rhesus monkeys showed that their swellings continued to increase in size into the last week before menstruation, and then decreased fairly rapidly so as to be minimal at menstruation. Swelling started again slowly in the first week of the next cycle.

Swellings like those of the rhesus, which are principally a phenomenon of adolescence, though they also recur briefly in adult animals after long acyclic intervals, were described as "maturing" (that is, ceasing to appear) by Zuckerman *et al.* (1938). These swellings are actually characteristic of nonfertile females; the young rhesus first conceives just about the time her swellings cease. This type of swelling may be clearly distinguished from those of the baboon or mangabey: the female baboon swells during her first and every succeeding menstrual cycle, and is fertile at the time the first swelling reaches maximum size. [Baboon swellings have also been described as "maturing" by Gilman and Gilbert (1946), but in this case they seem to have been recording the slow increase in swelling size that occurs when females are prevented from becoming pregnant and undergo repeated cycles — an abnormal condition for this species (Rowell, 1970b).]

Finally, we should not forget that many, perhaps the majority of Old World primates have no sexual skin, and that the phenomenon is confined to Catarrhines, plus the tarsier (Hill, 1953). Discussion of the possible behavioral functions of sexual skin will follow, but there are important implications of the above survey. Zuckerman *et al.* (1938) stated that sexual swellings were homologous throughout the group. This seems to be true, however, only in their response to exogenous hormones. In anatomical origin, in relation to the menstrual cycle, and in relation to the animals' life cycle, there are wide differences, so that homology in the usual sense must be discarded. Moreover, it is quite clear that, either the response of the tissues to endogenous hormones is not identical in different species, or the pattern of estrogen secretion in the menstrual cycle varies. Here we have yet another reason for discarding the biomedical concept of *the* monkey.

Many of the New World species (for example, marmosets, spider, and woolly monkeys) have enlarged female genitalia, notably clitorides. These are not described as changing appearance during reproductive cycles, and they seem to be a quite separate development from the sexual skin of the Catarrhines. Where behavioral observations have been made, these structures seem to be used in scent marking. Klein (1971) gives an excellent description of this behavior in a spider monkey, *Ateles belzebuth,* and points out that the complex structure of the pendulous clitoris in this species is precisely related to the method of marking, so that the theory that the structure mimics the penis (Wickler, 1967) is redundant — it does not in any case at all resemble the penis of this species. There was no apparent change in scent marking or response by males with female reproductive cycle here.

Lemurs have elaborate displays associated with scent marking, and the output of the scent glands is greatly increased during the brief breeding season — quite possibly some scents are produced only at this time. Michael and Keverne (1970) have demonstrated that even the microsmatic rhesus monkey can use olfactory cues from a vaginal pheromone produced only by estrogen-treated females.

III. Reproductive Cycles and Copulation

The definition of estrus was about quantitative changes in copulatory behavior, so these will be considered first. Copulation is behavior with the advantage that there is little disagreement about its definition, and it can also be detected, without actual behavioral observation, by the presence of semen in the vagina. Thus information on this particular point tends to be rather better than on other aspects of behavior.

A. Copulation during Menstrual Cycles

It was noticed very early that monkeys and humans are willing to copulate for much more of the time than domestic animals like dogs, cats, and cattle. Heape (1900) referred to "abnormal oestrus" — willingness to mate outside the time when conception was possible. Miller (1931), reviewing the literature then available, said that all higher primate females were willing to mate at any time, although acknowledging periods of more intense sexual activity in baboons and chimpanzees associated with perineal swelling. Continuous, or nearly continuous, female availability was also stressed by Zuckerman (1932). This author, from zoo data and the examination of twelve specimens of chacma baboon shot in South Africa, concluded that there was no evidence of an annual breeding season in any primate higher than the lemuroids, although quoting a considerable body of naturalists' observations to the contrary (Zuckerman, 1931a). Zuckerman related two uniquely primate features—the menstrual cycle and a social organization in which animals of both sexes and all ages remain together permanently. He suggested that the main cohesive factor in these social groupings was sexual attraction, and that the extended female receptivity characteristic of the primate menstrual cycle made permanent associations possible. Since that time annual birth seasons in wild monkey populations have been amply documented (Lancaster and Lee, 1965), though some species in some localities do breed regularly throughout the year, including Zuckerman's chacma baboons (Hall, 1962; Rowell, 1969b), and seasonal changes in conception rate are not necessarily correlated with behavioral changes in nonconceiving females (Rowell, 1970a; Loy, 1969a). The uniqueness of primate social organization is also less clear now that there is more information on other mammals (see Kühme, 1965, on the Cape hunting dog, *Lycaon pictus;* Klingel, 1967, on the zebra). Neither of these advances necessarily destroys Zuckerman's hypothesis, which becomes a part of more complex explanations, having been for nearly forty years a most powerful stimulant to primate research.

The prosimians were excluded by Zuckerman, being known then to have limited breeding seasons. *Lemur catta* (Evans and Goy, 1968) and *Galago crassicaudatus* (Eaton *et al.,* 1972) also have limited estrous periods, closely associated with ovulation, at least when caged singly except for testing, and from Jolly's (1966) observations, probably also in the wild.

In the first detailed study of sexual behavior in free-ranging monkeys, Carpenter (1942) stressed a clearly defined period of estrus in rhesus monkeys and noted a total absence of sexual behavior later in the year when the majority of females were pregnant. Estrus was said to occur about mid-cycle, and to last about a third of the cycle; besides mating, it was associated with a reddening of the perineal skin, fighting, and a rise in social rank.

Carpenter, like Zuckerman, studied groups of monkeys that had been newly made from strange adults recently captured and imported. Since later studies have more and more stressed the importance of long-term personal relationships in determining interaction patterns, both of these studies must now be approached with reservations.

Rather earlier than Carpenter's study, a distinct estrus, coinciding with maximal perineal swelling, was established for the chimpanzee at the Yerkes laboratory (Yerkes and Elder, 1936). Copulation was not confined to this time but was much more frequent then. More recently, writers have tended to assume that extended or continuous estrus is a product of the boredom of captivity and lack of alternative occupation, and that copulation in the wild is less frequent and more markedly periodical. "Estrus cycle" has been used synonymously with "menstrual cycle" even when no information on mating was available. The position is further confused by the use by some monkey species of copulatory movements in nonsexual contexts. Some authors have felt that the motor patterns were indistinguishable (male–male mountings of baboons may include ejaculation) and have used a purely motor definition (Rowell, 1967a); others (e.g., Kaufman, 1965) have felt that they could separate dominance mounting from sexual mounting. The difficulty is especially apparent in field studies, and it is also usually impossible under field conditions to distinguish reliably between mounts with and without intromission, ejaculation, etc. Species differences are probably also important.

As a final blow to the concept of continual receptivity, Michael, Herbert, and their co-workers have demonstrated that the continuous receptivity of the cycling rhesus monkey in captivity, described by Hartman (1932), does not withstand quantitative analysis. Ball and Hartman (1935) had already described some variation of receptivity during the cycle. Using a rather crude scoring technique, summing three separate female behavior patterns, they found a rise in receptivity just before ovulation and a fall just after. They noted considerable variation in their animals, and some did not show the effect. The examples illustrated, however, suggest that individual females were rather constant in the amount of behavior change in different cycles. Michael and Herbert first showed (1963) that quantitative studies of behavior of pairs of animals under rigorously controlled conditions demonstrated a cyclic variation in the quantity of sexual behavior observed, with a clear mid-cycle peak in ejaculation frequency corresponding to the time of ovulation. A mid-cycle peak in the probability of mating by laboratory macaques was confirmed by Phoenix et al. (1968), who showed that this behavior change was strongly related to ovarian conditions. Michael, Herbert, and co-workers went on to show that these changes could be reproduced by using spayed animals given estrogen–progesterone therapy. They were able, by comparing male and female responses to different methods of administering hormones, to separate the two concepts of receptivity and attractiveness of females, an important distinction which led to the discovery of the vaginal pheromone mentioned above. This long series of papers has recently been reviewed by Herbert (1970); the reader is referred to that article for detailed references.

The rhesus estrous cycle was demonstrated by Michael and Herbert in isolate-living females paired with males in daily 60-minute tests. Monkeys normally live in very different circumstances, with partners of both sexes continually available. Even in the pair test situation there was variation among both males and females, and when a second female was introduced into the situation the level of male–female interaction was no longer highly predictable from a knowledge of the female's hormone levels alone (Herbert, 1968). With further complication of the social situation one may speculate whether the cyclic effect might even be submerged almost entirely.

In group-living animals it is difficult to keep complete records of all copulatory activity, and records typically consist in whether or not copulation (as decided by observed copulation to ejaculation, traces of fresh ejaculate in the vulva, or presence of sperm in vaginal lavage) occurred on a given day. Though less detailed, such records are probably biologically adequate in the sense that one full copulation in twelve hours will probably suffice for conception. Using such records from small groups of four female rhesus monkeys to a male, copulation was found to occur most frequently in the luteal (postfertile) part of cycles. There was no clear peak, the most salient feature being the infrequency of copulation immediately before and during menstruation (Rowell, 1963). Rather similar distributions of copulations during the menstrual cycle occurred in breeding groups of *Cercopithecus mitis* (Sykes') and *C. aethiops* (vervet) monkeys — a more or less level distribution with a fall just before and a rise just after menstruation (Rowell, 1970a). In all three species these aggregated data were found not to be representative of individual behavior, but a sum of extremely varied patterns. In the rhesus colony, nearly half the copulations were due to two favorites (in separate groups), which were also the highest ranking animals in their groups; except for a slight reduction over menstruation, these animals copulated equally often throughout their cycles. Data from the other eleven animals showed a peak in the week before the next menstruation. In the Sykes' group (six females) running records of vaginal contents showed clear estrous periods: an individual would have sperm in four or five successive alternate-day samples, and then none for three or more weeks. These estrous periods were not, however, related to a specific period of the menstrual cycle. Individual female's records showed peaks in early, middle, or late cycle, and one showed an even distribution of copulations throughout cycles. In the vervet group, vaginal contents included sperm on most days, and estrous cycles were not apparent. Struhsaker (1967) records estrous periods of "at least 45 days" in a wild population. Sexual behavior was also observed in the caged group during standard watches; it showed no variation in frequency during menstrual cycles. One female showed most sexual behavior when cycling, another when pregnant, and the other three showed no differences. Copulation was not recorded in the first five weeks of lactation

(Rowell, 1972). Hanby *et al.* (1971) also found no cyclicity of behavior during two breeding seasons in a colony of *Macaca fuscata*. Like the vervets, these females did not mate during early lactation.

The possibility that estrous periods might not be associated with specific stages in the menstrual cycle has been given little previous attention. In no field or free-range study of macaques in which estrous periods were described was it possible to record menstruation (with the recent exception of Loy, 1970). Jay (1965) could observe menstruation, and confirm a mid-cycle estrus, in some females of a troop of langurs, *Presbytis entellus*. The usual nonbehavioral criterion of estrus in studies of free-ranging macaques has been intensity of color of face and rump (Kaufman, 1965; see also Bernstein, 1963), but this is reliably associated with estrus in only half of cycles (Carpenter, 1942), or less (Rowell, 1963). Moreover, color may be rapidly affected by social changes. (Compare also the baboon swelling: DeVore (1965) observed deflation after a fight between wild baboons; the swelling of caged baboons decreased in size and became soft after handling and immobilizing with Sernylan; gentle stroking of the swelling caused it to become taut and shiny again in a few moments.) So the possibility remains that estrous periods in these conditions may not be mid-cycle as generally assumed but could have variable relationships with cycles, or perhaps be determined primarily by exogenous (social) factors. It is quite likely that some individuals will be more influenced by hormonal factors than others (cf. common human experience).

In review, estrous periods of free-ranging rhesus monkeys have been made to sound rather constant, but in original reports one is struck more by their variability. For instance, Carpenter (1942) is usually quoted on a mean estrous period of 9.2 days, or about a third of the cycle. His data, however, show a range of 4 to 15 days, with no peak in frequency of any length (45 cycles). In a later, more extensive study, Kaufman (1965) found a range of estrus length from 1 to 95 days, with a mean of 11 days. Given the known fluctuations of estrogen–progesterone balance in the average 28-day cycle of this species, it is difficult to imagine these estrous periods all being related to an equivalent hormonal state. Conaway and Koford (1965) give complete mating data for 31 females throughout one breeding season, and no regularity of occurrence or duration of estrus is apparent in their data. Loy (1970) has recently called attention to another explanation of the occurrence of estrus in the rhesus monkey. He recorded menstruation while observing behavior of free-living females and was able to establish perimenstrual estrous periods that did not differ, either in mean duration or included behavior, from estrous periods that were essentially mid-cycle. He points out that premenstrual increases in sexual activity were in fact recorded by several workers on laboratory rhesus (Michael *et al.*, 1967; Herbert, 1967; Phoenix *et al.*, 1968; see also Erikson, 1967, using an artificial stimulation technique), although in all cases the authors stressed only the mid-cycle peaks they also recorded. A second, postovulatory peak in estrogen excretion has been demonstrated in the rhesus monkey (Chatterjee and Anand, 1967), chimpanzees (Fish *et al.*, 1941), and women (Pedersen-Bjergaard and Pederson-Bjergaard, 1948). Loy links the perimenstrual estrus he observed with this second rise in estrogen secretion and therefore feels that a useful correlation between estrogen levels and estrus could still be maintained, but since he observed estrous periods occurring before, during, and after menstruation, this correlation cannot be very precise. Chimpanzees show no perimenstrual estrus, but women, if they report any change in receptivity with cycle, commonly mention a premenstrual increase (Ford and Beach, 1951).

Conaway and Koford (1965) mention longer and behaviorally more obvious estrus in older than in younger animals. A similar relationship of intensity of heat to age was noted by Goodall (1969) in wild chimpanzees. A comparison of three elderly (over 12 years) and four young female baboons also showed longer estrous periods in the older animals (mean length for former 11.7, for the latter 7.5, $P < 0.01$) (Rowell, personal observation). Old *Macaca fuscata* females, however, were less persistently sexually active during the breeding season than younger animals (Hanby *et al.*, 1971).

There seems to be no generalization that can be made about the relationship of copulation frequency to menstrual cycle in primates. Some species, probably only those with limited perineal swellings, copulate almost exclusively during a mid-cycle estrus associated with the swelling. In anubis baboons (Rowell, 1967a) and in the white-cheeked mangabey (Chalmers, 1968; Rowell and Chalmers, 1970), estrus terminates abruptly: once the swelling has shown the smallest sign of decreasing, copulation is as infrequent as when the perineum is quite flat. In the chacma baboon, Saayman (1970) found a higher incidence of sexual activity during deflation, decreasing gradually with the size of the swelling. In rhesus macaques a similarly timed, but still less abruptly demarcated, period of estrus can be demonstrated in simplified conditions, but it virtually disappears in normal social groups, and in this species there is evidence of two estrous peaks in the menstrual cycle. A pattern of clear estrous periods not at all related to specific stages of the cycle has been observed once and may be more general, since the possibility has not previously been taken into account. And finally there are species in which some, probably the majority, of individuals mate throughout the cycle at an even rate. At least these last three patterns may occur in different individuals of the same group, and we have as yet no idea of their relative frequency. There is urgent need for data on a wider range of species.

B. COPULATION DURING PREGNANCY

Periods of estrus in early pregnancy were first observed by Ball (1936) in laboratory rhesus monkeys. She described a single estrus three to four weeks after conception and believed that only a single estrus was possible in a normal pregnancy, because sexual behavior was suppressed when the placenta took over the major part of progesterone secretion from the corpus luteum after the first month. In two of her animals a second estrus was accompanied by abortion, suggesting that the placenta had failed in its secretory takeover. Estrus during pregnancy was confirmed by Conaway and Koford (1965) and by Kaufman (1965) in the free-ranging Cayo Santiago colony. In the breeding season reported by Conaway and Koford, no less than a third of the estrous periods they observed were later found from observed birth dates to have occurred during pregnancy; several females had two or more periods during pregnancy, and one old female mated almost continually throughout gestation. It is difficult to relate this observation to the finding by Michael *et al.* (1968) that progesterone depressed sexual behavior. In perineal-swelling species, copulation is very rare unless there is a swelling; I have seen only very small swellings in pregnant baboons and mangabeys, too small to be associated with copulation. Goodall (1969) reports full swellings, with estrous behavior, in pregnant wild chimpanzees, however. In nonswelling species, copulation during pregnancy occurs, but probably less frequently than during menstrual cycles. Captive gorillas have been observed to copulate up to the sixth month of pregnancy. Occasional copulations were recorded in four of five Sykes' monkey pregnancies, and the fifth included a very clear estrous period about four weeks after conception. Vervet females also varied, from one extreme female which showed sperm in every vaginal lavage taken throughout pregnancy up to the day before birth, to another which mated only rarely when pregnant. Jay noted at least two estrous periods during pregnancy in a wild *Presbytis entellus* group (personal communication). *Macaca fuscata* females actually copulated more frequently after conception than before, but pregnant females stopped mating earlier in the season, the sooner they had conceived (Hanby *et al.,* 1971).

C. THE LACTATION INTERVAL

After a live birth the reproductive tract becomes highly atrophied during the lactation interval, and sexual behavior is effectively absent (though male rhesus in caged groups have been observed to mount females during and immediately after birth; see photo in Hinde *et al.,*

1964). This interval, if suckling continues, lasts two to three years in the chimpanzee, five to six months in the olive baboons, three to four months in the Sykes' monkey, and as little as five weeks in the vervet. In all species menstrual cycles begin again well before lactation is finished — lactation is, in fact, usually continuous in a healthy female, the new infant replacing the previous one at the breast or even sharing nursing (e.g., Lancaster, 1972, on the vervet). In species with a defined annual breeding season, the lactation interval seems to last until the next breeding season, when the infant is about six months old, and in these species there is a "lactation interval" even if the infant dies, which continues until the breeding season (I. C. Kaufman, personal communication, on *M. nemestrina*). Rhesus females that do not conceive during the breeding season on Cayo Santiago continue to show menstrual cycles, with estrus, throughout the pregnancy and lactation of the majority, (Loy, 1969b). In baboons, on the other hand, menstrual cycles begin again two to three weeks after abortion, stillbirth, or death of infant, and a similar interval occurred in one *Cercopithecus mitis* and two *Miopithecus talapoin* whose newborn infants died.

The first sign of resumption of cycles in the baboon is a slowly developing perineal swelling, and copulation begins when it becomes large, suggesting that the reproductive tract is prepared by the usual histological changes for mating before it occurs. In a Sykes' monkey the order was rather different: vaginal lavage at twelve weeks after birth was almost devoid of cells. A week or two later came a sample that contained sperm, but no other cells except the occasional parabasal. Only a week or two after this did the vaginal epithelium begin to show signs of activity. Thus in this case sexual behavior preceded reproductive tract regrowth. This single observation is of interest, not for itself, but in the context of current work on seasonally breeding rhesus monkeys. When the majority of females give birth and go into lactation interval at about the same time, there is suddenly an almost total loss of mating behavior in the group, a situation which Zuckerman's old hypothesis would predict (p. 78) was potentially highly disruptive of social organization. However, Sade (1964) observed a big decrease in testicular activity coinciding with late pregnancy and lactation interval of the rhesus females of the Cayo Santiago group, showing that seasonal breeding was effected through both sexes. Vandenbergh and Vessey (1968) stated that the seasonal breeding of rhesus monkeys was synchronized by rainfall, possibly through its effect on plant growth, but their data are equivocal, and in tropical Africa, although there is again a general relationship between breeding seasons of *Cercopithecus* species and seasonal rainfall, the precise timing makes it difficult to postulate a convincing timing mechanism (Rowell, 1970a). Vandenbergh (1969) found that in the sexually inactive season male rhesus could be reactivated by exposure to females artificially brought into estrus. The reverse experiment has not yet been reported, but the observation on Sykes' monkeys quoted above suggests that artificially reactivated males might also stimulate females to show estrus. This in no way helps to clear up the problem of timing of breeding seasons, but does indicate that social as well as meteorological factors may participate in synchronization of breeding.

D. SUMMARY

In summarizing the relation between female reproductive cycles and copulation, the first generalization is that there is no reliable hormonal correlate of estrus in intact group-living animals. Primates show a great deal of Heape's "abnormal estrus" at times when they cannot conceive. There is such variation between species, however, that should the research problem require it, one can select a species, like a baboon, in which estrus and ovulation are relatively closely correlated. It would be very unwise to forget that estrus is a behavioral term in the majority of species about which there is any information, and there remains a tantalizing range of species to be investigated.

Not only do species vary, there is also variation within species, even between animals in the same group, in the same physical environment. We have seen that age is an important variable, females in at least three species increasing the duration and intensity of their sexual behavior as they grow older. There is a suggestion, which will be explored further in the next section, that at least in captive groups female rank may partly determine the pattern of her sexual behavior. Individual experience in other areas probably plays a role: Ransom and Ransom (1972) describe social relationships of infant baboons which probably influence their adult interaction pattern with males. Other sources of variation probably remain to be discovered once the variety, rather than the average, is accepted as a subject of interest.

IV. SECONDARY SEXUAL BEHAVIOR

Copulation in monkeys is usually accompanied by a complex of courtship behavior. Unlike copulation itself, many of the behavior patterns involved in courtship have been variously interpreted by different authors. They may occur outside the context of copulation, between pairs of animals other than adult male and female, and they are therefore considered separately from mating itself in this review. Behavior patterns of courtship include spatial adjustments—following of one partner by the other, sitting together, separation of the pair from the rest of a group; contact—handling, nosing, or mouthing genitals, touching other parts of the body, grooming; facial gestures like lipsmacking or pouting; and presenting of the anogenital region by the female. All these have been classed as specifically sexual behavior by some authors, but they seem to have more general significance.

A. CONSORT BEHAVIOR

Courtship behavior is obvious and prolonged in baboons, some macaques, and chimpanzees, but it is much more subtle in some other groups. As an example, even after a year of regular observation of a groups of vervets, the author was not always able to predict copulation, since there was no constant prior modification of the male–female interaction pattern. In Sykes' monkeys an exchange of glances could often be detected, and sometimes copulation was preceded by following and circling behavior (nasogenital investigation by both animals simultaneously). Carpenter (1964) commented on the lack of courtship preceding copulation in howler monkeys (*Alouatta palliata*), although he described a reliably occurring exchange of gestures – rhythmic tongue movements between male and female preceding copulation. In earlier field studies of several species (e.g., Haddow, 1952) copulation was not observed and was assumed to take place at night. In retrospect it seems likely that observers expecting complex and long-lasting courtship might easily miss copulations of *Cercopithecus* species under field conditions.

In a few species – *Papio anubis* and *M. mulatta* especially – the formation of consort pairs has attracted much attention. A female at the height of estrus is escorted, groomed, and mounted by a single, high-ranking male, which apparently prevents her from copulating with other males. This behavior has been thought to have genetic effects, the high-ranking males, presumed to be genetically superior, copulating when conception is most likely, and thus producing more offspring. There has even been discussion as to how, if dominance is thus selected for, subordinate animals continue to be produced. Several observations throw doubt on this theory. [For discussion of the value of the concept of dominance as a heritable quality, see Rowell (1966b).] Firstly, we have seen that estrus in many species is not closely associated with ovulation. Conaway and Koford (1965) noted that some of their high-ranking, frequently mating rhesus males formed long-lasting consort relations with older females who were already pregnant. Frequency of copulation by male baboons is generally, but not very precisely, correlated with rank (DeVore, 1965), the very highest ranking males being sometimes too involved in "police work" to have much time for sexual behavior. Conaway and Koford found only a partial correlation of mating frequency with rank in 1960, but in 1962 Kaufman found a very high correlation in the same groups (Kaufman, 1965). Consort relationships are not always exclusive. Though DeVore (1965) reports consort pairs lasting several days in anubis baboon troops, in a troop observed by Rowell (1967a) estrous females were observed to be "in consort" with each of the five adult males in their group during the course of a single day: as each male tired and became less eager to follow, he was abandoned by the female in favor of the next. Saayman (1970) found both patterns in a troop of chacma baboons: individual consort pairs lasting 1 to 15 days (mean 2.7 days) were observed, and there were also consort pairs with subadult males lasting less than 1 day. Of Conaway and Koford's thirty-two rhesus females, only four consorted with a single male, and more than half consorted with four or more. Kaufman found a higher proportion of females that were monogamous within a single estrus— twenty-three of ninety estrous periods were monogamous—but the majority were associated with more than one male.

Competition for females in an extreme form was described by Zuckerman (1932) in a hamadryas baboon group with a very high proportion of males. Field observers, however, have frequently commented on the absence of interference by high-ranking males in the copulations occurring close to them (Goodall, 1969, on chimpanzee; Rowell, 1967a, on anubis baboons; Saayman, 1970, on chacma baboons; Simonds, 1965, on *M. radiata*, the bonnet macaque). DeVore (1965) reported harassment of copulating males by other adult males and described this as competition for the female, though the harassing male never succeeded in obtaining the female. Adult male Japanese macaques of high rank also harassed frequently, and again did not succeed in breaking up mating pairs (Hanby *et al.*, 1971). Harassment of copulations by infants and juveniles, however, often but not always the female's own child, is very commonly seen in many species. Overall, direct evidence of competition for females by potent males, which might lead to sexual selection, is limited. A final consideration on the genetic value of consort pair formation is that, as more long-term studies become available, it is more apparent that male status is as much a matter of changes with age as an individual characteristic (see Kummer, 1968), so that any mating advantage that accrues from consort pairing of middle-aged adult males will only perpetuate the rather general characteristics that have allowed survival to that age.

Choice of mate may be determined by criteria other than rank. Both Kummer (1968) and Ransom and Ransom (1972) describe interactions between males and infants and juvenile females that could be the origin of the strong personal attachments between adult pairs seen in *P. hamadryas* and *P. anubis*, respectively. Stable pair relationships carrying over for several years were reported in rhesus groups by Kaufman (1965). On the other side, there is evidence of a possible partial "incest tabu" in chimpanzees, where Goodall observed no son-mother matings, in rhesus, where Sade (1968) found a much lower incidence of son–mother mating than would be expected by chance, and in *M. fuscata*, where sons were not seen to ejaculate with mothers (Hanby *et al.*, 1971).

Consort pairing does occur in chimpanzees, but more commonly the swollen female travels with group of males, mating with all of them frequently. It does not occur in all macaques. Simonds (1965) comments specifically on the absence of consorting in *M. radiata*. It is not generally recorded for other group-living species with no sexual skin, but Ullrich (1961) described consort pairs in black and white colobus (*C. guereza*). Animals that live in groups containing only a single pair of adults such as gibbons and *Callicebus* are rather a special case and are not considered in this context.

It is worth noting that behavior corresponding exactly to the descriptions of consort pairs, except for copulation, may occur outside the context of estrus. The most striking example is that of baboons, where the adult male follows the mother of a newborn infant, attending and grooming her just as he would a swollen female (Ransom and Ransom, 1972). A similar relationship may be seen between females when one has a newborn infant, the other often being a young nulliparous animal (in baboons, also in vervets, Lancaster, 1972).

A note may be made here on the behavior of pregnant females—by far the least studied aspect of our topic, attention having been concentrated on menstrual cycles and on mother–infant interaction. In a caged baboon group (Rowell, 1969a) pregnant females showed small but consistent reduction of social activity with other females, both in initiating friendly interaction and in avoiding other females. They seemed on the whole rather more lethargic than usual. In the wild (Rowell, 1966a) pregnant females also interacted less with other females to some extent, but this was associated with a change of behavior the reverse of lethargic. Pregnant females were usually among the furthest out from the troop center during foraging and responded less quickly to change in direction and activity of the main troop; they seemed less anxious generally about maintaining normal close contact, comparable to some of the more senior males. Perhaps it is because of this change in behavior during pregnancy, in some ways the reverse of consort activity, that the brilliant rump of the pregnant female, easily identified from several hundred yards, has been developed.

Whether consort behavior is mentioned, or stressed, by an observer is going to depend on the sort of relationship obtaining between adult males and females outside the estrous situation (and if estrus is readily definable, which verges on the tautologous). For example, in a caged baboon group the highest ranking female was a "good friend" of the adult male and always spent a lot of time with him. Apart from copulation, her interaction with him hardly changed during her swelling. At the other extreme, the lowest ranking female carefully avoided the male except when she was swollen, when she approached him, copulated, groomed, and was followed, in dramatic contrast to her nonswollen behavior. In her case one thought in terms of consort behavior; in the case of the alpha female this description did not seem appropriate. This problem is perhaps best considered in terms of a more detailed analysis of individual behavior patterns: three of those most commonly associated with copulation are discussed below.

B. PRESENTING

Among baboons, mangabeys, macaques, and chimpanzees, presenting the hindquarters is a universal gesture of "politeness" used by all ages and both sexes. In these groups, which all have sexual skin on the rump, and may also have a sexual swelling, it is an obvious and readily identified gesture, even though there may be several modifications within the species—for example, presenting is accompanied by a vertical tail if a presenting baboon is frightened; a foot may reach back to touch the animal presented to; the hips may be slewed and the legs partly bent if presenting is to a very small infant (this has been interpreted by some observers as an invitation to climb on the back of the presenter); the rump may be thrust under the nose of the other animal; or the presenter may be several feet away. Similarly the present of the chimpanzee varies from a straight-legged posture used in most greetings to a prostrate crouch of females in high estrus (Crawford, 1940). In spite of this variability one can nearly always say with confidence when one animal is presenting to another. Presenting may be followed by grooming the rump, or by mounting the presenter, among other responses. It is said to be used to avert aggression, though I have myself never seen presenting to an animal at all likely to attack: more frequently it is seen during reconciliation after an agonistic interaction. In the few studied species without sexual skin, presenting is much less easily defined, and anyone used to baboons or macaques might well say it does not occur, as did Hall *et al.* (1965) of the patas (*Erythrocebus patas*). In *Cercopithecus aethiops* and *C. mitis* the rump may be presented for grooming, though rarely; and copulation is sometimes preceded by the female standing in a slightly more four-square posture than usual, with the tail slightly raised, glancing at the male of her choice but with the rump not necessarily turned toward him. Simply standing might be a useful signal in most species of monkeys, which are normally seated or lying if not moving. If Hall *et al.* observed similar behavior in patas, they would have been quite justified in refusing to classify it as presenting as normally understood. Jay (1965) describes slightly more obvious presenting by female langurs, with turning of the rump toward the male and *lowering* of the tail which is normally carried over the back in this species, and also a characteristic head gesture and shuddering. The talapoin, although it has an extensive area of sexual skin, presents in the subtle Cercopithecus-like way in my colony. On the other hand, Scruton and Herbert (1972) describe presenting as a clearly definable pattern, and from the remarks of Herbert (1970) seem to regard it as little different from the presenting of rhesus monkeys. There are perhaps individual or race differences in this species.

Female chimpanzees (Crawford, 1940) show big increases in frequency of presenting when they are swollen, and fully swollen baboons present about seven times as often as they do when the perineum is flat. A mid-cycle increase in presenting in some, but not all, female rhesus was reported by Trimble and Herbert (1968). There is a general assumption that presenting is primarily a means of attracting attention to the sexual skin, and so communicating the female's willingness to mate. Use of this gesture in other contexts is regarded, on this hypothesis, as secondary, and the value of the gesture in conciliation is derived from its sexual connotation. This view is expounded by Wickler (1967). Bopp (1953) took an opposing view of presenting by baboons, calling it an *Inferioritätsreaktion*. He suggested that, since, in the animals he observed, presenting to both sexes, and not just to males, increased during the female's swelling, this could hardly be described as a sexual gesture. He attributed the increase to a lowering of rank at that time, an increase in inferiority. There is evidence that, as a sexual invitation, presenting of the swollen perineum by baboons is not effective, at least in producing an immediate sexual response. The proportion of presenting which was followed by mounting was about the same whatever the state of the female's perineum and was never high—between 4% and 14%. Most copulations were initiated by the male approaching a seated female whose perineum was not visible (Rowell, 1967a). These observations were made on wild and caged *P. anubis* groups. In a wild chacma (*P. porcarius*) group, however, Saayman (1970) did not confirm this observation. Presenting by swollen chacma females produced a higher percentage of sexual responses than did presenting by nonswollen females, though again most copulations were initiated by males. Perhaps this difference might be related to the greater size and conspicuousness of the chacma swelling. The *number* of mountings preceded by the presentation of swollen, compared with nonswollen, perinea was much higher in both cases because the swollen females presented so much more often. There was a suggestion, from field data, that the association between swelling and estrus might be learned by males, since from infancy to adulthood they became steadily more selective of fully swollen females for copulation attempts. On the other hand, there was little evidence from the analysis of the behavior of the caged baboon group that presenting could be regarded as an "inferiority reaction." Half of the presenting seen in that group was by females to males and could therefore also be described as being directed by subordinate to dominant animals. A third of the presenting seen, however, was between females, and here the consistency of rank direction was not particularly high— 67% of presentings were by subordinate to dominant females (Rowell, 1966b). In analyzing female interactions by cycle state, presenting was unfortunately not separated from other gestures of conciliation. This group of behavior patterns as a whole showed no consistent changes with reproductive state. The two highest ranking females presented less to other females when fully swollen; the two highest ranking presented more to other females when their swellings were increasing (Rowell, 1969a). These data differ from those of Bopp (1953) and were interpreted in relation to changes in agonistic behavior which will be discussed later (Section V).

C. GROOMING

Mutual grooming occupies more time than any other activity in all studied groups of primates, and it occurs in sexual as well as in other social contexts. Among Old World primates, adult females spend most time grooming each other, especially within matrilines (Sade, 1965), but they also groom adult males and juveniles. Adult males of some species—for example, baboons and *M. nemestrina* (Rosenblum *et al.*, 1966)—spend relatively little time grooming. They frequently initiate bouts with females, but quickly turn to solicit reciprocal grooming. Male chimpanzees (Goodall, 1969), talapoins (Wolfheim, 1970), and bonnet macaques (Simonds, 1965) groom other males rather than females, at least outside a sexual context. This presumably also applies to those species in which all-male groups occur.

During consort relations of baboons and macaques, the mates groom each other. Michael and Herbert (1963) found that grooming between opposite sexed rhesus paired for short test periods varied reciprocally during the menstrual cycle, females grooming males more before and after menstruation, while males groomed females almost exclusively at mid-cycle. For these animals grooming partners were available only during the tests, so observed grooming rates were very high. It is possible that the reciprocal pattern was an artifact of the almost continuous grooming produced by the experimental conditions, and the fact that rhesus monkeys do not groom each other simultaneously. Lindburg (in press) in a field study found a rather different pattern: more than half of male-to-female *and* female-to-male grooming occurred in consort pairs—that is, when females were in estrus—although they were in estrus only 8.5% available time. Thus grooming by both sexes varied together, not reciprocally. Similarly, in a caged group of baboons where grooming partners of all types· were continuously available (Rowell, 1968), males still groomed swollen (equivalent to rhesus mid-cycle) females more, but females also groomed males more as they moved into a sort of consort relationship (this behavior change cannot be seen in full in captivity). The total amount of grooming by the female did not change, but, now sitting with the male, she groomed him more, and other females correspondingly less. The female was groomed rather more frequently when swollen, because the increase in grooming by the male more than compensated for the reduction in female grooming. The amount of the change varied between individuals. As discussed earlier (p. 89), this difference could be partly related to rank, the highest ranking female showing no change in grooming frequency, while two females lower in rank groomed with the male only when fully swollen. The beta female was disliked by the male, who rarely copulated with her, and she actually groomed him slightly less when swollen than when her perineum was flat.

When these changes during the menstrual cycle are related to the females' overall reproductive cycle, they are insignificant compared with the increase in grooming received by mothers of newborn infants. Pregnant females tended to be groomed rather less than the overall average rate, though significantly so in only two of five cases. The amount of grooming of other animals did not vary with the females' reproductive state, though, as we have seen, the partners changed.

Chimpanzee males groomed swollen females more, though still not as often as they groomed other males (Goodall, 1969). This author does not discuss changes in female grooming with reproductive state. In captive animals, Young and Orbison (1944) state that grooming (between oppositely sexed pairs) is "less closely related to the cycle than in rhesus monkeys."

In a captive group of vervet monkeys, *Cercopithecus aethiops,* males and females groomed each other most when the females were pregnant, but in a similar group of *C. mitis* there was no consistent change in intrasexual grooming with reproductive state. Between females of both species, mothers with small babies were groomed more frequently than females in other reproductive states; there were no changes within the menstrual cycle (Rowell, 1972).

It appears that there is much variation, both between species and between individuals, in the relations between frequency of grooming and reproductive cycles among the Old World monkeys.

D. Handling, Nosing, and Licking Genitals

Since handling is very frequently followed by putting the fingers to the muzzle, these behavior patterns are probably best considered together as chemical sampling of the genitalia. This has become especially interesting in view of the recent demonstration that pheromones of vaginal origin play an important part in sexual response by rhesus males in the pair test situation (Michael and Keverne, 1970). Interestingly, handling or nosing of genitals other than the animal's own has not been listed as a behavior pattern of group-living rhesus, though several exhaustive catalogs of sexual and other social behavior have been published (Carpenter, 1942; Hinde and Rowell, 1962; Altmann, 1962). Smelling of the genitals is recorded for the bonnet macaque by Simonds (1965), however. This species has no reliable change in color or swelling of the rump skin during the menstrual cycle, but was mentioned by Zuckerman (1930) as showing a "copious vaginal discharge" at mid-cycle, so perhaps it relies more heavily on chemical than on visual cues.

In chimpanzees, males touch females' swellings most frequently when the swelling is deflating, and often when it is increasing, but not at full swelling (Goodall, 1969). A sub-adult male baboon touched or inspected female perinea about equally often at all stages in which there was some enlargement, but an adult male mainly touched fully swollen perinea (Rowell, 1967a).

All the foregoing species have well-developed "sexual skin." Handling and nosing genitals seems to be a more common part of the mating sequence, as judged by the weight given in published descriptions, in monkeys with no sexual skin. Male nosing of female genitals was recorded by Gartlan (1969) during copulation of wild vervets, and mutual genital nosing in a circling movement may precede copulation in Sykes' monkeys. In caged groups of these species, genital nosing by Sykes' monkeys was more common with cycling than noncycling females, and perhaps most frequent at mid-cycle, though data were few. In the vervet group, however, it occurred with about the same frequency in all reproductive states.

The importance of olfactory stimuli from the female genitalia in New World monkeys has already been mentioned (p. 77). All descriptions of precopulatory behavior include handling or licking the genitalia of the female (Carpenter, 1964, on howler and red spider; DuMond, 1968, on the squirrel monkey; Moynihan, 1964, on the night monkey, *Aotes*). This is in addition to the attention paid to urine markings in these species. Similarly, olfactory stimuli are important in precopulatory behavior of lemurs: scent-marking and genital nosing are prominent in Jolly's (1966) description of the breeding season of *Lemur catta* and *Propithecus verreauxi*. It is not clear from most descriptions of either New

World monkeys or prosimians whether genital handling and nosing generally occur outside the sexual context, or whether olfactory communication is then only by means of the various elaborate scent-marking methods found in both groups. For the black spider monkey, *Ateles belzebuth,* Klein (1971) states that handling of female genitals does occur in nonsexual situations, but is most frequent in precopulatory behavior. In *Lemur catta* female genital marking was not related to estrus, but male investigation of female genitalia and male scent marking displays were significantly more frequent to estrus than to non-estrus females Evans and Goy, 1968).

In summary then, we have some association of genital sampling of females with cycling rather than with pregnancy or lactation, and with estrus where this is clear within cycles. But the differentiation is not as obvious in group studies as might have been expected from the rather dramatic findings of Michael and Keverne on laboratory-tested macaques. Perhaps with the stimulus of their recent work more attention will be paid to this point with future studies.

V. RANK AND AGONISTIC BEHAVIOR

In his account of the behavior of captive hamadryas baboons, Zuckerman (1932) stated that the female rose to highest rank when her perineal swelling reached maximal size. Carpenter (1942) came to a similar conclusion from his observations of newly released macaques on Cayo Santiago, noting that females coming into estrus were often severely wounded, implying that, besides being attacked by males when too importunate, they fought their way up the female hierarchy at that time. Both these authors seem to have used proximity to a high-ranking male as an index of female rank — a somewhat androcentric view which becomes tautologous in the context of estrus. Changing rank as assessed by social interaction patterns has not been confirmed in captive or wild hamadryas (Kummer, 1956, 1968) nor in caged anubis baboons (Rowell, 1966b). Hall and DeVore (1965) assumed female rank changes with cycle state in wild baboons but describe them as subtle, and this apparently derives from DeVore's observations, since in Hall's earlier paper (1962) he did not describe changes in rank with reproductive state in chacmas. Bernstein (1963) found no rank changes with cycle in female rhesus in a caged group, and Kaufman (1965), though discussing the effect of rank on breeding behavior, did not mention changes of rank with cycle. It seems, therefore, that earlier accounts may be discounted, and females of these species should not be expected to change rank, as assessed by social criteria, during the menstrual cycle. Rank changes with cycle have been considered only for baboons and macaques, because these species show relatively high rates of agonistic behavior which make analysis possible. In field studies of most species, and in caged studies of *Cercopithecus* species, agonistic exchanges are so rare that sufficient data cannot be collected. This would imply that changes with cycle are unlikely to be important, even should they eventually be shown to exist.

Several authors have considered rank change with cycle in chimpanzees, but here the criterion has been that originally used by Yerkes — priority of access to food reward in pairs of caged animals. Yerkes (1939) found a tendency for females with swellings to become higher ranking than male partners on this criterion, but felt that this was not a true rank change, but rather a "granting of privilege" by the male, and made comparisons with human prostitution. Crawford (1940) made the same tests on all-female pairs, and again found a general tendency for swollen females to get a higher share of the rewards, but the effect was unreliable and depended on individual relationships. Birch and Clark (1945, 1946a,b, 1950) investigated the problem as a hormone effect, using castrated chimpanzees and the same food competition test. They found that androgens increased the rank of castrated animals of both sexes, while estrogen decreased the rank of males, but increased that of females. Estrogen also produced perineal swellings in the females, an effect that could be suppressed by giving amounts of progesterone simultaneously with the estrogen, which had no effect on behavior when administered alone. Females given estrogen and progesterone, and therefore showing no swelling, did not rise in rank, and the authors felt that this demonstrated that the increase in rank was due to the presence of the swelling. Since for many species the combination of estrogen and progesterone has very different effects on behavior from either hormone alone, this conclusion does not seem to me to be valid. Mirsky (1955), reviewing experiments on chimpanzees, contrasted the rather clear-cut effects reported by Birch and Clarke with the complex and variable results of the earlier workers. He tried to replicate the chimpanzee studies on castrated male and female rhesus monkeys, using single-sex pairs and also groups of five, but found no effect on rank of implanting either estrogen or androgens (thus confirming the remarks on this species made earlier). Goodall (1969) makes no mention of rank in relation to cycle in wild chimpanzees, perhaps suggesting that the effect reported by Birch and Clarke is of no great moment in normal life.

If actual rank changes do not occur during menstrual cycles, this does not preclude smaller changes in agonistic interaction patterns. There is a general tendency to be involved in more agonistic behavior during menstrual cycles than when pregnant or in lactation interval. This has been found in free-living rhesus monkeys (Wilson, 1968), in caged baboons, vervets, and Sykes' monkeys (Rowell, 1969a, 1972), and in mangabeys (Chalmers and Rowell, 1971). In baboons there is also a big increase in avoidance of friendly approaches by mothers in the first few weeks after birth, in response to the overenthusiastic attentions of would-be "aunts." In vervets, where adult females are less interested in other females' infants ("aunt" behavior being shown mainly by juvenile females: Lancaster, 1972), this rise in avoidance was not apparent (Rowell, 1972).

Within cycles, the picture is less clear. Chimpanzees, in the dominance studies cited above, were described as more aggressive when swollen; caged baboons overall were both attacked more and attacked more themselves when fully swollen; vervet females were also avoided most in mid-cycle but the differences were not significant (Rowell, 1969a, 1972). On the other hand, Young and Orbison (1944) mention chimpanzees which were more aggressive during menstruation; Hartman (1932) states that around menstruation caged rhesus monkeys were "more restless and irritable." In small breeding groups of rhesus the incidence of being bitten was highest immediately before menstruation, and there was a tendency for higher ranking animals to be unusually aggressive just after menstruation, but the figures were too small to be reliable without confirmation (Rowell, 1963). This may come from Sassenrath (in preparation) who is finding a similar rise in bite wounds around menstruation in laboratory group-caged females. Ivey and Bardwick (1968) found a sharp rise in negative affect (anxiety and hostility scores measured by word counts in recorded spoken material) just before menstruation in human subjects, and premenstrual irritability and anxiety have been well documented by Dalton (1964, 1966). A difficulty here is the lack of comparability of data: "irritable" as a description of a woman and of a monkey probably has rather different meanings, and would be based on different behavioral observations. How, for instance, can bite wounds be compared with word-count changes? Changes in agonistic relations over menstruation may also turn out to be a complex of related events: Paige (1969), whose study included both normal cycles and those of women using contraceptive hormone dosages, found differences in the time course relative to the cycle of "anxiety" and "hostility" scores, though both are classed as negative affect; similarly, the more frequent agonistic behavior in Rowell's macaques was different before and after menstruation. This is an area in which further research on nonhuman primates is urgently needed. If "mood" changes related to menstruation could be confirmed and further explored in the rhesus, for example, many of the current hypotheses used to explain human behavior changes, involving such factors as embarrassment or tabus about menstrual blood, or still more abstract constructs about feminine role fulfillment, would probably have to be discarded. On the other hand, Young and Orbison (1944) found that behavior at menstruation could not be separated from that at other nonswollen stages of the menstrual cycle in chimpanzees. For the most part studies on nonhuman primates have concentrated on the estrus/nonestrus comparison and have simply not considered menstruation as a behavior-influencing variable (but see Loy, 1970).

The effect of the menstrual cycle on agonistic behavior depends on the social status of the female. Probably the latter factor is the more powerful and may completely mask the potential for cyclical change in a group situation. Thus in a group of caged baboons with a very clear linear hierarchy, each of five adult females showed a different pattern of significant change in agonistic behavior during her menstrual cycle. The highest ranking female showed almost no change in relation to her own cycle, the lowest ranking fluctuated most, and the others were intermediate. Outside the menstrual cycle, differences were consistent: there was a general reduction in frequency of avoiding while pregnant (see p. 88) and an increase in avoiding of friendly approaches in lactation interval (see above).

Higher ranking females attacked other females with different frequencies according to the cycle state of the attacked animal, and the choice of cycle state to be attacked again varied with the attacker's rank. The alpha female attacked swollen females, the beta female attacked deflating females, the gamma female attacked both inflating and deflating females, but neither beta nor gamma female attacked swollen females, perhaps because of their proximity to the male (Rowell, 1969a).

In summary, there seem to be reliable differences in agonistic behavior between cycling, pregnant, and lactating females. Within the menstrual cycle changes in agonistic behavior, sometimes even expressed in rank changes, seem to be more reliably demonstrable, the further the conditions used are from the normal hormonal and social environment of the female. Further studies are required before we can say how far this potential effect of hormone fluctuation produces real changes in socially living monkeys.

VI. AGONISTIC BEHAVIOR BETWEEN MALES

There are several studies which indicate that male hierarchical relationships may be affected by the reproductive cycles of their associated females, with disruption of an established hierarchy at the onset of a breeding season. Jolly (1966) found that in wild *Lemur catta* and *Lemur macaco* troops females were dominant over males. Within sexes, the male hierarchy was clear-cut, the female very much less so. At the beginning of the brief mating season, *L. catta* males began to fight about four times as often and much more severely than usual, and the hierarchy established outside the breeding season was no longer valid while it lasted. Kaufman (1965), Vandenbergh and Vessey (1968), and Wilson and Boelkins (1971) found a similar increase in male fighting at the onset of the breeding season among rhesus monkeys on Cayo Santiago. In this case, besides fighting more, the males also moved to other troops much more often (Wilson, 1968), and this also involved change in established male hierarchies. Lindburg (1969) reports similar movements of males in a wild population in the mating season. DeVore (1965) and Ransom (1970) found increases in fighting and threatening between adult males in the presence of swollen females in wild anubis baboon groups.

VII. The Converse: Effect of Agonistic Behavior and Rank on Female Reproductive Cycles

Gilman and Gilbert (1946) noted that chacma baboons under stress — newly captured, transported long distances, or fed an inadequate diet — often either became acyclic or underwent unusually long cycles (the distinction is very difficult to make). Rowell (1970b) showed a correlation between social stress and an increase in the length of the follicular phase of the menstrual cycle — specifically in the time from day 1 to the onset of estrus. Stress had to take place around the time of menstruation, and in this study usually meant repeated beating-up by another female, but capture and removal from the familiar group (a procedure which involved no physical damage) had the same effect. Young and Yerkes (1943), discussing various factors that caused changes in menstrual cycle length in chimpanzees, reported that social factors had no effect. Their conditions, however, did not permit extensive investigation of the point. It is perhaps relevant that the average menstrual cycle length reported for captive chimpanzees, kept singly or in pairs (Yerkes and Elder, 1936), was shorter than that noted by Goodall (1969) in the wild. Similarly, the average menstrual cycle length of singly caged baboons (Hendrickx and Kraemer, 1969) was shorter than that of group-living caged baboons (Rowell, 1970b). This suggests that social understimulation might produce shortened menstrual cycles.

There is an accumulation of monkey-keepers' lore which suggests that social position might affect reproductive cycles more generally. In the last few years the author has established new breeding colonies of six separate species of Old World monkeys, starting in each case from groups of mutually strange adult females. In these circumstances females first form a rather rigid hierarchy. In all cases the highest ranking females were the first to breed, and, with few exceptions, females became pregnant in order of descending rank. Higher ranking females also tend to end their lactation intervals sooner in these groups, an effect first pointed out to me by I. C. Kaufman (personal communication), who had the same impression from *Macaca nemestrina*. These observations have no scientific merit and are offered solely in the hope of stimulating proper research into this subject which has potentially exciting implications.

VIII. Conclusions

In reviewing the literature on this subject, I was first impressed by the uneven distribution of our knowledge, with a reliable body of information on only a handful of species. Comparisons between these species, and with the fragmentary information available from some of the rest of the group, gave first an impression of variety. The menstrual cycle is a distinguishing character of the primates, and, as might be expected, innovation in reproductive processes has been accompanied by rapid divergence, giving a wide range of anatomical, behavioral, and probably physiologidal characters. In the past, generalizations have been made about primate reproductive cycles and behavior on the assumption that the few well-known species are representative of the group. Such generalizations underemphasize the differences between the known species, and there is now enough evidence that even these differences by no means represent the full range found in the group. For example, variations in female willingness to mate range in magnitude from small or absent to periodic complete disruptions of normal behavior; and their timing from brief episodes precisely related to endocrine changes within the menstrual cycle, through as yet unexplained fluctuations with about the same periodicity as the menstrual cycle but varying in relationship with it, to fluctuations that are more usefully related to seasonal changes than to menstrual cycles.

Conclusions on the relationship between all types of social behavior and female reproductive cycles have varied according to the conditions under which observations were made. In general, the simpler the social situation, and the more restricted the physical environment of the animals, the better the correlation between hormone levels and behavior. It is clear that these correlations exist, but also that they must be extremely labile, responding to environmental influences of every kind from the food supply to the previous learning experience of the female. As a result there are few examples of behavior changes that could reliably be predicted, in many individuals, from knowledge of endocrine changes in group-living female primates, with differences between cycling, pregnancy, and lactation interval being more reliable than changes within the menstrual cycle.

Miller (1931) suggested, and Zuckerman (1932) expanded the suggestion, that prolonging estrus would have enabled primates to evolve a way of life in permanent groups. Conversely, it seems reasonable to suggest that pronounced, hormonally regulated estrus would become less necessary for successful conception as animals came to live in enduring bisexual groups in which relationships are based on experience with individuals as well as responses to age/sex classes. These two trends should be mutually supportive, so that sexual behavior becomes less and less distinct in the interaction pattern of the group. We are then left with the paradox that the baboons and mangabeys, with some of the most highly developed social organizations yet described, also have some of the most clearly identified, short, and precisely timed estrous periods known. Clearly, we are only at the beginning of investigation of the relations between the factors so far identified.

References

Altmann, S. A. 1962. A field study of the sociobiology of rhesus monkeys, *Macaca mulatta*. *Ann. N.Y. Acad. Sci.* **102**, 338–435.

Ball, J. 1936. Sexual responsiveness and temporally related physiological events during pregnancy in the rhesus monkey. *Anat. Rec.* **67**, 507–512.

Ball, J., and Hartman, C. G. 1935. Sexual excitability as related to the menstrual cycle in the monkey. *Amer. J. Obstet. Gynecol.* **29**, 117–119.

Bernstein, I. S. 1963. Social activities related to rhesus monkey consort behavior. *Psychol. Rep.* **13**, 375–379.

Birch, H. G., and Clark, G. 1945. Hormonal modification of social behaviour: I. The effect of sex-hormone administration on the social dominance of a male castrate chimpanzee. *Psychosom Med.* **7**, 321–329.

Birch, H. G., and Clark, G. 1946a. Hormonal modification of social behaviour: II. Effects of sex hormone administration on social dominance status of the female castrate chimpanzee. *Psychosom. Med.* **8**, 320–331.

Birch, H. G., and Clark, G. 1946b. Hormonal modification of social behaviour: III. The effects of stilboestrol therapy on social dominance in female chimpanzees. *Bull. Can. Psychol. Ass.* **6**, 15–18.

Birch, H. G., and Clark, G. 1950. Hormonal modification of social behaviour: IV. The mechanism of estrogen-induced dominance in chimpanzees. *J. Comp. Physiol. Psychol.* **43**, 181–193.

Bopp, P. 1953. Zur Abhängigkeit der Inferioritätsreaktionen vom sexualzyklus bei Weiblichen Cynocephalen. *Rev. Suisse Zool.* **60**, 441–446.

Carpenter, C. R. 1942. Sexual behaviour of free ranging monkeys. I. Specimens, procedures, and behavioral characteristics of estrus. II. Perioidicity of estrus, homosexual, auto-erotic, and non-conformist behavior. *J. Comp. Psychol.* **43**, 143–162.

Carpenter, C. R. 1964. "Naturalistic Behavior of Nonhuman Primates." Pennsylvania State Univ. Press, University Park, Pennsylvania.

Chalmers, N. R. 1968. The social behaviour of free-living mangabeys in Uganda. *Folia Primatol.* **8**, 263–281.

Chalmers, N. R., and Rowell, T. E. 1971. Social behaviour of a caged group of mangabeys (*Cercocebus albigena*). *Folia Primatol.* **14**, 1–14.

Chatterjee, S., and Anand, B. K. 1967. Estimation of oestrogen from female monkey's urine. *Ind. J. Med. Res.* **55**, 973–980.

Conaway, C. H., and Koford, C. B. 1965. Estrous cycles and mating behaviour in a free ranging herd of rhesus monkeys. *J. Mammal* **45**, 577–588.

Crawford, M. P. 1940. The relation between social dominance and the menstrual cycle in the female chimpanzee. *J. Comp. Physiol. Psychol.* **30**, 483–513.

Dalton, K. 1964. "The Premenstrual Syndrome." Thomas, Springfield, Illinois.

Dalton, K. 1966. The influence of mother's menstruation on her child. *Proc. Roy. Soc. Med.* **59**, 1014.

DeVore, I. 1965. Male dominance and mating behaviour in baboons. *In* "Sex and Behavior" (F. A. Beach, ed.), pp. 266–289. Wiley, New York.

DuMond, F. V. 1968. The squirrel monkey in a semi-natural environment. *In* "The Squirrel Monkey" (L. A. Rosenblum and R. W. Cooper, eds.), pp. 88–146. Academic Press, New York.

Eaton, G., Slob, A. K., and Goy, R. W. 1970. Report on work in progress.

Erikson, L. B. 1967. Relationship of sexual receptivity to menstrual cycles in adult rhesus monkeys. *Nature (London)* **216**, 299–301.

Evans, C. S., and Goy, R. W. 1968. Social behaviour and reproductive cycles in captive ringtailed lemurs (*Lemur catta*). *J. Zool.* **156**, 181–197.

Everett, J. W. 1961. The mammalian female reproductive cycle and its controlling mechanisms. *In* "Sex and Internal Secretions" (W. C. Young, ed.), pp. 497–555. Williams & Wilkins, Baltimore, Maryland.

Fish, W. R., Young, W. C., and Dorfman, R. I. 1941. Excretion of oestrogenic and androgenic substances by female and male chimpanzees with known mating behaviour records. *Endocrinology* **28**, 585–592.

Ford, C. S., and Beach, F. A. 1951. "Patterns of Sexual Behaviour." Harper, New York.

Fujiwara, T., Uchino, I., Howjo, S., Imaizumi, K., and Imamichi, T. 1967. Normal range of the menstrual cycle of Cynomolgus monkeys under laboratory conditions. *Jap. J. Med. Sci. Biol.* **20**, 505–507.

Gartlan, J. S. 1969. Sexual and maternal behaviour of the vervet monkey, *Cercopithecus aethiops. J. Reprod. Fert. Suppl.* **6**, 137–150.

Gilman, J., and Gilbert, C. 1946. The reproductive cycle of the chacma baboon with special reference to the problems of menstrual irregularities as assessed by the behaviour of the sex skin. *S. Afr. J. Med. Sci.* **11**, Suppl., 1–54.

Goodall, J. van L. 1969. The behaviour of free-living chimpanzees in the Gombe Stream Reserve. *Anim. Behav. Monogr.* **1**, 165–311.

Haddow, A. J. 1952. Field and laboratory studies on an African monkey, *Cercopithecus ascanius schmidti. Proc. Zool. Soc. London* **122**, 297–394.

Hall, K. R. L. 1962. The sexual, agonistic and derived social behaviour patterns of the wild chacma baboon (*P. ursinus*). *Proc. Zool. Soc. London* **139**, 283–327.

Hall, K. R. L., and DeVore, I. 1965. Baboon social behaviour. *In* "Primate Behaviour" (I. DeVore, ed.), pp. 20–52. Holt, New York.

Hall, K. R. L., Boelkins, R. C., and Goswell, M. J. 1965. Behaviour of Patas, *Erythrocebus patas* in captivity, with notes on natural habitat. *Folia Primatol.* **3**, 22–49.

Hanby, J. P., Robertson, L. T., and Phoenix, C. H. 1971. The sexual behaviour of a confined troop of Japanese macaques. *Folia Primatol.* **16**, 123–143.

Hartman, C. G. 1932. Studies in the reproduction of the monkey, *M. rhesus*, with special reference to menstruation and pregnancy. *Contrib. Embryol., Carnegie Inst. Wash.* **23**, 1–161.

Heape, W. 1900. The sexual season of mammals and the relation of pro-oestrum to menstruation. *Quart. J. Microsc. Sci.* **44**, 1–70.

Hendrickx, A., and Kraemer, D. C. 1969. Observation on the menstrual cycle, optimal mating time, and pre-implantation embryos of the baboon, *P. anubis* and *P. cynocephalus. J. Reprod. Fert. Suppl.* **6,** 119–128.

Herbert, J. 1967. The social modification of sexual and other behaviour in the rhesus monkey. *In* "Progress in Primatology" (D. Starck, ed.), pp. 232–246. Fischer, Stuttgart.

Herbert, J. 1968. Sexual preference in the rhesus monkey (*Macaca mulatta*) in the laboratory. *Anim. Behav.* **16,** 120–128.

Herbert, J. 1970. Hormones and reproductive behaviour in rhesus and talapoin monkeys. *J. Reprod. Fert. Suppl.* **11,** 119–140.

Hill, W. C. O. 1953. The female reproductive organs of *Tarsius* with observation in the physiological changes therein. *Proc. Zool. Soc. London* **123,** 589–598.

Hinde, R. A., and Rowell, T. E. 1962. Communication by posture and facial expression in the rhesus monkey (*Macaca mulatta*). *Proc. Zool. Soc. London* **138,** 1–21.

Hinde, R. A., Rowell, T. E., and Spencer-Booth, Y. 1964. Behaviour of socially living rhesus monkeys in their first six months. *Proc. Zool. Soc. London* **143,** 609–649.

Ivey, M. G., and Bardwick, J. M. 1968. Patterns of affective fluctuation in the menstrual cycle. *Psychosom. Med.* **30,** 336–345.

Jay, P. 1965. The common langur in Northern India. *In* "Primate Behaviour" (I. DeVore, ed.), pp. 197–249. Holt, New York.

Jolly, A. 1966. "Lemur Behavior." Univ. of Chicago Press, Chicago, Illinois.

Kaiser, H. 1947. Absence of coiled arteries in the endometrium of menstruating New World monkeys. *Anat. Rec.* **99,** 353–367.

Kaufman, J. H. 1965. A 3 year study of mating behaviour in a free ranging band of monkeys. *Ecology* **46,** 500–512.

Klein, L. 1971. Copulation and seasonal reproduction in 2 species of spider monkeys, *Ateles belzebuth* and *A. geoffroyi. Folia Primatol.* **15,** 233–248.

Klingel, H. 1967. Soziale Organisation und Verhalten freilebender Steppenzebras. *Z. Tierpsychol.* **24,** 580.

Kühme, W. 1965. Frielandbeobachtungen zur soziologie des Hyänenhundes (*Lycaon pictus*). *Z. Tierpsychol.* **22,** 495–541.

Kummer, H. 1956. Rang-Kriterian bei Mantelpavianen. Der Rang adulter Weibchen im Sozialverhalten, den Individualdistanzen und im Schlaf. *Rev. Suisse Zool.* **63,** 288–297.

Kummer, H. 1968. "Social Organization of Hamadyas Baboons." Karger, Basel.

Lancaster, J. B. 1972. Play mothering: the relationship between juvenile females and young infants among free-ranging vervet monkeys. *In* "Primate Socialization" (F. Poirier, ed.), pp. 83–104. Random House, New York.

Lancaster, J. B., and Lee, R. B. 1965. The annual reproductive cycle in monkeys and apes. *In* "Primate Behaviour: Field Studies of Monkeys and Apes" (I. DeVore, ed,), pp. 486–513. Holt, New York.

Lindburg, D. G. 1969. Rhesus monkeys: mating season mobility of adult males. *Science* **166,** 1176–1178.

Lindburg, D. G. Grooming as a regulator of social interaction in rhesus macaques. *In* "Behavior Regulators of Behavior in Primates" (C. R. Carpenter, ed.), Pennsylvania State Univ. Press, University Park, Pennsylvania (in press).

Loy, J. 1969a. Estrous cycles among free-ranging rhesus monkeys. *Amer. J. Phys. Anthropol.* **31,** 262.

Loy, J. 1969b. Estrous behaviour of free-ranging rhesus monkeys (*Macaca mulatta*) a study of continuity and variability. Ph.D. Thesis, Northwestern Univ., Evanston, Illinois.

Loy, J. 1970. Peri-menstrual sexual behaviour among rhesus monkeys. *Folia primatol.* **13,** 286–297.

Manley, G. H. 1966. Reproduction in lorisoid primates. *Symp. Zool. Soc. London* **15,** 493–509.

Matthews, L. H. 1956. The sexual skin of the gelada baboon (*Theropithecus gelada*). *Trans. Zool. Soc. London* **28**, 543–552.

Michael, R. P., and Herbert, J. 1963. Menstrual cycle influences grooming behaviour and sexual behaviour in the rhesus monkey. *Science* **140**, 500–501.

Michael, R. P., and Keverne, E. B. 1970. Primate sex pheromones of vaginal origin. *Nature (London)* **225**, 84–85.

Michael, R. P., Herbert, J., and Welegalla, J. 1967. Ovarian hormones and the sexual behaviour of the male rhesus monkey (*Macaca mulatta*) under laboratory conditions. *J. Endocrinol.* **39**, 81–98.

Michael, R. P., Saayman, G., and Zumpe, D. 1968. The suppression of mounting behaviour and ejaculation in male rhesus monkeys by administration of progesterone to their female partners. *J. Endocrinol.* **41**, 421.

Miller, G. S. 1931. The primate basis of human sexual behavior. *Quart. Rev. Biol.* **6**, 379–410.

Mirsky, A. F. 1955. The influence of sex hormones on social behaviour in monkeys. *J. Comp. Physiol. Psychol.* **48**, 327–335.

Moynihan, M. 1964. Some behaviour patterns of Platyrrhine monkeys: I. The night monkey (*Aotes trivirgatus*). *Smithson. Misc. Collect.* **146**, 5.

Paige, K. 1969. The effects of oral contraceptives on affective fluctuation associated with the menstrual cycle. Ph.D. Thesis, Univ. of Michigan, Ann Arbor, Michigan.

Pedersen-Bjergaard, G., and Pederson-Bjergaard, K. 1948. Oestrogenic and gonodotrophic substances in the urine from a woman with normal menstrual cycles and normal pregnancies. *Acta Endocrinol. (Copenhagen)* **1**, 263–281.

Phoenix, C. H., Goy, R. W., Resko, T. A., and Koering, M. 1968. Probability of mating during various stages of the ovarian cycle in *M. mulatta*. *Anat. Rec.* **160**, 378.

Pocock, R. I. 1925. The external characters of catarrhine monkeys and apes. *Proc. Zool. Soc. London* pp. 1479–1579.

Ransom, T. 1970. Ecology and behaviour of the baboon, *Papio anubis*, at the Gombe Stream National Park Tanzania. Ph.D. Thesis, Univ. of California, Psychol. Dep., Berkeley, California.

Ransom, T., and Ransom, B. 1972. Special adult-infant relationships among baboons and the formation of social bonds. **16**, 101–113.

Rosenblum, L. A., Kaufman, I. C., and Stynes, A. J. 1966. Some characteristics of adult social and suto-grooming patterns in 2 species of macaque. *Folia Primatol.* **4**, 438–451.

Rosenblum, L. A., Nathan, T., Nelson, J., and Kaufman, I. C. 1967. Vaginal cornification cycles in the squirrel monkey (*Saimiri sciurea*). *Folia Primatol.* **6**, 83–91.

Rossman, I. D., and Bartelmez, G. W. 1946. Delayed ovulation, a significant factor in the variability of the menstrual cycle. *Amer. J. Obstet. Gynecol.* **52**, 28–33.

Rowell, T. E. 1963. Behaviour and reproductive cycles of female macaques. *J. Reprod. Fert.* **6**, 193–203.

Rowell, T. E. 1966a. Forest living baboons in Uganda. *J. Zool.* **149**, 344–364.

Rowell, T. E. 1966b. Hierarchy in the organization of a captive baboon group. *Anim. Behav.* **14**, 430–443.

Rowell, T. E. 1967a. Female reproductive cycles and the behaviour of baboons and rhesus macaques. *In* "Social Communication in Primates" (S. Altman, ed.), pp. 15–32. Univ. of Chicago Press, Chicago, Illinois.

Rowell, T. E. 1967b. A quantitative comparison of the behaviour of a wild and caged baboon group. *Anim. Behav.* **15**, 499–509.

Rowell, T. E. 1968. Grooming by adult baboons in relation to reproductive cycles. *Anim. Behav.* **16**, 585–588.

Rowell, T. E. 1969a. Intra-sexual behaviour and female reproductive cycles of baboons (*Papio anubis*). *Anim. Behav.* **17**, 159–167.

Rowell, T. E. 1969b. Long term changes in a population of Ugandan baboons. *Folia Primatol.* **11**, 241–254.

Rowell, T. E. 1970a. Reproductive cycles of two Cercopithecus monkeys. *J. Reprod. Fert.* **22**, 321–338.

Rowell, T. E. 1970b. Baboon menstrual cycles affected by social environment. *J. Reprod. Fert.* **21**, 133–141.

Rowell, T. E. 1972. Organisation of caged groups of captive *Cercopithecus* monkeys. *Anim. Behav.* **19**, 625.

Rowell, T. E., and Chalmers, N. R. 1970. Reproductive cycles of the mangabey, *Cercocebus albigena. Folia Primatol.* **12**, 264–272.

Saayman, G. S. 1970. The menstrual cycle and sexual behaviour in a troop of free-ranging chacma baboons, *Papio ursinus. Folia Primatol.* **12**, 81–110.

Sade, D. S. 1964. Seasonal cycle in size of testes of free-ranging *Macaca mulatta. Folia Primatol.* **2**, 171–180.

Sade, D. S. 1965. Some aspects of parent-offspring and sibling relationships in a group of rhesus monkeys, with a discussion of grooming. *Amer. J. Phys. Anthropol.* **23**, 1–18.

Sade, D. S. 1968. Inhibition of son-mother mating among free-ranging rhesus monkeys. *Sci. Psychoanal.* **12**, 18–38.

Scruton, D. M., and Herbert, J. 1972. The menstrual cycle and its effect on behaviour in the talapoin monkey. *J. Zool.* (in press).

Simonds, P. E. 1965. The bonnet macaque in South India. *In* "Primate Behaviour" (I. DeVore, ed.), pp. 175–196. Holt, New York.

Struhsaker, T. 1967. Behaviour of vervet monkeys. *Univ. Calif. (Berkley), Publ. Zool.* **82**, 1–64.

Trimble, M. R., and Herbert, J. 1968. The effect of testosterone or oestradiol upon the sexual and associated behaviour of the adult female rhesus monkey. *J. Endocrinol.* **42**, 171–185.

Ullrich, W. 1961. Zur Biologie und Soziologie der Collobusaffen (*C. guereza caudatus* Thomas). *Zool. Garten* **25**, 305–368.

Vandenbergh, J. G. 1969. Endocrine coordination in monkeys: male sexual responses to female. *Physiol. Behav.* **4**, 261–264.

Vandenbergh, J. G., and Vessey, S. 1968. Seasonal breeding of free-ranging rhesus monkeys and related ecological factors. *J. Reprod. Fert.* **15**, 71–79.

Wickler, W. 1963. Die biologische Bedeutung auffällend farbiger, nackter Hautstellen und inner-artliche Mimikry der Primaten. *Naturwissenschaften* **50**, 481–2.

Wickler, W. 1967. Socio-sexual signals and their intra-specific imitation among primates. *In* "Primate Ethology" (D. Morris, ed.), pp. 69–147. Weidenfeld & Nicolson, London.

Wilson, A. 1968 . Social Behaviour of free-ranging rhesus monkeys with an emphasis on aggression. Ph.D. Thesis, Univ. of California, Berkeley, California.

Wilson, A. P., and R. C. Boelkins, 1971. Evidence for seasonal variation in aggressive behavior by *Macaca mulatta. Anim. Behav.* **19**, 4.

Wolfheim, J. 1970. Social interaction in a group of talapoin monkeys. M.S. Thesis, Univ. of California, Zool. Dep., Berkeley, California.

Yerkes, R. M. 1939. Social dominance and sexual status in the chimpanzee. *Quart. Rev. Biol.* **14**, 115–136.

Yerkes, R. M., and Elder, J. H. 1936. The sexual cycle of the chimpanzee. *Anat. Rec.* **67**, 119–143.

Young, W. C., ed. 1961. "Sex and Internal Secretions." Williams & Wilkins, Baltimore, Maryland.

Young, W. C., and Orbison, W. D. 1944. Changes in selected features of behaviour in pairs of oppositely-sexed chimpanzees during the sexual cycle and after ovariectomy. *J. Comp. Psychol.* **37**, 107–143.

Young, W. C., and Yerkes, R. M. 1943. Factors influencing the reproductive cycle in the chimpanzee: the period of adolescent sterility and related problems. *Endocrinology* **33**, 131–154.

Zuckerman, S. 1930. The menstrual cycle of the primates. I. General nature and homology. *Proc. Zool. Soc. London* pp. 691–754.

Zuckerman, S. 1931a. The menstrual cycle of the primates. III. The alleged breeding season of primates, with special reference to the chacma baboon, *P. porcarius. Proc. Zool. Soc. London* **101**, 325–343.

Zuckerman, S. 1931b. The menstrual cycle of the primates. IV. Observation on the lactating period. *Proc. Zool. Soc. London* **101**, 593–601.

Zuckerman, S. 1932. "The Social Life of Monkeys and Apes." Kegan, Paul, London.

Zuckerman, S. 1935. Variation in the sensitivity of different species of monkeys to oestroin. *J. Physiol. (London)* **84**, 191–195.

Zuckerman, S. 1937. The duration and phases of the menstrual cycle in primates. *Proc. Zool. Soc. London* **107**, 315–329.

Zuckerman, S., and Parkes, A. S. 1932. The menstrual cycle of the primates. V. The cycle of the baboon. *Proc. Zool. Soc. London* **102**, 139–191.

Zuckerman, S., van Wagenen, G., and Gardiner, R. H. 1938. The sexual skin of the rhesus monkey. *Proc. Zool. Soc. London* **108**, 385–401.

The Onset of Maternal Behavior in Rats, Hamsters, and Mice
A Selective Review

ELIANE NOIROT[1]

CENTRE NATIONAL DE LA RECHERCHE SCIENTIFIQUE
INSTITUT DE NEUROPHYSIOLOGIE ET DE PSYCHOPHYSIOLOGIE
MARSEILLE, FRANCE

I. INTRODUCTION

The term "maternal behavior" is used in this paper to include nest-building, activities during parturition, retrieving, cleaning, and nursing pups. Such a grouping is unjustified if it leads to postulating a common causation for these different activities, but it remains convenient for description and chapter headings (for discussion and comments see, e.g., Hinde, 1959, 1966; Rowell, 1960; Lehrman, 1961; Noirot, 1964a; Richards, 1967a).

The term "naïve" refers to rodents that have never previously encountered pups, except for their own litter-mates. When such animals are first presented with pups they display either maternal, avoidance, aggressive, or exploratory behavior. Exploration is used here in a broad sense which includes initial approach — avoidance or ambivalence and establishment of contact by sniffing the pup.

Naïve animals, other than parturient females, usually display a succession or combination of different types of behavior when they first encounter a pup: for instance, avoidance followed by aggression,

[1]Present address: Laboratoire de Psychologie Experimentale, 117, Av. A. Buyl, 1050 Bruxelles, Belgique.

ambivalence followed by maternal retrieving, and aggression switching over now and then to sniffing or licking of the pup are frequently observed sequences. The first reaction of such animals is rarely maternal. They need a certain time during which they are caged with pups before they overcome their initial tendency to avoid, explore, or attack, and become fully maternal. The amount of time needed varies greatly with species and environmental circumstances: it can be as short as 1 or 2 minutes or as long as 2 weeks. The mechanism through which exposure to pups leads to the onset of maternal behavior is usually referred to as "sensitization" in most studies on rats and as "priming" in studies on mice. The data concerning this process will be reviewed in the first section.

The second section is concerned with the effects of gestation and parturition on the onset of maternal behavior. Naïve parturient females, unlike most other naïve animals, display immediate maternal behavior as soon as they give birth, except for some rare infanticidal or indifferent mothers, Mice, rats, and hamsters do not avoid, sniff, or explore their newborns, not even the first one to which they give birth. As soon as it emerges from the vagina, they lick it, and as soon as the cord has been severed, either by the mother herself or accidentally during the process of giving birth, they clean it (Beniest-Noirot, 1957, 1958; Rowell, 1959, 1961b; Rosenblatt and Lehrman, 1963). This difference between the behavior of naïve mothers and naïve animals other than mothers suggests that gestation and parturition favor a very rapid establishment of maternal behavior. Evidence for such effects will be presented.

Attempts to create a humoral state similar to that of a pregnant or newly parturient female by the administration of hormones to virgin animals have, until now, failed to exert any positive effect on the onset of maternal behavior. However, plasma transfer from a newly parturient female to a virgin (Terkel and Rosenblatt, 1968) and cross-transfusion between two such animals (Terkel, 1970a) considerably speeded up the establishment of maternal behavior in the virgin. These experiments will be reviewed in the third section.

A general discussion comparing these different ways of inducing maternal behavior – sensitization or priming, gestation and parturition, plasma transfer or cross-transfusion – will be presented in the fourth section.

II. SENSITIZATION OR PRIMING

Wiesner and Sheard (1933) observed what they described as spontaneous maternal behavior, in that 16% of 250 virgin female rats, presented with a pup aged 1[2] to 3 days, retrieved it. The other females were reported to nose (that is, explore) the pup, and sometimes to manipulate it or carry it to some place in the cage other than the nest. Many of these initially nonmaternal animals retrieved pups and/or gave other maternal responses (cleaning, nest-building, or crouching in the lactation position) after one or more days of "concaveation" or "sensitization" during which one or several pups remained continuously in the cage with the female. Wiesner and Sheard, however, never observed postparturitional behavior in virgin females. Although they presented a number of females with fetuses obtained by cesarian section, in their membranes and still attached to the placenta, the females never removed the membranes, cleaned the pup, or ate the placenta. Nevertheless they all very readily accepted and ate raw meat. Unfortunately the authors did not specify how many females were tested, how long the presentations with the fetuses lasted, or how many presentations each animal was given. In a recent study Sachs (1969) reports that, when he presented intact or ovariectomized virgin rats of his population with living fetuses and placentas, almost all the animals ate the placenta but about half of them also ate the living fetus. Ovariectomized and intact virgins behaved in the same way as far as placentaphagy and cannibalism was concerned. The report does not describe the behavior of the noncannibalizing females.

Wiesner and Sheard's finding that contact with pups could lead to the onset of maternal behavior in animals other than mothers has apparently not aroused much interest at the time, nor has it stimulated research in the area. Only during the last few years have similar findings been reported again. Rosenblatt (1967) has now demonstrated that, provided sensitization was prolonged sufficiently (at most up to 15 days), practically all the naïve male and female rats ended up by displaying maternal responses. The proportion of immediately maternal animals, and the length of sensitization required to elicit maternal behavior in the others, varied greatly from one population to another, and even sometimes from one experiment to another within a population.

A summary of such data is given in Table I. It shows that in some colonies immediate maternal behavior was never reported in animals other than mothers (e.g., Lott and Fuchs, 1962), whereas in another colony 50% of naïve virgin females immediately retrieved a newborn pup (Roth et al., 1968). These differences cannot be explained by strain

[2]Some authors (e.g., Wiesner and Sheard, 1933) describe the day following parturition (generally at night) as day 0, others as day 1. For the sake of consistency, the latter denomination has been systematically adopted, and the original numbering changed to conform.

TABLE I

DATA ON THE BEHAVIOR OF NAÏVE ADULT RATS WITH PUPS

Subjects	Age of pups presented (days)	Number or percentage showing immediate maternal behavior	Sensitization experiments with initially nonmaternal animals			References
			Length of experiment (days)	Number of successful cases (retrieving)	(Mean) day(s) of the onset of retrieving	
250 virgin ♀	1–3	16%				Wiesner and Sheard (1933)
11 virgin ♀[a]	1–4	2	4	2	1	
29 virgin ♀[a]	1–4	1	4	10	1–4	
40 virgin ♀[a]	1–4	9	4	17	1–4	
8 virgin ♀[a] (Wistar)	1	2	29	3	1–7	
10 virgin ♀	1	3				Leblond (1937, 1940)
21 virgin ♀ (Wistar)	Not reported	0	5	2	2–3	Lott and Fuchs (1962)
8 virgin ♀	1–7	Not reported	7	?[b]	?[b]	Cosnier (1963)

14 virgin ♀	5–10	–c	10–15	14	5.5 ± 3d	Rosenblatt (1967)
12 virgin ♂	5–10	–	10–15	12	6.5 ± 5	
(Sprague-Dawley Charles River)					(mean ± d.)	
70 virgin ♀	1	About 50%				Roth et al. (1968)
(Sprague-Dawley)						
17 virgin ♀ (1)e	5–10	–c	15	17	3.0 ± 0.5	Terkel (1970a)
16 virgin ♀ (2)	5–10	–	15	16	3.5 ± 1.0	
6 virgin ♀ (3)	5–10	–	15	6	4.5 ± 1.0	
5 virgin ♀ (4)	5–10	–	15	3	12.0 ± 1.0	Terkel and Rosenblatt (1972b)
(Sprague-Dawley Charles River)						

a Experiments with progressively older females.

b A combined score (x points for retrieving +y points for nest-building, etc.) considerably increased with successive days.

c The rats were pretested, and spontaneous retrievers (about 20%) were excluded (Terkel, personal communication, 1970).

d These data do not correspond to the numbers originally published by Rosenblatt (1967), which were, respectively, 6.5 and 7.5. The author had referred to the first test, when the exposure time to pups was in fact null, as day 1, and to the second test, after 24 hours of exposure, as day 2. Therefore exposure duration was 1 day less than his published figures. Rosenblatt has changed the original numbering in all his later papers which now systematically refer to the actual exposure durations.

e Animals housed in cages with an area of (1) 36, (2) 126, (3) 360, and (4) 468 square inches.

differences in the readiness to display maternal behavior, such as those reported by Mc Iver and Jeffrey (1967). The latter authors' measures (responsiveness of mothers toward own pups) were similar for Sprague-Dawley and Wistar animals, whereas Long-Evans rats obtained higher scores. The difference in the proportion of spontaneously maternal animals with different colonies may be partly due to the fact that the experimenters used pups of different ages and thus probably of different effectiveness for eliciting maternal behavior.[3]

The length of the sensitization period (5 to 6 days), established by Rosenblatt (1967) for his Sprague-Dawley rats (see Table I), refers to the mean day of the onset of retrieving, but other maternal responses tended to occur earlier (for example, licking of pups on day 5.5 in all 14 females, on day 3.5 in 10 out of the 12 males). Differences in the same direction were found for nest-building and crouching.

The large differences in the sensitization period reported by Terkel (1970a) for four groups of naïve virgin females from the same strain apparently depended only on the size of their cage, small cages leading to an early onset of maternal behavior (mean: 2 days), large ones to a late one (mean: 10 days). Rosenblatt (1967), who had used animals of the same strain and cages of an intermediate size between the two types used by Terkel, found an intermediate value for the sensitization period. Terkel (1970a) reports that in the small cage, unlike the large ones, the pups can crawl toward the virgin and establish rapid bodily contact with her. He suggests that such contact favors maternal behavior. An additional possible explanation is that stimulation from pups, such as olfactory and auditory[4] cues, have a greater chance of being perceived by the adult and of exerting positive effects on maternal responses, the nearer the sources of stimulation are. Evidence for this will be provided by data on mice (see p. 119).

A recent analysis of the behavior of virgins during sensitization (Rosenblatt, 1972) shows considerable initial avoidance and ambivalence as suggested between the lines by Wiesner and Sheard's (1933) reports. Usually the female starts sniffing the pup with closed eyes and without making nose contact, and then runs away quickly. She may return many times during the first few minutes and hours to sniff the pups, progressively establishing nose contact, but she quickly runs away each

---

[3]Mice and probably also rats are optimal at birth, hamsters at the age of 5 to 10 days (Leblond, 1940; King, 1963; Noirot, 1964b; Wiesner and Sheard, 1933; Rowell, 1960; Richards, 1966a).

[4]Auditory cues from rodent pups mainly involve ultrasonic distress calls (Schleidt, 1951; Zippelius and Schleidt, 1956; Hart and King, 1966; Noirot, 1966a,b, 1968; Sewell, 1968; Noirot and Pye, 1969; Okon, 1970a,b). A review on this subject is in preparation (Noirot, 1972).

time. This resembles closely the behavior of mice with novel objects such as boxes containing a ticking watch or perfume (Noirot, 1969a, 1970b, and unpublished observations, 1970). After this initial period during which the rat principally avoids the pups and moves away if it happens to crawl to her, Rosenblatt describes two successive changes in the female. She first tolerates body contact with pups after they have themselves reached her. She remains, eyes closed, in a stiff, freezing position (shown clearly by Terkel's film (1970b). A second change occurs when she adjusts her body to the pup's movements, allows them to get under her, and starts licking them. Once this stage has been reached, further establishment of maternal behavior is much more rapid, and the female will clean the pups, collect them together in a corner by retrieving, adopt a crouching position, and display nest-building.

Attacking or killing pups is rare during sensitization, but does happen sometimes. The behavior seems slightly more frequent in male than in female rats, but disappears with successive presentations of pups in favor of maternal responses (Wiesner and Sheard, 1933; Cosnier, 1963; Rosenblatt, personal communication, 1970).

Immature naïve female rats become responsive to pups more readily than do adult ones. Thirty-day-old females all retrieved pups immediately or very quickly, but 45- and 60-day-old females required on average 3 to 4 days of sensitization before they gave this response. In parallel groups of males, different results were obtained. At the age of 30 days, the animals needed a similar amount of exposure to pups as adult males, about 6 days. At the age of 45 days this latency increased up to 8 days, but it then returned to its initial value of 6 days in a group of 60-day-old males.

The change in the animal produced by sensitization and leading to maternal behavior does not seem to require the contribution of a specific endocrine process. Indeed, exposure to pups is sufficient for eliciting maternal behavior in immature and in adult rats, and the sensitization period is of a similar length in adult intact males and virgin females, in castrated males and females, and in hypophysecto-mized animals (Rosenblatt, 1967).

In mice, naïve animals, other than mothers, display maternal behavior with an optimal (1- to 2-day-old) pup after a short period of ambivalence and exploration during which they first sniff the pup from a distance with closed eyes, then "nose" it (that is, sniff the pup while touching it with the snout), and, in between these bouts of investigation, run between the pup and the nest, apparently in an approach–avoidance conflict. This period is much shorter than in the rat, but, again, varies between colonies. According to Leblond (1938b) it lasted from some minutes up to 4 days in his population of pure A, CHI, and CBAN mice, but in an outbred colony (Beniest-Noirot, 1958) practically all adult males and females displayed maternal responses, usually starting with retrieving, after 1 or 2 minutes of preliminary exploration. Since 1936, Leblond and Nelson have tried to draw attention to the fact that all adult mice, males as well as females, even when castrated or hypophysectomized either before or after puberty, display maternal behavior with 1- or 2-day-old pups. They published a long series of papers both in French (Leblond, 1937, 1938a; Leblond and Nelson, 1936, 1937b) and in English (Leblond, 1938b, 1940; Leblond and Nelson, 1937a), but for many years most other authors took neither their findings nor those of Wiesner and Sheard (1933) into account when planning experiments on maternal behavior (see p. 128).

Some years later, Horner (1947) reported that male white-footed deermice took care of their pups. Several of Leblond and Nelson's findings were confirmed by Beniest-Noirot (1957, 1958, 1959) studying a mixed (albino, black, and agouti) outbred mouse population. In a first experiment, adequate parturition activities were observed in 9 out of 10 naïve virgin females and in 8 out of 10 naïve males presented with two newborn pups, one still attached to the placenta and one detached but still having an umbilical cord as long as possible. The two pups were presented in random order. All the positively responding animals first ate the placenta (when present), then (or first) chewed the cord, and next cleaned the pup. Pups provided with a placenta seemed to be given more intense care. A third group of 10 naïve males and 10 naïve females, each given one of the placentas severed by the experimenter, all immediately and voraciously ate it. Unfortunately, during this experiment no special attention was paid to sniffing and nosing the pups and to initial ambivalence before the occurrence of parturition activities, but it was noticed that some animals made contact only after a long latency which included sniffing from a distance. This observation, and also the fact that the three initially aggressive or indifferent animals needed two presentations with newborns in order to behave in an adequate way, seem to show that initial ambivalence was present in these naïve animals, whereas it is apparently absent in parturient naïve females.

It is possible that Wiesner and Sheard (1933) did not observe parturition activities in any of their virgin female rats because the animals had not been exposed long enough to the fetuses. Rats may require a long sensitization period in order to display cleaning of newborns, just as they do for other maternal responses. Mice, on the whole, need much less exposure to pups before giving maternal behavior.

Another experiment on mice compared the incidence of retrieving and licking pups, nest-building, and the adoption of the lactation or crouching position in groups of adult animals other than mothers, and in primiparous control females. All the animals were given a standard 5-minute test with three optimal (1- to 2-day-old) pups, starting from the moment they touched or nosed one of them. No differences were found between the proportions of control animals displaying each of these activities and the proportions of naïve females pregnant for the first time (late pregnancy), naïve males and virgin females, females having weaned a litter, and experienced males who had lived with a female and at least one litter from birth till weaning.

Infanticides rarely occurred, and those animals that were aggressive were usually found to have had an unusual previous life history. Thus one male and one female had been hand-reared from 8 days on, one male had lived with only female litter-mates, and a black female had been fostered by an albino mother. Black and agouti animals seemed more inclined to commit infanticides than albino animals (Beniest-Noirot, 1957).

A third series of experiments studied the behavior of immature mice, 20- to 39-day-old males and females, with 2-day-old pups. The tendency to care for pups developed gradually, some responses appearing earlier in life than others: first licking, then retrieving, and next nest-building. The lactation position was extremely rarely seen (in 3 out of 80 cases) before maturity. This development was, however, considerably accelerated in animals that had been living for 5 days with young pups from a subsequent litter, conceived during the estrus postpartum of their mother. Such animals explored the test pups less, and in the younger age groups (20 to 29 days) more frequent retrieving occurred. In animals aged 30 to 39 days, the incidence of retrieving was similar in both the naïve and exposed animals (this behavior seeming to have matured spontaneously in the unexposed mice), but nest-building was given by more exposed animals. Some immature animals apparently did not retrieve because the task was too difficult. They did a great deal of running to and fro between the pup and the nest, but, especially in the exposed animals, this behavior did not always seem to reflect an approach–avoidance conflict, as it does in adults. Some of them returned as quickly to the pup as they ran away from it, and they soon nosed the pup and stopped closing their eyes when approaching it. Intuitively, one was tempted to describe their running toward the nest as "anticipated" retrieving rather than as avoiding.

These data show similarities to those obtained earlier by Leblond (1938b) during a study comparing the behavior of naïve immature and naïve adult mice toward 1-day-old pups. He reported that immature animals needed more sensitization (usually 4 days) than adult animals in order to become maternal as measured by the onset of retrieving.

Although naïve mice seem more readily maternal than naïve rats, they undergo a change, apparently analogous to sensitization in the rat, during first contact(s) with pups. The above results with immature animals already suggested a positive influence of the proximity of young pups, but the change can be more clearly demonstrated by experiments using less effective test objects, such as older mouse pups, dead (drowned) newborns, or live young rats. Naïve mice only rarely displayed maternal responses during standard tests with such objects. The older pups were frequently groomed in a friendly fashion by naïve adults, sometimes initiated crouching, but elicited practically no retrieving and only occasionally some nest-building (Noirot, 1964b). The dead newborn was most frequently sniffed from a distance, nosed, and then avoided; sometimes it was carried to the food or the feces corner, and sometimes it was eaten. However, maternal responses were displayed during the first test by a (usually small) proportion of naïve animals. With the live 1- to 2-day-old rat pup, naïve mice showed a severe approach–avoidance conflict. They were extremely hesitant about approaching it, and extremely quick at running away from it, returning each time back to the nest. Afterward many of them tried to "bury" the pup. They threw bedding material on top and around it, moving their front legs in a way opposite to the one that is usually displayed during nest-building. When nest-building, mice tend to scratch material around their own body, whereas in this situation they threw it to a distance. Similar behavior commonly occurs when unusual objects with a strange odor are placed in home cages (Noirot, 1969a, and unpublished observations, 1970). Attacking was rare with all three of these stimulus objects.

After initial contact(s) with optimal pups, the tendency to give maternal behavior with these less effective patterns was greatly increased. Only 4 out of 20 naïve females retrieved a 10-day-old pup, but 15 naïve females first given nine successive 5-minute presentations with an optimal pup all subsequently retrieved a 10-day-old pup. Similar though smaller increases were seen in nest-building and the lactation position, but licking (already frequent in the first group) was not affected (Noirot, 1965). It was next shown that one single 5-minute contact with an optimal pup was as efficient in inducing the increase in maternal behavior as repeated presentations. A dead newborn mouse was retrieved and other maternal responses were given by very few naïve males and females (respectively, 3 and 4 out of 20 animals brought it into the nest), but each of 20 females and 19 out of 20 males retrieved it after one 5-minute contact with a 1- to 2-day-old live mouse pup. The tendency to display other maternal responses was also highly increased. This change is a long-term one. Some maternal responses with the dead pup were more frequent when the interval between the presentations of the optimal and the weak pattern lasted between 2 and 8 days, as when it was only a few minutes (Noirot, 1964c). The higher scores with the long interval could be explained by the fact that the animals observed with the short interval had recently performed maternal responses with the optimal pup. This can cause short-term decreases in responsiveness for some activities—namely, for licking and nest-building (though others, in particular retrieving, are extremely resistant to extinction, and crouching increases with successive presentations (Noirot, 1965).

Further experiments progressively showed that the increase in maternal behavior depended merely on exposure to cues from the (optimal) pups and not on performance. When the strong pup was placed in the nest so that the adults were unable to retrieve it, they nevertheless all ($N = 15$) subsequently retrieved a weak (dead) pup during a standard test (Noirot, 1964c). In another experiment, naïve animals were prevented from giving any adequate maternal behavior during an initial exposure to an optimal pup, the latter being hidden in a small perforated metallic box, so that it could provide only olfactory and auditory (mainly ultrasonic distress calls) cues. The animals were allowed to explore the box containing the pup for 5 minutes, and then tested 2 to 8 days later with the (weak) drowned newborn pup. They retrieved, licked, and performed nest-building much more frequently than completely naïve controls who had not previously been exposed to a hidden pup (Noirot, 1969a). In this experiment the pattern presented during the initial exposure (hidden live pup) and during the later test (drowned newborn) probably provided no common cues. Only ultrasonic distress calls and olfactory stimulation could have been received from the hidden pup: the drowned newborn of course did not call, and whether it had olfactory cues in common with the live pup remains an open question but seems unlikely. For this reason, and also for its independence of performance, the change in maternal behavior seems different from an associative learning process. Hinde (1966) suggested that priming might be a suitable term, and this was adopted in later papers (Noirot, 1969a, 1970a).

It was next shown that the two types of cues selectively prime different maternal responses—olfactory cues acting on licking, and ultrasonic distress calls (probably those elicited by cold stress) acting on maternal nest-building. Naïve females exposed only to olfactory cues from pups (a perforated box containing a nest where a litter had been living for 4 days) licked a 1- to 2-day-old live pup presented afterward more frequently and intensively than did control females exposed previously to an empty box. Naïve females exposed only or mainly to ultrasonic distress calls from pups (a box without perforations containing a 4- to 6-day-old live pup) showed more maternal nest-building than did controls.

Recent findings by Charton *et al.* (1971) show that smell from pups is easily detected by adults and probably favors maternal licking and cleaning, as it does in the mouse. Female and male rats, given the choice between pure drinking water and water containing a smear from the perineal region of a newborn pup, showed a preference for the latter solution. Rat pups, whose perineal regions were covered with collodion, were less licked by their mothers than control pups, whose backs were covered with collodion. Removal of the olfactory bulb decreased licking of the litter by the mother.

At first sight, the positive effect on maternal nest-building induced by the exposure of naïve animals to hidden pups seems to contradict the previous results obtained by Koller (1952) on nest-building in mice. He found that this behavior could be considerably increased in females caged with young mice, but not when the pups were placed under a wire cover so that the female could not retrieve or touch them (see also Lehrman, 1961, for comments). Similarly, one of our attempts to prime nest-building by continuous exposure to an inaccessible litter has failed (Noirot, 1966b). Naïve females were housed singly in large observation cages each containing a small living cage with either a pregnant female for the experimental animals, or a virgin female for the control animals. Nest-building was measured by Koller's technique: daily removal and weighing of the nest, built with straw available ad libitum from a device on the top of the cage. The sudden presence of a litter in the small cages did not increase nest-building, as measured by the amount of straw collected daily. It was noticed that many experimental females spent a great deal of time on the roof or near the small cages as if they were seeking to make contact with its inhabitants. However, after removal of the small cages containing the virgin female or the mother with her litter (5 days after the birth in the latter case), nest-building tended to increase in the experimental animals. Furthermore, when the females of both groups were presented afterward with a dead pup, the experimental animals displayed significantly more retrieving, licking, and nest-building than did the controls. A possible explanation for the failure to obtain an increase in nest-building with this measure *during* exposure to inaccessible pups comes from the observation that naïve animals display maternal responses in a definite serial order when first presented with a pup (Noirot, 1969b). Retrieving is always the first and crouching (when occurring) the last response given. Licking and nest-building are displayed in between, their order depending on the adequacy of retrieving: when the pup is rapidly brought into the nest, licking occurs next, but when the pup is often dropped, short bouts of nest-building are likely then to occur. It is possible that this restriction in the serial order of maternal responses merely induced searching and attempts to make contact with the distant pups, and that the failure of these attempts prevented (some) or most animals from giving subsequent responses. After removal of the pups, priming or nest-building could have become noticeable because the direct source of stimulation for establishing contact and retrieving was no longer present, whereas a direct source of stimulation for nest-building (straw) remained accessible.

On the other hand, this explanation seems inconsistent with the fact that some naïve females (5 out of 20), exposed to a 1-day-old pup hidden in a box, displayed intense nest-building during a 5-minute test (Noirot, 1969a). This, however, was a short observation period, and the measure (improving the nest with previously collected material) is of course different, and reflects perhaps a different aspect of nest-building behavior, from the one used previously (that is, the amount of new material collected and brought daily to the nest site). With the same amount of material one nest can be built better than another one (see Stone *et al.*, 1954, 1955, cited in Lehrman, 1961).

Priming of maternal behavior can probably take place in mice exposed to cues from pups living in neighboring cages. The few completely naïve animals of our colony which had actually given maternal responses with the drowned pup (see p. 116) were all housed very near breeding cages and sometimes separated from pups by only a thin metallic wall. Also, the proportion of naïve mice taking care of weak stimulus objects varied surprisingly from one period to another, as shown by the data in Table II. The proportion of immediately maternal animals seemed to increase with the amount of breeding in the animal room. It thus seemed likely that cues from distant pups living·in neighboring cages could affect naïve animals and increase their tendency to display maternal behavior. Animals living either from birth onward in a breeding room, or from weaning onward (25 days) in a room where no pups

TABLE II

PROPORTIONS OF NAÏVE MICE FROM AN OUTBRED ALBINO POPULATION GIVING
MATERNAL RESPONSES DURING A STANDARD FIVE-MINUTE TEST WITH A WEAK
STIMULUS (A DROWNED NEWBORN MOUSE), AT DIFFERENT PERIODS.

Group	Ss	Retrieving	Licking	Nest-Building	Crouching	Year of observation	Published
1	20 ♀	3	2	2	0	1962	Noirot
2	20 ♂	4	3	2	1	1962	(1964c)
3	20 ♀	11	7	12	0	1964	Noirot (1969a)

were present, behaved differently during a first standard test with a
1- to 2-day-old pup. When previously housed with neighboring pups,
they seemed to have acquired some familiarization with the test situation. They explored less and retrieved the pup more rapidly than did
the animals that had been living in an environment without pups (Noirot,
unpublished data).

Factors like this can be possible sources of artifacts during studies on
maternal behavior. The presence or absence of olfactory and auditory
cues from distant pups perhaps accounts for differences in the maternal
behavior of naïve animals reported by different authors. Leblond's
(1938b) mice, requiring apparently much longer exposure to pups (up
to 4 days) than Beniest-Noirot's (1958), might have been housed in
rooms where little breeding was going on or in cages permitting less
exposure to cues from distant pups; for example, some materials will
throw shadows for ultrasonic distress calls, whereas others will permit
their passage; and transmission of smell might be more or less intense,
depending on the ventilation systems used (Valenta and Rigby, 1968).

Similarly, the great differences reported by different authors in the
proportion of immediate retrievers among rats, and in the length
of sensitization required for eliciting maternal behavior (see p. 111),
could result from differences in the richness of the environment in
stimulation from distant pups.

The distance between the animal and such sources of stimulation
seems an important factor. A litter in a neighboring cage has a less
marked positive effect on maternal behavior in the naïve mouse than an
inaccessible litter or a pup hidden in a box, placed in the subject's home
cage (Noirot, 1969a). The same process might partly account for Terkel's
finding (1970a) that the sensitization period in the rat decreases with the
area of the test cage (see Table I, p. 111). In addition to the fact that
bodily contact is more rapidly established in a small cage, cues from
nearby pups might be more stimulating than cues from more distant
ones.

Unlike rats, which at first tend to avoid pups, and mice, which rapidly
give maternal responses, naïve hamsters, other than mothers, most
frequently attack pups on the first encounter. Very young pups are
killed by the attack and then eaten, while older ones are treated like
an adult intruder—threatened, bitten, and often injured. Only with
optimal patterns—that is, 5- to 10-day-old pups— may naïve animals
display maternal responses, but even in such cases some initial aggression is frequent, and the maternal responses do not seem to be as efficient
as those from experienced animals. For instance, retrieving is often
preceded by carrying the pups to a place different from the nest site,
and several such removals of the pup are often common even if it is

eventually deposited into the nest (Rowell, 1959, 1961a; Richards, 1965a, 1967a). Most authors relate this aggressive behavior with pups to the fact that hamsters, unlike rats and mice, are solitary mammals and thus systematically defend their territory against intrusion by strangers, except during short periods of mating. Another possible and not incompatible explanation already mentioned above (Richards, 1966a) is that the phylogenetically recent shortening of the gestation period in hamsters produces newborns that are not yet fully equipped for eliciting intense maternal behavior and for inhibiting possible adult aggression. This fits with the fact that optimal pups are older in hamsters than in species with a longer gestation. Rowell's report (1961b) of relatively frequent infanticides in mother hamsters, either at parturition or during the very first days of the lactation period, also agrees with this point of view.

In hamsters too, first contact with pups exerts a positive effect on later maternal behavior, although complicated interactions occur with attacking and eating pups. This was shown in an experiment comparing the behavior of four groups of virgin females during a standard test with 5-day-old pups. The females of one (control) group were naïve; those of the other groups had been given one previous 15-minute contact with either 1-, 5-, or 9-day-old pups. All the females initially presented with the 1-day-old pups attacked, killed, and ate them. All but one of the females presented initially with the 5-day-old pups attacked, but killing and eating were less frequent than in the former group, and some maternal behavior was seen. Only half of the females presented initially with the 9-day-old pups showed some attacking without injuring the pups, and all the animals gave some maternal responses. During the subsequent presentation with the 5-day-old pups, which took place about 48 hours later, numerous differences were found between groups. Maternal responses in the form of nest-building activities and carrying pups were more frequent and intense in the animals previously presented with either 1- or 9-day-old pups than in the naïve controls, but similar scores were obtained for crouching both in these and in the control groups. Latency before attacking was shortened after previous contact with 1-day-old pups, but the numbers of animals attacking and the median numbers of attacks were unaffected, and the number of pups killed and eaten was significantly reduced. After previous contact with 9-day-old pups, all the measures reflected less marked aggression than those from the control group. The animals presented twice with the 5-day-old pups only showed more nest-building on the second presentation than the controls and gave similar scores of attacking and eating pups (Noirot and Richards, 1966; see also Richards, 1967a,b, for comments). The fact that maternal behavior had been increased after the animals' initial contact with 1-day-old pups shows that, as in rats and mice, the change is independent of the performance of maternal responses. Indeed, in this group all the females had attacked, killed, and eaten only 1-day-old pups, and none of them had displayed any sort of maternal care. Therefore, again the increase seems to result from the animals' mere exposure to cues from the pups, and resembles the process described as sensitization in the rat, and as priming in the mouse. The small effect exerted by the repeated presentations of 5-day-old pups (only increased nest-building) could be explained by the fact that the very similarity of the two situations favors stereotyping (aggression is particularly likely to evolve in such a way, Scott, 1946; Beniest-Noirot, 1958). Systematic investigations of sensitization or priming in the hamster are unfortunately expensive because of the frequency of infanticide: continuous exposure as practiced by Rosenblatt (1967) with rats (that is, caging an adult with pups) would necessitate an enormous quantity of breeding animals and pups. A more suitable technique might be to expose naïve hamsters to pups in small (perhaps wire) cages in order to prevent the adults from killing or injuring them during the initial presentations.

Rowell (1961b) found that immature hamsters, especially those living in large families, did not kill or attack sucklings but responded maternally. They licked and cleaned them from a very early age onward. Maternal retrieving apparently occurred as soon as the young hamster had the physical strength to perform this task. Nest-building and crouching were seen in slightly older (but still immature) animals. Agonistic behavior with pups appeared after puberty and thus coincided more or less with the age for establishment of territories.

These data show similarities with Rosenblatt's reports (1972) on maternal behavior in juvenile rats, which also more readily displayed maternal behavior with pups than did adult animals (see p. 113). The opposite, however, seems to happen in mice (Leblond, 1938b; Beniest-Noirot, 1958; also see p. 115). This might be related to the fact that competition with other types of behavior which appear with maturity, namely aggression, exploration, and fear, is less acute in the mouse than in the rat or hamster. As a result, maternal behavior benefits less from the absence of this competition before puberty in the mouse.

III. EFFECTS OF GESTATION AND PARTURITION

As pointed out by the previous data and description, most naïve rodents other than mothers show more or less prolonged initial avoidance, exploration, or aggression when first presented with pups. Naïve parturient females, in contrast, display immediate and adequate maternal behavior with their newborns. This suggests that gestation and parturition exert positive effects on maternal behavior.

As long ago as 1933, Wiesner and Sheard found that some females very readily become responsive to pups when they reach the end of their gestation period. They described this phenomenon as a "disruption" between parturition and the establishment of maternal behavior.

Lott and Rosenblatt (1969; see also Rosenblatt, 1969, 1970) showed that late pregnant female rats needed progressively less exposure to pups before reacting maternally. The mean latency before the onset of retrieving was about 6.5 days in 11-day pregnant females (that is, similar to the latency of naïve virgin female rats), but it dropped considerably afterward and was about 3.5 days in 17-day pregnant females.

In a subsequent experiment (Lott and Rosenblatt, 1969), the same authors showed that terminating pregnancy by cesarian section exerted, from the tenth day of gestation onward, an additional positive effect on the onset of retrieving. After such an intervention, practiced between the sixteenth and the nineteenth day of gestation, retrieving occurred even earlier (after about 2 days of exposure) than in intact pregnant females.

They thus described two successive effects, related to gestation, favoring maternal behavior. The first, called "gestation" effect, becomes observable, with their measures, around the sixteenth day of gestation and progressively increases until the end of the gestation period. A second "termination of pregnancy" effect becomes noticeable from the tenth day of gestation onward, when cesarian deliveries are practiced. The authors suggest that the second effect might operate through the activation of the ovaries which accompanies experimental or normal termination of gestation. This idea is supported by the finding that cesarian delivery practiced at various days (10 and 16) of gestation fails to elicit the additional positive (termination of pregnancy) effect when, in addition, the ovaries are removed. This is at first sight inconsistent with the habitual failure of ovarian hormones to influence maternal behavior (see p. 128), but these extracts may exert such effects only when they interact with some other change.[5]

In mice, late gestation coincides also with an activation of maternal behavior. Rabaud (1921) observed two pregnant female mice living together in the same cage. To his great surprise he noticed that, after one of them had littered, both females took care of the newborns. According to his statement, it was impossible to distinguish the behavior of the real mother from the behavior of the other mouse, which was still pregnant. He therefore concluded that gestation already activates

[5]For more discussion, see also Rosenblatt (1970).

the maternal "instinct." Although the conclusion is probably right, his observation, of course, lacked a proper control: a virgin female mouse might have been as maternal as the pregnant one, under similar circumstances. The fact, however, that maternal behavior could occur in mice, whatever apparently their physiological state, was not yet known at that time.

Goyens (1969) and Noirot and Goyens (1971) tested independent groups of 20 intact females, pregnant for the first time, on days 1, 4, 14, and 19 of gestation (all the subjects gave birth on day 20). The animals were given a standard test with a 2-day-old pup, and their results were compared with those from virgin controls. Since mice of this colony display very rapid maternal behavior on a first encounter with pups, an event recorder was used for registering initial sniffing and all subsequent maternal responses over a 15-minute period starting from the moment the adult first touched the pup.

The results showed an unexpected negative effect on the first day of gestation after recent fertilization (maximum 19 hours earlier), followed by a progressive positive effect. With the advance of gestation, the females spent less time sniffing the pup before performing a maternal response, and more time giving maternal behavior. The virgin control level was regained in 4 to 14 days of gestation and slightly exceeded on day 19. The difference in the time spent giving care to the pups was entirely due to very frequent and long-lasting bouts of licking the pup. Nest-building and crouching tended, on the contrary, to be slightly less frequent and intense than in the control group. This might simply be a consequence of the very high and predominant tendency to perform cleaning activities, but other explanations must be considered. For instance, the heavy 19-day pregnant females cannot arch their back upward while crouching. As a consequence, the pups might get crushed and try to make the female switch over to another behavior, perhaps by emitting inhibiting distress calls. The pups could also try to initiate the lactation position less with the heavy pregnant than with lighter virgin or lactating females. It was noticed that the serial order in which the naïve pregnant females gave maternal responses during the test did not show the same rigidity as that observed in other naïve animals. Virgin female and male mice always first retrieved a pup (Noirot, 1969b), whereas pregnant females sometimes first licked it.

The positive change observed in the maternal behavior of the mouse during late gestation is consistent with Lott and Rosenblatt's (1969) data on the termination of pregnancy effect. The negative effect of early gestation on the maternal behavior of the mouse was very marked. Four out of 20 subjects only sniffed the pup and did not display any response of care. One female attacked the pup. Such a proportion of negative reactions is extremely unusual in naïve animals of that colony under any other physiological condition (Beniest-Noirot, 1958; Noirot, 1969b). When they did show maternal behavior, the females of this early gestation group did so after a latency similar to that of the controls, but they spent less time giving maternal responses than the latter, except perhaps for crouching. As already mentioned, however, crouching is at least partially initiated by the pup and can reflect a low tendency to perform the other maternal responses, which occur earlier in the test situation (Noirot, 1969b).

A similar negative effect of early gestation on maternal behavior has not been found in the rat by Lott and Rosenblatt (1969), who report that maternal responsiveness is not influenced by gestation during the first 10 days. This might be because they used a different measure or perhaps because they did not observe very recently fertilized females. The large individual differences found in our group of recently fertilized mice suggests that part of the negative effect could be a short-term one. If so, it might be easily missed during experimental investigations.

Data on hamsters similarly show positive effects of gestation on maternal behavior. In a first study, Rowell (1961a) failed to demonstrate this because she tested her subjects with only one hamster pup, which was often immediately killed and eaten. Using a different technique which provided more exposure to the test pups (standard tests for maternal behavior with three newborns), Richards (1966b) demonstrated changes in the pregnant hamster similar to those found by Lott and Rosenblatt (1969) in the pregnant rat. He compared attacking, eating, and maternal behavior in three groups: naïve virgin females, females during the last day of their first gestation, and newly parturient primiparous females within 24 hours after parturition. The virgin females, as usual, all attacked, killed, and ate the pups, displaying little maternal behavior apart from some sniffing and licking. The pregnant females all attacked and eventually killed or ate one or two pups, but they usually mothered the second and the third one fairly intensively. Indeed, in the end they obtained scores for maternal behavior similar to those of lactating females, which, except for one animal, did not attack or eat test pups, but performed only maternal responses. Richards thus concluded that gestation and parturition coincide with positive effects on maternal behavior (probably progressive from midpregnancy onward: Richards, personal communication, 1970). The change observable after parturition might be analogous to the termination of pregnancy effect observed in the rat by Lott and Rosenblatt (1969) but could also or partly result from the changes taking place in the female when she is giving birth.

Although active participation at parturition does not seem to be necessary for the establishment of adequate maternal behavior in the mother, it could have a facilitating effect. Most authors who have practiced cesarian deliveries on rats, more or less near to term, report that the operated females successfully reared their litters afterward (Wiesner and Sheard, 1933; Labriola, 1953; Moltz et al., 1966; Lott and Rosenblatt, 1969). Little information, however, was given in the earlier studies about the operated mother's *first* reaction with pups. Wiesner and Sheard (1933) operated their animals 1 to 3 days prior to parturition and presented them with newborns on the day after the operation. They observed retrieving in 7 out of 8 animals but did not comment on latency or mention possible initial ambivalent sniffing. Labriola (1953) left his subjects unobserved with pups for 24 hours and then observed adequate maternal behavior. Moltz et al. (1966) report that females, delivered by cesarian section just prior to parturition (on the twenty-second day of gestation), needed a few hours of exposure to pups before maternal responses occurred. Lott and Rosenblatt (1969) reported a slightly longer sensitization period (about 24 hours) before the onset of retrieving, with an earlier cesarian delivery after 16 to 19 days of gestation. On the whole, these data tend to show that the substitution of cesarian delivery for parturition slightly delays the onset of maternal behavior in the rat. This delay, however small, can be given several nonexclusive explanations. First, the animals might need to recover from the operation, but this could perhaps also apply to parturition. Second, cesarian-delivered pups usually do not survive (e.g., Wiesner and Sheard, 1933), and, as a consequence, the animals are given foster pups. There is evidence that mother rats can recognize their own young from strange ones of the same age on the basis of olfactory cues (Beach and Jaynes, 1956). It is possible that the mothers need some time to get used to a foreign odor from the foster pups. The same argument can be used even when their own pups are returned, since handling by experimenters or instruments could add a strange smell to the pups. Finally, the process of giving birth (eating placentas, chewing umbilical cords, and contacting newborns) might have a positive effect on maternal behavior.

Some authors (e.g., Richards, 1967a; Terkel, 1970a) assume that the placenta contains an orally active substance, estrogen, which, at a certain dose, favors maternal behavior. This was apparently supported by the results from a study on cross-fostering by Denenberg et al. (1963). These authors found that fostering of newborns to 10-day lactating females was more often successful when the young were transferred with their cord and placenta (which were eaten by the foster mothers), than when they had been previously cleaned by their own mothers. When fostering took place earlier during the lactation period, at day 1 or 5, the presence or the absence of the placenta did not affect survival. Denenberg and his collaborators proposed to explain this result by the fact that, at these times, the foster mothers still benefited from the effect of the estrogen ingested when they had eaten the placentas of their own pups. Indeed, they found in a subsequent experiment (same reference) that the injection of a certain critical dose of estrogen was apparently able to compensate for the absence of the placenta in the later fostering condition.

However, the measure used by Denenberg *et al.* (1963) — survival of foster pups — does not necessarily reflect the adequacy of the foster mother's maternal behavior. It can also reflect the aptness of the foster pups to survive, which, of course, could have been influenced differently by the different experimental treatments. As Rosenblatt (1970) has pointed out, this study remains inconclusive with regard to the role of the orally hormones from the placenta in maternal behavior, and it shows rather the importance of maintaining a synchronized relationship between the mother and her litter for optimal pup survival. His main objections were of three types. First, Bruce (1961) has found that lactation was almost stopped when newborn pups were transferred to mothers nursing older pups. This could explain why more foster pups survived when given to 1-day lactating females than when given to 10-day lactating females (see also Grota, 1968, who found that the 10-day lactating females were in fact better retrievers than foster mothers given pups at day 1). Second, the finding that survival was higher in foster pups transferred with their cord and placenta than in pups previously cleaned by their own mothers is not necessarily due to poor mothering but could result from a deficiency in the pups. Finally Rosenblatt questions the interpretation of the results according to which the administration of substitutes for the hormones present in the placenta did change the survival of the pups in the cases fostering to 10-day lactating females (see Rosenblatt, 1970, for more discussion).

Contact with the newborns during parturition probably also exerts positive effects on maternal behavior. The newborns could present stimuli similar to those from parts of the female's own body, in particular to the genital region, which she has been increasingly contacting and cleaning during gestation (Rosenblatt and Lehrman, 1963; Roth and Rosenblatt, 1967). This could explain the apparent immediate familiarity of the mother with her pups. This idea resembles Birch's (1956) view that increased self-licking of the genital region during gestation leads to intense familiarization with this region, as well as to gentle treatment and inhibition of biting anything presenting a similar odor. The evidence on which he based his assumption was that females prevented by collars from self-licking of genital regions during gestation killed their pups at parturition. This argument, however, is not convincing (see also Beach, 1951; Lehrman, 1961; Richards, 1967a). In addition, several authors (e.g., Roth and Rosenblatt, 1967) who have collared pregnant female rats did not observe systematic cannibalism at parturition, and other workers (Friedlich, 1962; Christopherson and Wagman, 1965; Kirby and Horvath, 1968) who have tried to repeat Birch's experiment failed at duplicating his results.

Other cues received from newborns during parturition might also influence the mother's behavior. Once the pup is breathing regularly, it could emit ultrasonic inhibiting calls, elicited by thorough cleaning, and thereby prevent too rough handling by the female (Zippelius and Schleidt, 1956; Noirot, 1966a; Okon, 1970b). Afterward, before getting into a cold coma (Okon, 1970a), the pup could emit abandon calls, and this could start the priming of maternal activities, such as retrieving and nest-building (Noirot, 1972). When the pups are collected together they can, by bodily contact, initiate crouching. Their typical head-shaking and balancing movements probably lead to their reaching functional nipples and subsequently to suckling.

IV. HORMONAL TREATMENTS, PLASMA TRANSFER, AND CROSS-TRANSFUSION

Exposure to pups, provided it lasts long enough, invariably leads to the establishment of maternal behavior in naïve rats and mice, and probably also in hamsters. Up to now physiological correlates of this change have not been found. Changes during gestation also lead to the onset of maternal behavior in the absence of previous contact with pups (except for early cohabitation with own litter-mates, which is usually uncontrolled), and at least one of these changes (the "termination of gestation" effect) seems related to an endocrine process (Lott and Rosenblatt, 1969; Rosenblatt, 1969; cf. p. 123).

On the other hand, the administration of any type or any mixture of female hormones has systematically failed to produce a positive effect on the onset of maternal behavior in the virgin. Although some early experimenters claimed a positive effect of some hormones on maternal behavior, their data must be disregarded because most of the experiments were inadequately planned. Once Wiesner and Sheard (1933), and Leblond and Nelson 1936, 1937a,b, Leblond, 1940) had shown that maternal behavior could occur in intact, untreated naïve rats and mice, it was invalid to test the effect of a certain hormone on maternal behavior, without comparing the treated experimental with untreated control animals. In addition, the phenomenon of sensitization, also reported early by Wiesner and Sheard and by Nelson and Leblond, excluded the possibility of using treated animals as their own controls, since this involves an increasing exposure to pups, which alone can exert positive effects. Instead of inspiring these precautions, the phenomenon received little attention, and even in 1956 Klein referred to Leblond and Nelson's observations as "contradictory findings, difficult to interpret" (Klein, 1956). His own experiments (on maternal behavior in rabbits) lacked proper control, and so also did numerous experiments on rodents which were planned with the implicit assumption that maternal behavior occurs only in mothers (for review, see Beach, 1951; Lehrman, 1961; Richards, 1967a,b; for additional comments see also Lott and Fuchs, 1962; Noirot, 1966a; Rosenblatt, 1969).

Another type of experimental technique, frequently practiced to demonstrate the hormonal basis of maternal behavior, consisted in upsetting the endocrine balance of a recently parturient mother, usually by the administration of large doses of estrogens (e.g., Hain, 1942; Weichert and Kerrigan, 1942; Spoujitch et al., 1960; all three studies on rats), and demonstrating the consequent negative effects on her behavior with the litter. Several criticisms can be made. A negative argument is (as always) uncertain: if maternal behavior disappears with a certain change in the animal's physiological state, it cannot be concluded that it was *necessarily* determined by the previous physiological state. The technique interferes with milk letdown, which can be stopped or reduced. As a consequence the pups starve, and this may lead to the mother killing and eating them. Some authors (Spoujitch et al., 1960) themselves reported that the mothers also changed in many other respects: some refused to eat, and most apparently behaved as sick animals. Finally, maternal behavior can be upset or abolished by a great number of experimental treatments, other than hormonal ones—for example, mild lead poisoning (Dalldorf and Williams, cited in Beach, 1951), manganese-deficient diets (Orent and Mc Collum, 1931), fertilization postpartum under conditions of poor diet (Beniest-Noirot, 1958; Noirot, 1969c).

More recent, adequately controlled experiments, testing the effects of the administration of various (combinations of) hormones on the onset of maternal behavior, have failed to demonstrate any positive influence. Lott (1962) and Lott and Fuchs (1962) tested the effect of prolactin, and Beach and Wilson (1963) tried various combinations of prolactin, progesterone, and estrogen, without success. Roth et al. (1968) investigated the effects of numerous treatments on castrated female rats, including one that was supposed to create a physiological state similar to the one that normally occurs at parturition, but found no effect on maternal behavior. Rosenblatt (1969, quoting unpublished data) failed to maintain maternal behavior in newly parturient or cesarian-delivered females deprived of pups, by injections of prolactin and oxytocin.

Only nest-building activities have been reported to increase after the administration of progesterone[6] to female mice (Koller, 1952, 1956), and of estrogen and progesterone to female hamsters (Richards, 1969). However, this behavior when occurring in the absence of pups, or in the absence of other responses for the care of pups (when the latter are present), must not necessarily be considered as a maternal response (Noirot, 1962).

These consistent failures of hormone administrations to exert any positive effect on maternal behavior are surprising when one considers, for instance, that the positive effect of the termination of gestation seems to be related to the intense reactivation of the ovary and its secretions. Such an apparent discrepancy could indicate that these endocrine changes intervene in a complex way—for instance, affecting maternal behavior only when they interact with another physiological change, which may also be related to gestation.

Such a view agrees with the fact, demonstrated by Terkel and Rosenblatt (1968), that blood plasma from newly parturient rats contains substances that exert positive effects on maternal behavior. One single injection of about 3.5 ml of blood plasma from a recently parturient animal considerably speeded up the onset of maternal behavior in virgin females: only a mean sensitization period of 2.25 days was needed for eliciting retrieving. Control females injected with blood plasma from proestrus[7] females or with a saline solution behaved like untreated animals and needed longer sensitization (about 4.5 days), but a third group injected with blood plasma from diestrus females apparently underwent a contrary change and needed much longer exposure to pups (7 days) than the females from the two other control groups.

This negative effect is not commented upon by the authors: it can perhaps be compared with the negative effect from early pregnancy on maternal behavior in mice (Noirot and Goyens, 1971). Both diestrus and recently pregnant females (before implantation) are supposed to be in a relatively similar humoral condition.

The success of the plasma injection experiment led to the idea that continuous blood exchange between a mother and a virgin animal might perhaps be the most efficient way of establishing maternal behavior in the virgin. A similar point of view had, much earlier, been tested by Stone (1925) when he realized a parabiotic union between two female rats. He joined the integuments of one female with that of the other from the shoulder to the hip, transforming them into a particular type of Siamese twins. After one of the females had given birth, the other fe-

[6]Lisk (1972) has demonstrated that it is in fact an interaction between both progesterone and estrogen levels that induces an increase in nest-building by the female mouse.
[7]The recipient females were in the same estral phase as the donors.

male, which had remained virgin, did not display maternal behavior. The technique thus failed. Terkel (1970a) supposed that this was due to the fact that a parabiotic union only permits selective transmission of substances carried by the blood. He then developed a "cross-transfusion" technique, using a single, chronically implanted heart catheter between two freely moving rats. This procedure apparently achieves rapid, continuous, and complete blood exchange between the two partners.

Terkel's technique proved indeed to be extremely successful for rapidly eliciting maternal behavior in virgins. Retrieving occurred in seven out of eight virgins within 48 hours after continuous blood exchange with a newly parturient female had started. The mean length of sensitization required by the virgin before the onset of retrieving was 14.5 hours. This indeed is the shortest latency ever reported for naïve virgins of that colony (except, of course, for "spontaneous retrievers") (see also Terkel and Rosenblatt, 1972a).

The change in the blood, which most actively contributes to the establishment of maternal behavior under these conditions, seems to be a short-term one. In two other groups of eight pairs each, continuous blood exchange was started either 24 hours after parturition (M + 24 → V), or 24 hours before parturition was expected in the mothers (M − 24 → V). In these groups, respectively, one and three virgins retrieved within 48 hours after the onset of the blood exchange. Maternal behavior was thus much less stimulated in these two groups than when the blood exchange started immediately after parturition. This suggests that the termination of gestation effect related to the reactivation of the ovaries, and thus probably to the reversal of the estrogen–progesterone ratio (Lott and Rosenblatt, 1969), can be transmitted by cross-transfusion. The fact that these hormones probably do not cross a parabiotic union may explain Stone's failure to establish maternal behavior in a virgin rat, united in this way to a parturient female (Stone, 1925). Whether the positive gestation effect described by Lott and Rosenblatt (1969) is transmitted seems more doubtful: although the animals tended to be more stimulated for performing retrieving in group M − 24 → V than in group M + 24 → V, the difference was small. A comparison between results from the virgins receiving blood from 10- to 19-day pregnant females and those from late pregnant females would provide useful information on this point.

In a fourth group, again composed of eight pairs of females, Terkel achieved continuous blood exchange between sensitized (maternal) and naïve virgins. In this case, cross-transfusion had no influence on the latency for the onset of maternal behavior in the naïve animals. None of them displayed retrieving within the 48 hours after continuous blood exchange had started. Similarly, in a last group, blood exchange between each of eight spontaneous retrievers and each of eight unresponsive virgins failed to produce an effect. Only one virgin retrieved within 48 hours after the onset of blood exchange.

These data suggest that exposure to pups leads to maternal behavior through a different mechanism from gestation and parturition. Nevertheless, it is still possible that sensitization also involves a short-term change in the blood, difficult to locate in time. In such a case, the blood exchange between sensitized and naïve virgins might have been started too late, thereby resembling the case of cross-transfusion between a virgin and a mother that had littered more than 24 hours earlier (group M + 24 → V). Although such mothers remained maternal (mainly or only through stimulation from the litter: Rosenblatt and Lehrman, 1963; Rosenblatt, 1969), their blood had already lost the capacity for favoring maternal behavior in a virgin by cross-transfusion. This alternative also supposes that spontaneous retrievers have once been subject to a short-term change in the blood and remain under its long-term influence on maternal behavior.

Terkel (1970a) noticed that the serial order of maternal responses given by sensitized virgins was not the same as that given by virgins induced to become maternal either by plasma injection or by cross-transfusion with a parturient female. In the first animals nest-building activities occurred several days before retrieving, whereas in the latter, retrieving appeared before nest-building.

V. Conclusions: Comparison between the Different Ways of Inducing Maternal Behavior

When maternal behavior is established in a naïve animal by priming, the underlying mechanism seems different from that which occurs when it is established by gestation and parturition or by the administration of plasma or blood from a parturient female. First, the physiological correlates do not appear to be the same. Second, the serial order in which the different maternal activities occur differs. Finally, interactions with other types of possibly competitive behaviors, namely exploration and aggression, present a different picture. These three points will now be discussed.

A. Physiological Correlates

No physiological, and particularly no endocrine, correlate of priming has so far been found. Virgin female rats could not be induced to lactate (Bruce, 1961) and went on cycling normally (Rosenblatt, 1967) during continuous exposure to, or cohabitation with, pups. Laparotomies of three sensitized females that had intensively retrieved pups did not reveal any abnormalities, except for one case in which the ovaries seemed enlarged. Histological examination, however, led to the conclusion that they were normal (Wiesner and Sheard, 1933). As described above, cross-transfusion between sensitized (maternal) and naïve (nonmaternal) virgins failed to shorten the onset of maternal retrieving in the unresponsive animals, and so did cross-transfusion between spontaneous retrievers and initially nonresponsive virgins (Terkel, 1970a).

Exposure to pups invariably led to the onset of maternal behavior in immature rats and in adult intact or castrated rats of both sexes as well as in hypophysectomized females. Furthermore, the mean length of exposure required for eliciting several features of maternal behavior was similar in these different groups (Rosenblatt, 1967).

Similar findings were made for naïve mice. Maternal behavior could be seen in any immature or adult animal, whatever its apparent physiological condition, generally after a shorter period of initial ambivalence than in the rat (Leblond, 1937, 1938a,b, 1940; Leblond and Nelson, 1936, 1937a,b; Horner, 1947; Beniest-Noirot, 1957, 1958, 1959; Noirot, 1969b).

The effects of exposure to pups on maternal behavior in the naïve hamster have been studied much less, because of this animal's marked tendency to attack and kill strange pups. It has been shown, however, that virgin females can become maternal through repeated presentation of pups (Noirot and Richards, 1966).

There is thus no known humoral process whose contribution is necessary for the establishment of maternal behavior through priming. Although one can assume that a change must have taken place in the animal when it switches over from initial exploration, avoidance, or attacking to maternal activities, the nature of the physiological correlates remains an open question.

Gestation and parturition, on the other hand, coincide with numerous known endocrine changes, some of which could be involved in the onset of maternal behavior.

The gestation effect, which becomes noticeable on several measures of maternal behavior in rats, hamsters, and mice after mid-pregnancy could be related to several humoral processes. Until now, however, none of them has been identified as contributing to maternal behavior. Attempts at administering those hormones, whose levels are known to increase during gestation, have failed to favor maternal behavior in virgin animals. There is only some suggestion, but no definite evidence, that the blood from pregnant females (24 hours before parturition) can favor maternal behavior when cross-transfused (Terkel, 1970a). This does not mean that gestational endocrine changes are necessarily irrelevant with regard to the onset of maternal behavior in the mother. If they have an influence, they exert it in unknown ways, probably interacting with other processes coincident with gestation.

The termination of gestation effect apparently requires the contribution of the ovary, which is reactivated before parturition and is responsible for the estrogen–progesterone reversal. Indeed, experimental termination of gestation exerted a positive effect on the establishment of maternal behavior when the litter (with or without the uterus) was removed, but not when, in addition, the ovaries were removed (Lott and Rosenblatt, 1969). On the other hand, the blood from females just after parturition is able to accelerate the onset of maternal behavior in the virgin, either through plasma injections or more actively through cross-transfusion, but not through parabiosis (see Stone, 1925; Terkel and Rosenblatt, 1968; Terkel, 1970a). The fact that progesterone and estrogen are easily transmitted by cross-transfusion, and not by a parabiotic union, is an additional reason for supposing that they may play a part in the processes leading to maternal behavior. However, these hormones administered in various combinations to castrated females failed to exert effects on their behavior with pups (Roth et al., 1968). This again indicates that they probably need to interact with other processes in order to affect the onset of maternal behavior.

Parturition probably also speeds up maternal behavior in the mother, since cesarian sections seem to delay its onset slightly. Whether underlying endocrine changes (for example, sudden, high secretions of oxytocin and prolactin) contribute also remains an open question (Terkel, 1970a). Administration of these hormones did not maintain maternal behavior in mother rats deprived of their litter (Rosenblatt, 1969), and prolactin did not initiate maternal activities in virgin animals (Lott, 1962; Lott and Fuchs, 1962). The favorable effect on placentaphagy also remains questionable.

None of these endocrine changes is indispensable, however, for the establishment of maternal behavior. Female rats, ovariectomized on day 20 or 22 of gestation, displayed maternal behavior with their litter, although some animals, operated on day 20, had difficult deliveries and the operation interfered with milk letdown (Terkel, 1970a). The operated animals needed longer cohabitation with their pups before becoming fully maternal than did normal mothers. Terkel (1970a) supposes that Moltz and Wiener (1966) failed to observe maternal behavior in 50% of primiparous females, ovariectomized shortly before term, because they did not observe them long enough with the litters. Similarly, the effect of estrogen from the placenta is not indispensable for the occurrence of maternal behavior. Females delivered by cesarian section and given previously cleaned foster pups can rear them successfully, although, again, they seem to become maternal after a slight delay, as compared with normal mothers.

B. SERIAL ORDER OF MATERNAL RESPONSES

When a naïve adult virgin female or male rat is continuously exposed to pups, the first maternal response given is usually nest-building, the second one licking, and the third one crouching: retrieving generally occurs last. The average interval between the first and the last maternal response given is about 3 days (Rosenblatt, 1967).

The order in which pregnant rats display the different maternal activities was not commented upon by Lott and Rosenblatt (1969) when they studied maternal behavior during gestation, nor by Terkel and Rosenblatt (1968) when they demonstrated the positive effect of maternal blood plasma injections on the onset of maternal behavior in virgin females. Later, however, Terkel (1970a) reported that virgin females induced to become maternal by cross-transfusion with a parturient female displayed maternal activities in a different serial order from that shown by sensitized virgins. Unfortunately he discussed only retrieving and nest-building and not the other maternal activities. During cross-transfusion, virgins retrieve about 1 day before they start nest-building; during sensitization, as just mentioned, virgins start nest-building about 3 days before they retrieve.

Naïve virgin female and male mice display maternal behavior in an extremely predictable order during a first encounter with a 1- or 2-day-old pup. Retrieving always occurred first (in all of 115 cases), and the lactation position was generally the last response given. Some irregularity was seen between licking and nest-building, the order depending on whether retrieving was rapidly successful or not. If it was, licking occurred before nest-building, but if it was not, the reverse order was seen (Noirot, 1969b).

Pregnant mice did not display the same rigidity of serial order on a first encounter with a pup (Noirot and Goyens, 1971). Although the data have not yet been systematically analyzed, a preliminary examination has shown that some females lick the pup before they retrieve it to the nest.

The order in which virgin and pregnant hamsters display maternal activities has apparently not been studied.

Not enough data are yet available for a definite conclusion, but the fact that the serial order of maternal responses is not the same during priming as during gestation in both rats and mice suggests again that the process leading to the establishment of maternal behavior is probably different in the two cases.

C. Interactions with Exploration and Aggression

When an animal becomes maternal, either by priming or by gestation, one could suppose that its tendencies to perform other activities (mainly exploration or attacking) have been decreased, that its tendencies to display maternal activities have been increased, or that both these effects have been exerted simultaneously. The data available up to now do not permit one to determine, for any particular case, which of these three possibilities has occurred. A single change in only one type of behavior (for example, reduced preliminary exploration after a certain treatment or event, but no effect on maternal behavior, or vice versa) has apparently never been obtained, and usually at least two types of behavior are affected. For instance, a naïve mouse, once exposed to a series of pup distress calls, displays less approach–avoidance running and more maternal behavior than a previously unexposed naïve mouse during a first encounter with a pup (Noirot, 1970a). Although one is tempted to interpret these results as reflecting a combined action on both types of behavior—a decreased tendency to explore and an increased tendency to give maternal behavior—it could equally well be argued that the animal is only more stimulated for maternal behavior, or less stimulated for exploration, and for that reason displays a maternal response earlier in the test. Nevertheless it might be worthwhile to consider such interactions because they could focus attention on similarities or differences between the two main factors (priming and gestation) promoting maternal behavior, and this could perhaps contribute later to an understanding of the underlying mechanism.

The brief description (p. 112) of the exploratory behavior shown by a virgin rat exposed to pups shows that the animal goes through successive changes: approach–avoidance, avoidance, ambivalence, and maternal behavior (Rosenblatt, 1972). Similarly, during experiments on priming in mice, it was shown that, with repeated presentations of test pups, or after exposure to stimulus objects sharing common cues with pups, the animals showed less approach–avoidance running between the pup and the nest, and nosed it less before displaying maternal behavior, than naïve animals (Noirot, 1969a, 1970a). Comparisons with data on hamsters are unfortunately impossible. A similar experiment, showing that a process analogous to priming occurs in naïve hamsters, used only a single score for sniffing and licking (Noirot and Richards, 1966), for these two activities are extremely difficult to distinguish in a hamster presented with a pup.

From mid-pregnancy onward, a similar change is seen in the exploratory behavior displayed by mice and maybe also by rats with pups. This change does not require previous exposure to pups. Independent groups of naïve pregnant rats gave shorter mean latencies before the onset of maternal retrieving, the nearer they were to term (Lott and Rosenblatt, 1969), which could mean that they less avoided and explored. A similar experiment on independent groups of pregnant mice showed that initial nosing of a test pup before performing maternal behavior fell off with the advance of gestation (Noirot and Goyens, 1971). The study on changes in the behavior with pups during gestation in the hamster (Richards, 1966b) again groups together sniffing and licking; no comparison can thus be made. The fact, however, that exploration is absent in the female hamster giving birth (as in the rat and mouse) suggests that a similar change, leading to apparent immediate familiarity with her own pups, also takes place in this species.

Thus, with regard to exploration of pups, a similar change seems to coincide with priming and with gestation. Whether this is characteristic of exploration in general, so that the behavior of primed and pregnant females with various kinds of unusual stimuli is similarly affected, or whether the process is restricted to pups only, has apparently not yet been studied.

The picture of interactions between maternal and aggressive behavior during priming and gestation is more complicated. Attacking and eventual killing of pups can occur in the naïve rat exposed to pups, but has been reported to disappear with successive presentations (Wiesner and Sheard, 1933; Cosnier, 1963; Rosenblatt, personal communication, 1970). No systematic data on infanticidal behavior in this species seem to be available.

Naïve virgin female and naïve male mice occasionally attack an (even optimal) pup during a first encounter. With successive presentation they either become maternal or develop a stereotyped infanticidal behavior (Beniest-Noirot, 1957, 1958).

Naïve hamsters most frequently attack and kill pups on a first encounter (Rowell, 1960; Richards, 1965a, 1966a). As mentioned before, complex changes occurred in the hamster with successive presentations of pups (see pp. 121–122). Different measures of aggression changed in apparently contradictory ways: for instance, in one case latency before attacking decreased, whereas the number of attacks was unaffected and the number of pups killed or injured decreased (Noirot and Richards, 1966). It was suggested that this complexity could be explained by the fact that several changes had occurred with successive presentations. Aggression easily becomes stereotyped and is probably more likely to change in that way when the test pups and situations are similar on successive presentations. At the same time, cues from the pups, acting more slowly than those stimulating aggression, could have started to prime maternal behavior. As a consequence, animals can attack more readily, but also switch over to maternal behavior earlier during the test. A similar explanation could account for the change toward either systematical killing or maternal behavior in initially aggressive mice.

Changes with gestation in infanticide behavior have apparently not been studied in mice or rats, probably because such behavior is rare in both species. In the hamster, however, attacking of pups decreases as parturition approaches (cf. p. 125). Females just prior to parturition attacked and killed only one or two out of three 1-day-old test pups and displayed maternal behavior with the next one(s). Naïve virgin females, on the other hand, always killed all three test pups of this age (Richards, 1966b).

Some data are available concerning interactions between maternal behavior and territorialism — that is, aggression toward strange adults — in mice. Infanticidal behavior was correlated in the naïve males and non-pregnant females from a mixed, outbred mouse population with severe territorialism. Those animals that killed pups systematically attacked strange adults in a violent way; they tended to fight without previous sniffing or threatening, and were not very responsive to submissive postures by the intruder (Beniest-Noirot, 1958).

Some experiments, testing the effect of exposure to pups on territorialism, showed that this behavior was not affected in initially pacific animals, but that it might be reduced for a short period in territorial males presented for some time with a litter. Males, living in pairs each with a female, were presented daily with an intruder, alternatively male and female. They became progressively more aggressive with the advance of gestation in their partner, but, after the female had littered, a considerable short-term decrease was seen in their territorialism, as indicated by several measures of aggression (Beniest-Noirot, 1957, 1958).

This decrease might result from changes in the female, or from recent copulation during the estrus postpartum, but contact with the newborns might also have contributed, perhaps through an effect generalized from the pups' inhibiting distress calls. An attempt has been made to test this possibility by exposing moderately (nonstereotyped) aggressive males, living alone, to pups, and to check for possible effects on their subsequent behavior with strange adults. A change obviously occurred: the animals behaved differently from before their encounter with pups. They either seemed very inhibited and did not threaten or attack the intruder at all, or they fought it violently in an "impulsive" way — that is, without any preliminary investigation or threat. However, the males that no longer attacked seemed continuously on the point of doing so. They were extremely active and nervous, and displayed much running between the nest and the strange adult. Sometimes an unexpected noise, such as sneezing by the observer or the ringing of a bell, was followed by a violent and sudden attack by a previously tolerant male. These changes of various measures of aggression toward extreme values suggest that some mice, under the influence of inhibiting cues from pups, such as inhibiting calls, might have temporarily generalized this inhibition toward adult strangers, that some others had only reached a frail equilibrium, and that the remaining ones had not yet been sufficiently exposed to the pups. (This leaves open the question: why in the last case did the males become more violent than before their contact with pups?) The males of this last experiment had been given three 1-day-old pups for 1½ hours, on three consecutive days. The males from the first experiment had been observed for a minimum of 12 hours after their female had littered and thus after a longer and continuous period of contact with a greater number of pups.

Whereas infanticide behavior is correlated with severe territorialism in naïve males and nonpregnant females, a reversed relation seems to develop in the pregnant female. Fights with strange adults become more severe with the advance of gestation and reach a maximal intensity toward parturition. This moment, however, coincides with a high tendency to perform maternal behavior, and infanticides during parturition are rare. Even females that have previously attacked test pups rarely kill their own, and often rear them with success. This inverted relation, high territorialism and intense maternal behavior at the moment of parturition, could result from changes in the selectivity of the pregnant female's territorialism. Although fights become more and more violent, they are directed toward other types of intruders than when the female is not pregnant. Nonpregnant or early pregnant females attack strange females and tolerate strange males. Late pregnant females attack strange males and nonpregnant females, but they tolerate and in large population cages may even search to cohabit with other pregnant females (Noirot, 1969c).

When one considers these changes in territorialism, together with the major changes that occur simultaneously in the maternal behavior of the pregnant mouse—that is, progressively less preliminary exploration and more cleaning of test pups—a picture arises in which olfaction seems to play an important part. Indeed, territorialism in rodents (Steiniger, 1950; Eibl-Eibesfeldt, 1960; Mackintosh and Grant, 1966; Ropartz, 1967, 1968a,b), and exploration and cleaning of pups in mice (Noirot, 1970a) are known to be dependent on olfactory cues. It has been shown, on the other hand, that the odor emanating from an animal (rat) changes with its sexual state and that simultaneously its responsiveness to several odors also changes. Unfortunately these studies concentrated on estrous cycles and sexual arousal induced by hormonal treatments (Le Magnen, 1952a). Little work seems to have been done on pregnant subjects, except for a study on the human female (Le Magnen, 1952b). It nevertheless suggests that gestation could coincide with changes in responsiveness to certain odors.

It thus could be that the pregnant female's preference for certain odors evolves as parturition approaches. Such an explanation could account for the changes occurring in her territorial and maternal behavior. For instance, the female's preference for male odors decreases and gradually disappears. She therefore progressively treats strange males like strange females by intense fighting. Increased preference for "pregnancy" odors explains why she now distinguishes strange pregnant from strange nonpregnant females and fights only the latter. Simultaneously increased preference for "pup odors," which could share characteristics with the pregnant female's own odor, could inhibit attacking of animals with a similar smell and also stimulate licking and cleaning activities.

Another simpler explanation would be that the female's own odor changes with gestation and that she attacks animals with a different odor and tolerates animals with a similar odor (for example, pregnant females and her own newborns). Unfortunately this does not account for territorial behavior under other circumstances. Nonpregnant females attack strange females, which probably have an odor similar to their own, and tolerate strange males, which have a different odor. Indeed the changes in a female's odor with different sexual states seem quantitative, whereas the difference between male and female odors seems to be a qualitative one (Le Magnen, 1952a).

Thus, priming and gestation both involve a progressive decrease in preliminary exploration of pups before maternal activities occur. Infanticidal behavior may evolve differently. Repeated presentations of pups to naïve infanticidal animals leads either to stereotyped killing or to the progressive onset of maternal behavior. During gestation, infanticides seem to decrease, at least near to term. Interactions with territorial behavior are complex. High territorialism usually coincides with the absence of maternal behavior and with frequent infant-killing in males and in nonpregnant females. The contrary is seen in females on the point of giving birth. At that time, intense territorialism coincides with intense maternal behavior and with relatively rare infanticidal behavior.

Acknowledgments

Thanks are due to Paul Bertelson, Robert Hinde, David Pye, Jay Rosenblatt, and Joseph Terkel, who have read the manuscript and helped considerably to improve it. For the sake of editorial necessities only part of the very interesting material and comments, generously provided by Jay Rosenblatt, could be used here. This I regret very much. I am grateful to S. Cosnier, N. Freeman, J. Goyens, E. Okon, J. Rosenblatt, B. Sachs, and J. Terkel for permitting me to consult and quote unpublished data.

This review was written while I held a grant "Chercheur qualifié" from the Belgian "Fonds national de la Recherche scientifique." Part of my work described in this paper was sponsored by the Belgian "Fonds de la Recherche fondamentale collective."

References

Beach, F. A. 1951. Instinctive behavior: reproductive activities. In "Handbook of Experimental Psychology" (S. Stevens, ed.), pp. 387–434. Wiley, New York.

Beach, F. A., and Jaynes, J. 1956. Studies on maternal retrieving in rats. I. Recognition of young. J. Mammal. 35, 177–180.

Beach, F. A., and Wilson, J. 1963. Effects of prolactin, progesterone and estrogen on reactions of non-pregnant rats to foster young. Psychol. Rep. 13, 231–239.

Beniest-Noirot, E. 1957. Analyse du comportement dit "maternel" de la souris. Mémoire non publié, Univ. de Bruxelles.

Beniest-Noirot, E. 1958. Analyse du comportement dit "maternel" chez la souris. Monogr. Fr. Psychol. No. 1. CNRS, Paris.

Beniest-Noirot, E. 1959. Le comportement dit "maternel" de la souris. C. R. Reunions Strasbourg (1956), Bruxelles (1957), Sect. Psychol. Exp. Comportement Anim. Union Int. Sci. Biol., Strasbourg pp. 139–146.

Birch, H. G. 1956. Sources of order in the maternal behaviour in animals. Amer. J. Orthopsychiat. 26, 279–284.

Bruce, H. M. 1961. Observations on the suckling stimulus and lactation in the rat. J. Reprod. Fert. 2, 17–34.

Charton, D., Adrien, J., and Cosnier, J. 1971. Déclencheurs chimiques du comportement de léchage des petits par la Ratte parturiente. Rev. Comp. Anim. 5, 89–94.

Christophersen, E. R., and Wagman, W. 1965. Maternal behaviour in the albino rat as a function of self-licking deprivation. J. Comp. Physiol. Psychol. 60, 142–144.

Cosnier, J. 1963. Quelques problèmes posés par le "comportement maternel provoqué" chez la rate. C. R. Soc. Biol. 8/9, 1611.

Dalldorf, G., and Williams, R. R. 1945. Impairment of reproduction in rats by ingestion of lead. Science 102, 668–670.

Denenberg, V. H., Grota, L. J., and Zarrow, M. X. 1963. Maternal behaviour in the rat: analysis of cross-fostering. J. Reprod. Fert. 5, 133–141.

Eibl-Eibesfeldt, I. 1960. Beitrage zur Biologie der Haus und Ahrenmaus sebst einigen Beobnachtungen und anderen Nagern. Z. Tierpsychol. 7, 558–587.

Friedlich, O. B. 1962. A study of maternal behaviour in the albino rat as a function of self-licking deprivation. M. S. Thesis, Southern Illinois Univ, Carbondale, Illinois.

Goyens, J. 1969. Contributions à l'étude de l'évolution du comportement maternel au cours de la gestation chez la souris. Mémoire non publié, Univ. de Bruxelles.

Grota, L. J. 1968. Factors influencing the acceptance of cesarean delivered offspring by foster mothers. Physiol. Behav. 3, 265–269.

Hain, A. M., 1942. The effect a) of litter size on growth b) of oestrone administered during lactation (rat). Quart. J. Exp. Psychol. 25, 303–313.

Hart, F. M., and King, J. A. 1966. Distress vocalizations of young in two subspecies of Peromyscus maniculatus. J. Mammal. 47, 287–293.

Hinde, R. A. 1959. Unitary drives. Anim. Behav. 7, 130–141.

Hinde, R. A. 1966. "Animal Behaviour." McGraw-Hill, New York.

Horner, B. E. 1947. Paternal care of young mice of the genus Peromyscus. *J. Mammal.* **28**, 31–36.

King, J. A. 1963. Maternal behavior in *Peromyscus*. *In* "Maternal Behavior in Mammals" (H. L. Rheingold, ed.), pp. 38–93. Wiley, New York.

Kirby, H. W., and Horvath, T. 1968. Self-licking deprivation and maternal behaviour in the primiparous rat. *Can. J. Psychol.* **22**, 369–375.

Klein, M. 1956. Aspects biologiques de l'instinct reproducteur dans le comportement des mammifères. *In* "L'Instinct dans le Comportement des Animaux et de l'Homme" (Fondation Singer Polignac, ed.), pp. 287–344. Masson, Paris.

Koller, G. 1952. Der Nestbau der weissen Maus und seine hormonale Auslösung. *Verh. Deut. Zool. Ges., Freiburg* pp. 160–168.

Koller, G. 1956. Hormonale und psychische steuerung beim Nestbau weiser Mäuse. *Zool. Anz. Suppl.* **19.** [*Verh. Deut. Zool. Ges., Freiburg* pp. 123–132 (1955).]

Labriola, J. 1953. Effects of caesarian delivery upon maternal behavior in rats. *Proc. Soc. Exp. Biol. Med.* **83**, 556–557.

Leblond, C. P. 1937. L'instinct maternel: Nature et relations avec la glande mammaire, l'hypophyse et le système nerveux. *Rev. Fr. Endocrinol.* **15**, 457–475.

Leblond, C. P. 1938a. Mécanisme de l'instinct maternel. *Kongressber. Int. Physiol. Kongr., Zurich* pp. 14–19.

Leblond, C. P. 1938b. Extra-hormonal factors in maternal behavior. *Proc. Soc. Exp. Biol. Med.* **38**, 66–70.

Leblond, C. P. 1940. Nervous and hormonal factors in the maternal behavior of the mouse. *J. Genet. Psychol.* **57**, 327–344.

Leblond, C. P., and Nelson, W. O. 1936. L'instinct maternel après hypophysectomie. *C. R. Soc. Biol.* **122**, 548–549.

Leblond, C. P., and Nelson, W. O. 1937a. Maternal behavior in hypophysectomised male and female mice. *Amer. J. Physiol.* **120**, 167–172.

Leblond, C. P., and Nelson, W. O. 1937b. Présence d'instinct maternel sans stimulation hormonale. *C. R. Soc. Biol.* **124**, 1064.

Lehrman, D. S. 1961. Hormonal regulation of parental behavior in birds and infrahuman mammals. *In* "Sex and Internal Secretions" (W. C. Young, ed.), pp. 1268–1382. Williams & Wilkins, Baltimore, Maryland.

Le Magnen, J. 1952a. Les phénomènes olfacto-sexuels chez l'homme. *Arch. Sci. Physiol.* **6**, 125–150.

Le Magnen, J. 1952b. Les phénomènes olfacto-sexuels chez le rat blanc. *Arch. Sci. Physiol.* **6**, 285–331.

Lisk, R. D. 1972. Oestrogen and progesterone synergism and elicitation of maternal nest-building in the mouse *(Mus musculus)*. *Anim. Behav.* (in press).

Lott, D. F. 1962. The role of progesterone in the maternal behavior of rodents. *J. Comp. Physiol. Psychol.* **55**, 610–613.

Lott, D. F., and Fuchs, S. S. 1962. Failure to induce retrieving by sensitization or the injection of prolactin. *J. Comp. Physiol. Psychol.* **55**, 1111–1113.

Lott, D. F., and Rosenblatt, J. S. 1969. Development of maternal responsiveness during pregnancy in the rat. *In* "Determinants of Infant Behaviour" (D. M. Foss, ed.), Vol. 4, pp. 61–68. Methuen, London.

Mc Iver, A. H., and Jeffrey, W. 1967. Strain differences in maternal behavior in rats. *Behaviour* **28**, 210–215.

Mackintosh, J. H., and Grant, E. C. 1966. The effect of olfactory stimuli on the agonistic behavior of laboratory mice. *Z. Tierpsychol.* **5**, 584–587.

Moltz, H., and Wiener, E. 1966. Effects of ovarectomy on maternal behavior of primiparous and multiparous rats. *J. Comp. Physiol. Psychol.* **62**, 382–387.

Moltz, H., Robbins, D., and Parks, M. 1966. Caesarian delivery and the maternal behaviour of primiparous and multiparous rats. *J. Comp. Physiol. Psychol.* **61**, 455–460.

Noirot, E. 1962. Modifications de réactivité au niveau des réponses aux jeunes chez la souris. Thèse de doctorat, Univ. de Bruxelles.

Noirot, E. 1964a. Changes in responsiveness to young in the adult mouse. I. The problematical effect of hormones. *Anim. Behav.* **12**, 52–58.

Noirot, E. 1964b. Changes in responsiveness to young in the adult mouse. II. The effect of external stimuli. *J. Comp. Physiol. Psychol.* **57**, 97–99.

Noirot, E. 1964c. Changes in responsiveness to young in the adult mouse. IV. The effect of an initial contact with a strong stimulus. *Anim. Behav.* **12**, 442–445.

Noirot, E. 1965. Changes in responsiveness to young in the adult mouse. III. The effect of immediately preceding performances. *Behaviour* **24**, 318–325.

Noirot, E. 1966a. Untrasons et comportements maternels chez les petits rongeurs. *Ann. Soc. Roy. Zool. Bruxelles* **95**, 47–56.

Noirot, E. 1966b. Ultrasounds in young rodents. I. Changes with age in albino mice. *Anim. Behav.* **14**, 459–467.

Noirot, E. 1968. Untrasounds in young rodents. II. Changes with age in albino rats. *Anim. Behav.* **16**, 129–134.

Noirot, E. 1969a. Changes in responsiveness to young in the adult mouse. V. Priming. *Anim. Behav.* **17**, 542–546.

Noirot, E. 1969b. Serial order of maternal responses in mice. *Anim. Behav.* **17**, 547–550.

Noirot, E. 1969c. Interactions between reproductive and territorial behaviour in female mice. *Int. Mental Health Res. Newslett.* **11**, 10–11.

Noirot, E. 1970a. Selective priming of maternal responses by auditory and olfactory cues from mouse pups. *Develop. Psychobiol.* **2**, 273–276.

Noirot, E. 1970b. Observation de Divers Comportements de la Souris de Laboratoire. Film, réalisé pour la Télévision belge dans le cadre des émissions scholaires.

Noirot, E. 1972. Ultrasounds and maternal behavior in small rodents. *Develop. Psychobiol.* **5** (in press).

Noirot, E., and Goyens, J. 1971. Changes in maternal behavior during gestation in the mouse. *Horm. Behav.* **2**, 1–9.

Noirot, E., and Pye, D. 1969. Sound analysis of ultrasonic distress calls of mouse pups as a function of their age. *Anim. Behav.* **17**, 340–349.

Noirot, E., and Richards, M. P. M. 1966. Maternal behaviour in virgin female golden hamsters. Changes consequent upon initial contact with pups. *Anim. Behav.* **14**, 7–10.

Okon, E. E. 1970a. The effect of environmental temperature on the production of ultrasounds in non-handled albino mouse pups. *J. Zool.* **162**, 71–83.

Okon, E. E. 1970b. The ultrasonic responses of albino mouse pups to tactile stimuli. *J. Zool.* **162**, 485–492.

Orent, E. R., and Mc Collum, E. V. 1931. Effects of deprivation of manganese in the rat. *J. Biol. Chem.* **92**, 651–678.

Rabaud, E. 1921. L'instinct maternel chez les mammifères. *J. Psychol. Norm. Pathol.* **18**, 487–495.

Richards, M. P. 1965a. Aspects of maternal behaviour in the golden hamster. Ph.D. Thesis, Cambridge Univ., Cambridge, England.

Richards, M. P. 1965b. The behaviour of the pregnant golden hamster. *J. Reprod. Fert.* **10**, 285–286.

Richards, M. P. 1966a. Maternal behaviour in virgin female golden hamsters (*Mesocricetus auratus* Waterhouse): The role of the age of the test pup. *Anim. Behav.* **14**, 303–309.

Richards, M. P. 1966b. Maternal behaviour in the golden hamster: Responsiveness to young in virgin, pregnant, and lactating females. *Anim. Behav.* **14**, 310–313.

Richards, M. P. 1967a. Maternal behaviour in rodents and lagomorphs. In "Advances in Reproductive Physiology" (A. McLaren, ed.), Vol. 2, pp. 53–110. Academic Press, New York.

Richards, M. P. 1967b. Some effects of experience on maternal behaviour in rodents. In "Determinants of Infant Behaviour" (B. M. Foss, ed.), Vol. 4, pp. 69–77. Methuen, London.

Richards, M. P. 1969. Effects of oestrogen and progesterone on nest-building in the golden hamster. Anim. Behav. 17, 356–361.

Ropartz, P. 1967. Mise en évidence du rôle de l'olfaction dans l'aggressivité de la souris. Rev. Comp. Anim. 2, 97–102.

Ropartz, P. 1968a. Étude du déterminisme olfactif de l'effet de groupe chez la souris mâle. Rev. Comp. Anim. 2, 35–77.

Ropartz, P. 1968b. The relation between olfactory stimulation and aggressive behaviour in mice. Anim. Behav. 16, 97–100.

Rosenblatt, J. S. 1967. Nonhormonal basis of maternal behavior in the rat. Science 156, 1512–1514.

Rosenblatt, J. S. 1969. The development of maternal responsiveness in the rat. Amer. J. Orthopsychiat. 39, 36–56.

Rosenblatt, J. S. 1970. Views on the onset and maintenance of maternal behavior in the rat. In "Development and Evolution of Behavior: Essays in Memory of T. C. Schneirla" (L. R. Aronson, E. Tobach, D. S. Lehrman, and J. S. Rosenblatt, eds.), pp. 489–518. Freeman, San Francisco, California.

Rosenblatt, J. S. 1972. Psychobiology of Maternal Behavior. Report. Institute of Animal Behavior, Newark, New Jersey.

Rosenblatt, J. S., and Lehrman, D. S. 1963. Maternal behaviour of the laboratory rat. In "Maternal Behaviour in Mammals" (H. Rheingold, ed.), pp. 8–57. Wiley, New York.

Roth, L. L., and Rosenblatt, J. S. 1967. Changes in self-licking during pregnancy in the rat. J. Comp. Physiol. Psychol. 63, 397–400.

Roth, L. L., Richards, M. P., and Lisk, R. D. 1968. Effects of estrogen and progesterone on maternal behavior in virgin rats. Amer. Zool. November.

Rowell, T. E. 1959. Maternal behaviour in the golden hamster. Ph.D. Thesis, Cambridge Univ., Cambridge, England.

Rowell, T. E. 1960. On the retrieving of young and other behaviour in lactating golden hamsters. Proc. Zool. Soc. London 136, 265–282.

Rowell, T. E. 1961a. Maternal behaviour in non-maternal golden hamsters. Anim. Behav. 9, 11–15.

Rowell, T. E. 1961b. The family group in golden hamsters: its formation and break-up. Behaviour 17, 81–93.

Sachs, B. 1969. Behavior of maternal rats in the perinatal period. Amer. Zool. 9, 1068.

Schleidt, W. M. 1951. Töne Hoher Frequenz bei Mäusen. Experientia 1, 65–66.

Scott, J. P. 1946. Incomplete adjustment caused by frustration of untrained fighting mice. J. Comp. Psychol. 39, 379–390.

Sewell, G. 1968. Ultrasound in rodents. Nature (London) 217, 682–683.

Sewell, G. 1970. Ultrasonic communication in rodents. Nature (London) 227, 410.

Spoujitch, V., Arnovljevic-Brankovic, J., and Vidovic, V. L. 1960. Effets de l'injection d'hormones ovariennes sur le comportement maternel et le cycle oestral de la rate. Acta Neurol. Psychiat. Belg. 3, 247–269.

Steiniger, F. 1950. Zur Sociologie und sonstigen Biologie der Wanderratte. Z. Tierpsychol. 7, 356–379.

Stone, C. P. 1925. Preliminary note on maternal behaviour of rats living in parabiosis. Endocrinology 9, 505–512.

Terkel, J. 1970a. Some aspects of maternal behavior in the rat with special reference to humoral factors at the time of parturition. Ph.D. Thesis, No. 71-3109. Univ. Microfilms, Ann Arbor, Michigan.

Terkel, J. 1970b. I. Freely Moving Rats During Blood Exchange. II. Induction of Maternal Behavior in Rats Using the Cross-Transfusion Technique. Color Film (15 min.), Institute of Animal Behavior, Newark, New Jersey.

Terkel, J. 1972. Technique for continuous cross-transfusion between two freely-behaving rats using a single chronically implanted heart catheter. *Anim. Behav.* (submitted for publication).

Terkel, J., and Rosenblatt, J. S. 1968. Maternal behaviour induced by maternal blood plasma injected into virgin rats. *J. Comp. Physiol. Psychol.* **65,** 479–482.

Terkel, J., and Rosenblatt, J. S. 1972a. Humoral factors underlying maternal behavior at parturition in the rat: a study using cross-transfusion between freely moving animals with single chronically implanted heart catheters. *Anim. Behav.* (submitted for publication).

Terkel, J., and Rosenblatt, J. S. 1972b. Aspects of nonhormonal behavior in the rat. *Horm. Behav.* (submitted for publication).

Valenta, J. G., and Rigby, M. R. 1968. Discrimination of the odor of stressed rats. *Science* **161,** 599.

Weichert, C. K., and Kerrigan, S. 1942. Effects of estrogens upon the young injected lactating rats. *Endocrinology* **30,** 741–752.

Weisner, B. P., and Sheard, N. M. 1933. "Maternal Behaviour in the Rat," Oliver & Boyd. Edinburgh.

Zippelius, H. M., and Schleidt, W. M. 1956. Ultraschall-Laute bei jungen Mäusen. *Naturwissenschaften* **21,** 1–2.

Sexual and Other Long-Term Aspects of Imprinting in Birds and Other Species

Klaus Immelmann[1]

ZOOLOGISCHES INSTITUT DER TECHNISCHEN UNIVERSITÄT
BRAUNSCHWEIG, GERMANY

I. Introduction

For many years, the study of imprinting has concentrated mainly on the following reaction of precocial birds and on the stimuli eliciting this response, whereas the long-lasting effects of imprinting have been studied to a regrettably small extent. As a consequence, general reviews of the context and characteristics of imprinting also refer mainly to filial imprinting, and this in turn has frequently led to the impression that imprinting of the following response represents the "classical" example for the phenomenon as a whole.

However, besides its importance for infant–mother relations, early experience may also exert a marked influence on *adult* behavior, especially on the determination of sexual preferences but also on several other aspects of social and other behavior. It is therefore worth while to summarize the evidence for long-lasting effects of imprinting and to discuss its possible bearings on the general concept of imprinting.

[1] This review is based on a paper read at the XIIth International Ethological Conference in Edinburgh in September 1971. I should like to thank Dr. P. P. G. Bateson, Prof. R. A. Hinde, Prof. W. Sluckin, and Prof. F. V. Smith for kindly reading the manuscript and for many valuable suggestions.

147

II. Evidence for Early Determination of Sexual Preferences

Most of the evidence for long-range aspects of imprinting concerns the early establishment of sexual preferences, usually referred to as "sexual imprinting." As with filial imprinting, most data are available for certain species of birds. They can be divided into two groups:

1. *Intraspecific* sexual imprinting: In a number of domesticated species, individuals of one color breed which had been reared by foster parents of another color later proved to pair, regardless of their own plumage color, preferentially with members of their foster parents' color strain. This has been found for ducks (Schutz, 1965), domestic fowl (Lill and Wood-Gush, 1965), domestic and feral pigeons (Goodwin, 1958; Warriner *et al.*, 1963), zebra finches (Immelmann, 1969a; Walter, 1970), and Bengalese finches (Immelmann, 1970).

2. *Interspecific* sexual imprinting: In a larger number of domesticated as well as wild species of birds, sexual attachments have also been observed to be directed toward another species as a consequence of early experience with that particular species.

In the latter case one can distinguish between birds that became imprinted on humans and those that proved to be imprinted on another species of bird. Imprinting on humans occurs in birds that have – at least for a time – been hand-reared. Evidence comes from occasional and sometimes rather "anecdotal" observations on single individuals as well as from more detailed experimental investigations. So far, sexual imprinting on humans has been found in more than twenty-five species ranging from herons, storks, and eagle owls to small passerines such as bullfinches, hawfinches, and estrildine finches (see Table I) (for details, see Klinghammer, 1967).

Experimental data based on cross-fostering experiments between two species of birds, on the other hand, have been determined with fewer species, namely pigeons and doves (Craig, 1908, 1914; Whitman, 1919; Goodwin, 1948, 1958), ducks and geese, coot (*Fulica atra*), red jungle (*Gallus gallus*) and domestic fowl (Schutz, 1965, 1970), herring and lesser black-backed gulls (*Larus argentatus* and *L. fuscus*) (Harris, 1970), house and tree sparrows (*Passer domesticus* and *P. montanus*) (Cheke, 1969), and several species of estrildine finches (Immelmann, 1969, 1970, 1972; Goodwin, 1971; H. Mueller, personal communication, 1972).

In most cases (exceptions will be mentioned later), cross-fostered individuals showed strong sexual attachments to the species of their foster parents and – in free choice situations with conspecifics – directed their courtship and pairing activities preferentially toward members of the foster species. This has been observed, for instance, in male estrildine finches. Thus zebra finches (*Taeniopygia guttata*) raised by Bengalese

TABLE I

LIST OF BIRDS FOR WHICH SEXUAL ATTACHMENT TO HUMANS HAS BEEN DESCRIBED[a]

Lesser white-fronted goose (*Anser erythropus*) (Steven, 1955)
Purple heron (*Ardea purpurea*) (von Frisch, 1957)
Bittern (*Botaurus stellaris*) (Portielje, 1926)
White stork (*Ciconia ciconia*) (Löhrl, 1961)
Sparrowhawk (*Accipiter nisus*) (Mohr, 1960)
Broad-winged hawk (*Buteo platypterus*) (Mueller, 1970)
Golden eagle (*Aquila chrysaetos*) (Hamerstrom, 1970)
Peregrine falcon (*Falco peregrinus*) (Waller, 1942)
Domestic turkey (Räber, 1948; Schein, 1963)
Red jungle fowl (*Gallus gallus*) (Hess, 1959b)
Domestic fowl (Fisher and Hale, 1957; Schein and Hale, 1959; Guiton, 1962)
Corncrake (*Crex crex*) (Heinroth, 1924–1933)
Ring dove *(Streptopelia risoria)* (Craig, 1908; Klinghammer and Hess, 1964; Klinghammer, 1967).
Rock dove (*Columba livia*) (Heinroth, 1970)
Domestic pigeon (Goodwin, 1948)
Mourning dove (*Zenaidura macroura*) (Klinghammer, 1967)
Senegal parrot (*Poicephalus senegalus*) (Klinghammer, 1967)
Budgerigar (*Melopsittacus undulatus*) (Lorenz, 1955)
Eagle owl (*Bubo bubo*) (Heinroth, 1924–1933)
European roller (*Coracias garrulus*) (von Frisch, 1966)
Blue-winged siva (*Siva cyanouroptera*) (Thielcke, 1966)
European raven (*Corvus corax*) (Gwinner, 1964)
American crow (*Corvus brachyrhynchos*) (Klinghammer, 1967)
Jackdaw (*Coloeus monedula*) (Lorenz, 1935)
Zebra finch (*Taeniopygia guttata*) (Immelmann, 1969a; Kikkawa, 1969)
Bengalese finch (*Lonchura striata*) (Immelmann, 1969a)
Bullfinch (*Pyrrhula pyrrhula*) (Nicolai, 1956, 1959)
Hawfinch (*Coccothraustes coccothraustes*) (Kear, 1960)
Eastern meadowlark (*Sturnella magna*) (Nice, 1965)

---

[a]Sequence of orders and families according to Storer (1971).

finches (*Lonchura striata*) courted Bengalese finch females almost exclusively: this occurred even though, during the free choice experiments, the conspecific females usually showed strong sexual reactions and sometimes approached the male as soon as it was introduced into the test cage, whereas the females of the foster parents' species as a rule showed no such reactions but mostly tried to avoid the male's approach (Immelmann, 1969a).

Such preferences have been found not only under laboratory conditions but also under more natural circumstances. Under seminatural conditions cross-fostered individuals of several species of ducks have been reported to mate with members of their foster parents' species even in the constant presence of conspecifics (Schutz, 1965, 1970). In the two species of gulls mentioned above, mixed pairs were found even under completely natural conditions (Harris, 1970), and in the case of the house and tree sparrows, several cases of actual hybridization have been described as a result of interspecific mating in cross-fostered individuals (Cheke, 1969).

In mammals, evidence for sexual attachments meaningfully analogous to sexual imprinting in birds is still meager and much less conclusive. The only extensive experimental work has been carried out by Mainardi *et al.* (1965) with the house mouse (*Mus musculus*). In female house mice, Mainardi has found that intraspecific sexual preferences—that is, preferences for a certain subspecies—are strongly influenced by infantile learning of the parents' characteristics and that this infantile learning process has many of the characteristics of sexual imprinting. The same author gives also some possible evidence for *interspecific* imprinting, as mice fostered to a lactating rat mother preferred to spend time with rats rather than mice. Similar results have been obtained by Denenberg *et al.* (1963). However, no observations about possible sexual preferences are given.

Finally, as in birds, several examples of hand-reared mammals that became attached to humans have been reported. In addition to short-term attachments which have been called "maternal" imprinting and might be compared to filial imprinting in birds (cf. Klopfer *et al.*, 1964), there are also some long-lasting effects of hand-rearing. Several cases have been mentioned, for instance, by K. Heinroth from the Berlin Zoo (1970). The observations refer to a variety of species, such as polar bear, hippopotamus, Mongolian wild ass (Kulan), and many antelope and deer. In contrast to the majority of hand-reared birds, however, the behavior of these animals toward men was mainly aggressive rather than sexual (cf. also Hediger, 1950).

For other groups of animals, evidence for sexual preferences based on early experience is lacking almost altogether. An extensive experimental study has been carried out by Mainardi (1968) with *Drosophila melanogaster*. His results indicate that, in this species, courtship preferences can be affected by previous experience.

In summary, this brief survey indicates that sexual imprinting is a rather widespread phenomenon, at least among birds and perhaps also in other groups of animals. For birds the evidence clearly shows that imprinting occurs in groups of different systematic position and with very different ecological requirements. Owing to profound differences in motor and sensory development, and to differences in breeding biology and in many other factors, it is not at all surprising to find that sexual imprinting in birds, despite uniformity in its main characteristics, shows many differences in detail. For practical purposes, I should like to discuss the various characteristics of sexual imprinting separately.

III. Characteristics of Sexual Imprinting

Lorenz (1935) mentioned four main criteria that are characteristic for imprinting: (1) It can take place only during a restricted time period of the individual's life, the sensitive period. (2) It is irreversible—that is, it cannot be forgotten. (3) It involves learning of supra-individual, species-specific characters. (4) It may be completed at a time when the appropriate reaction itself is not yet performed. In subsequent years, these criteria have frequently been discussed and repeatedly criticized. However, since these discussions were concerned mainly with filial imprinting, and since the material on sexual imprinting that has recently become available may throw some new light on the problems in question, it seems worth while to discuss them again.

A. Sensitive Periods

The fact that social attachments can be determined only during specific stages in ontogeny, and consequently that the same experience may lead to *different* behavioral results at different ages, has always been regarded as one of the most important characteristics of imprinting. This does not mean that the probability of learning in other contexts may not also change with age, but imprinting presents a particularly clear-cut case (cf. Hinde, 1962). The period during which imprinting is possible has been called the sensitive period or critical period, but Bateson (1966) has given good reasons why the former should be preferred. For filial imprinting, several authors have recently used the two terms in slightly different contexts, reserving the name critical period for the period of "maximum imprintability" (Fabricius, 1964). In sexual imprinting, quantitative differences during the sensitive period have also been found (see below), but the change in sensitivity to exposure seems to be gradual and does not allow a sharp distinction into two periods.

Despite its common usage, however, the term "sensitive period" (or critical period if used as an equivalent for sensitive period) is not employed uniformly throughout the literature, and no exact definition seems to have been given. This becomes particularly clear in those cases where imprinting has been said to occur "beyond the sensitive period." In my opinion—and this has been generally agreed by the first international imprinting conference in Durham in September 1971—use of the term "sensitive period" seems to be justified (for theoretical and practical purposes) only in its broadest sense. It should, therefore, be defined as the *whole* space of time in the individual's life during which a particular preference can be determined or altered, whereas outside its limits social experience does *not* exert a similar influence. One has to be aware, however, that this definition should always be understood as an operational one, since the onset and offset of the sensitive period in any

one individual seem to depend upon the *kind* of experimental procedure used (see below).

For the following response of precocial birds, the sensitive period
tends to be early and brief, and it has been determined fairly accurately
for a number of species. For sexual imprinting, data are still scanty. This
is because the relevant period tends to be much longer and to show
much more individual variation, so that large numbers of animals have
to be tested before definite conclusions can be drawn. Therefore, only
very preliminary results are available. The most important are:

Mallard (*Anas platyrhynchos*): onset of sensitive period before 5 to 19
days of age, duration several weeks (Schutz, 1965)

Greylag goose (*Anser anser*): onset about 50 days of age, offset about
140 days (Schutz, 1970)

Mourning dove (*Zenaidura macroura*): onset before 7 days of age,
offset after 52 days (Klinghammer, 1967)

Bullfinch (*Pyrrhula pyrrhula*): onset unknown, offset as late as the
second year of life (Nicolai, 1956)

A rather brief sensitive period has been found in the zebra finch. The
results of cross-fostering experiments with more than 100 birds indicate
that sexual imprinting is possible only between about 13 and 40 days of
age, whereas social experience outside this period is without any influence on the subsequent choice of a mate (Immelmann, 1972).

Closely related to the problem of sensitive periods is the question of
the length of exposure—that is, the amount of experience—needed for
the establishment of sexual preferences. Again, very few data are available. In zebra finches it has been found that a brief exposure (sometimes
less than 5 days) during the early parts of the sensitive period has the
same effect as about twice that exposure toward its end. For the establishment of attachments in the ring dove (*Streptopelia risoria*), Klinghammer and Hess (1964) gave evidence for a period optimum at 7 to
9 days of age; this means again during the early parts of the sensitive
period.

Two conclusions can be drawn from these results:

1. The length of exposure required decreases through the sensitive
period.

2. Only a rather small part of the sensitive period is actually required
for imprinting. This latter finding is also supported by observations on
mallards, bullfinches, jackdaws (*Coloeus monedula*), and other species.
It points to the conclusion that the phenomenon of sensitive periods
may have two different aspects: (*a*) a *static* aspect, because the outer
limits of that period—which can only be determined experimentally
with a large number of individuals—seem to be largely species-specific;
(*b*) a *dynamic* aspect, because for the *individual* environmental factors

determine at which time during the sensitive period imprinting really does take place. Under natural circumstances, variation is probably fairly slight, as rearing conditions are similar for all individuals, but under controlled experimental conditions the whole period may be analyzed by varying the age of exposure.

A difficult problem related to the occurrence of sensitive periods concerns their possible *determinants*. For filial imprinting, some data are available and a number of possibilities have been discussed. Unfortunately, they often have been treated as if they applied to imprinting in general. Here, however, a clear distinction must be made between filial and sexual imprinting, because it is clear from the different age limits of sensitive periods that the developmental conditions must be different for both acquisition processes. Thus, for the onset of filial imprinting, increase in locomotor ability has sometimes been thought to be a main factor (cf. Hess, 1959a; Bateson, 1966). In the case of sexual imprinting, this is very unlikely. In doves and zebra finches, for example, the young are still in the nest during the first part of the sensitive period and do not move much. In the precocial ducks and geese, on the other hand, locomotor ability seems to be fully developed well in advance of the beginning of the sensitive period. For the end of that period the onset of fear has repeatedly been suggested as a determining factor (cf. Hess, 1959a; Hinde, 1962; Scott, 1962; Moltz, 1963; Sluckin, 1965; Bateson, 1966; Smith, 1969). Again, this does not apply to sexual imprinting, as fear responses occur well in advance of the end of the sensitive period.

For sexual imprinting many possible determinants have been suggested. Frequently, *hormonal factors* — that is, correlations between sexual imprinting and sexual development — have been mentioned. However, in almost all species investigated the sensitive period has come to a definite close *before* the birds have reached sexual maturity — that is, before they show any copulatory behavior. In many cases not even indications of any sexual activity are detectable at that time. In the zebra finch, for example, the testes of the young male at the end of the sensitive period have been found to be still only beginning spermatogenesis, containing only spermatogonia and very few primary spermatocytes. The first courtship sequences occur about 20 days later, and full sexual maturity (copulatory behavior, occurrence of spermatozoa in the testis tubules) is attained about 30 to 50 days after the end of the sensitive period (Immelmann, 1970). These results do *not* exclude the possibility that some sort of "precocious sexual behaviour" as observed in some altricial birds, or some kind of "infantile sexual arousal" as has been presumed in the literature (cf. Guiton, 1962; Andrew, 1964; Bateson, 1966), which could be due to the onset of secretory activity of the Leydig cells, may contribute to the establishment of mating preferences. So far, however, this is only an assumption, and final proof is lacking. This problem could be solved only through large-scale experiments with artificial hormone treatment.

Another possibility is a correlation with *sensory* or *neural development*. In some cases, the determination of subsequent preferences seems to start as soon as the sensory organs and their neural connections have reached a developmental state that allows the nestling to acquire the information necessary for the establishment of such preferences. In the zebra finch, for example, the sensitive period begins before the 13th day of life. The eyes of the nestling are not fully open before the 11th day of life, so perhaps visual imprinting starts as soon as the birds are able to perceive and process optical stimuli (Immelmann, 1972). The same correlation with the development of sensory discriminatory abilities may apply to other altricial birds and has been discussed for the following responses of precocial birds (cf. Hinde, 1962; Kovach *et al.*, 1966). But it does not apply, for example, to sexual imprinting in the greylag goose where the sensitive period begins late, long after perceptual capacities are fully developed.

The end of the sensitive period may also be a consequence of neural development. For many animals the number of neurons and synapses is not complete at birth, but the division of neurons and the formation of new synapses continue for several weeks, months, or (in the case of larger mammals and man) years (cf. Richter, 1966). It is possible, therefore, that the great sensitivity early in life and the great stability of early experience could be correlated with the formation of new synapses, and that the end of the sensitive period could be associated with the end of mitotic activity. But again this is highly speculative, and further research, especially histological investigations about brain development, is urgently needed.

Other possible determinants are, for example, biochemical changes in the brain (cf. Bateson *et al.*, 1969; Smith *et al.*, 1970), the degree of general arousal, and various other factors of growth and maturation (cf. Fuller and Waller, 1962). For filial imprinting, it has also been suggested that imprinting brings about its own end—that is, that the amount of sensory input leads to a certain degree of satiation or reduces the range of effective stimuli (cf. Sluckin and Salzen, 1961; Sluckin, 1965; Bateson and Reese, 1969). Similar mechanisms may perhaps also be involved in sexual imprinting.

The few examples mentioned indicate that the question of the determinants of the sensitive period is a complex one, that many factors probably are involved simultaneously, alternately, or successively, and that more data are needed before definite conclusions can be drawn.

The problem becomes even more complicated if we realize that within any one organism *each* response may have its own sensitive period and hence must be related to different determining factors (cf. Hinde, 1962; Schutz, 1968; Goodwin and Hess, 1969).

B. Persistence of Sexual Preferences

Next to the existence of sensitive periods, the great persistence of preferences has always been regarded as one of the most important characteristics of imprinting and is usually referred to as irreversibility.

The following evidence for the persistence of sexual preferences established early in life is available. Guiton (1962) mentions that sexual fixations on humans in domestic fowl are not lost within the first 12 months of life. Schein (1963) reports that hand-reared turkeys proved to be imprinted on humans at 5 years of age, when they still preferred to court humans even in the presence of female turkeys. The same was reported by Hess (1959b) for a red jungle fowl cock. Schutz (1969) now has 9-year-old mallards which had been foster-reared by other species of ducks and geese and which still prefer to pair with members of their foster parents' species even though—despite their active courtship behavior—they do not get many positive reactions from the strange females. In both these cases, with the males already 5 or 9 years old, there is no reason to expect that the preferences will change over the rest of their lives.

Similar results have been obtained with two species of altricial birds, the zebra and Bengalese finches. More than 80 cross-fostered males that, in a free choice situation with conspecific females and females of the foster parents' species, had proved to be sexually imprinted on the latter have been kept together with conspecific females for several months or years without any possibility of seeing or hearing members of the foster parents' species. More than 30 of these males have even been forced to pair with a conspecific female: they were kept with one such female in a breeding cage in a sound-proof chamber. Being thus deprived of any visual or acoustic contact with the foster parents' species, most of these males eventually accepted the female as a substitute, and the pair finally raised one or several broods. After 9 months to 7 years of intraspecific experience, all males were separated again and tested in the usual free choice situation. The results revealed as strong a sexual preference for the foster parents' species as was found before the long-term experiments. Even after 7 years of intraspecific breeding experience and the joint raising of up to nine broods the males still preferred their foster parents' species as soon as they were again given the choice (Immelmann, 1972). In other words, in the zebra finch imprinting is absolutely irreversible even in the face of very intense and long-lasting experience with other objects. To the best of my knowledge, this seems to be the first case where, under very strictly controlled conditions, definite irreversibility has been proved for a period of time which markedly exceeds the life expectancy of these birds under natural conditions.

On the other hand, the concept of irreversibility is the one that has most frequently been attacked by critics, and some real or imaginary counterevidence has been produced. These disagreements, however, are at least in part due to variations in procedure, and hence may not be quite as important as has been concluded. Here I should like to stress the following three points:

1. Lorenz has emphasized from the outset that imprinting always affects the *preferential* rather than the exclusive response to sexual and social stimuli, and consequently that objects other than the imprinted one may be courted occasionally. This applies mainly to situations where the imprinted object is not available and hence other objects may be accepted as a substitute, as in the case of Bengalese-imprinted zebra finches breeding with conspecific females. Therefore, any conclusions about the possible reversibility or irreversibility of sexual preferences can be drawn only if the animal is tested in a free-choice situation. This has been omitted by many investigators.

2. Not all living things are equally suitable as objects for sexual imprinting. Humans, for example, are much less suitable as a stimulus object than members of a closely related species of birds (see below). When testing persistence of sexual imprinting, therefore, one should always take care that two objects of approximately equal suitability are presented during the free-choice experiments. This also has been omitted frequently.

3. Finally, many investigators seem to have tested irreversibility at the wrong time—that is, too early in the individual's life, when the sensitive period was not yet terminated. As mentioned above, the actual imprinting process does not require the whole length of the sensitive period but only a (sometimes rather small) part of it. It follows that, if the animal is imprinted during the first part of the sensitive period, a second, longer subperiod occurs during which sexual preferences, although already established, are not yet irreversible so that, under certain circumstances, they may still be redirected onto another object. Experimental evidence is available again for zebra finches. Young males that had been foster-reared by Bengalese finches and had been isolated on their own during adolescence always proved to be sexually imprinted on Bengalese finches. But males that, after separation from their foster parents, had been kept in an aviary together with conspecifics for the same amount of time subsequently proved to prefer conspecific females.

From comparison with the first group it is clear that they also must have been imprinted on their foster parents' species at the time of separation, but that this preference had been altered through subsequent intra-specific experience. Such reversal is possible, however, only if intra-specific contact begins before the birds are about 40 days old. After that date experience does not affect sexual preferences any more, and absolute irreversibility is reached (Immelmann, 1972).

In other words, imprinting may be reversible or irreversible according to the *age* of the bird. Up to the very end of the sensitive period pref-erences can still be changed and the principle of primacy before recency (Hess, 1959a) is not yet realized. But this is not new information: it was mentioned explicitly and substantiated with several examples by Lorenz (1935), but this fact seems to have been overlooked by many investigators who claimed to have disproved irreversibility.

For this definite end of the sensitive period, after which alteration of preferences is no longer possible, a separate name is perhaps justified. The best proposal seems to be "critical point" (Klinghammer, 1967). With regard to primary socialization, Scott (1962) has introduced the term "turning point." But as has been stressed earlier (see above), this critical point may not be absolute but may depend in any one individual on its previous experience, and this in turn depends, for example, on the kind of experimental procedure used.

Of course, the existence of more or less complete irreversibility in some groups of birds does not exclude the possibility that in others sexual preferences may be less persistent, and actual examples will be mentioned below when sexual differences in imprintability are discussed (cf. also Thorpe, 1963, p. 407). The purpose of the enumeration of possible methodical omissions was only to explain some of the differ-ences which have been reported in the literature to avoid further mis-understandings among experimenters.

C. GENERALIZATION

The third characteristic of imprinting mentioned by Lorenz, the learning of supra-individual, species-specific characters, can be treated very briefly. In all cross-fostering experiments, it has been found that sexual preferences for the foster parents' species are not restricted to particular individuals — for example, the foster mother or foster siblings — but, in spite of sometimes pronounced individual differences, for example in sexual activity, apply to all members or at least to all mem-bers of the opposite sex of that particular species. It follows that in sexual imprinting a certain amount of generalization is to be observed, whereas in filial imprinting preferences sometimes really do seem to be restricted to one particular individual (cf. Cushing and Ramsey, 1949; Schutz, 1965).

The amount of generalization found in sexual imprinting cannot be explained as due to inability to discriminate between individuals, because it has been proved—for example, in zebra finches—that after pair formation the birds may well develop a definite individual preference for a particular female. This preference, however, has nothing to do with experience early in life, but is due to subsequent learning. Consequently, such preference for a particular female—quite in contrast to the more generalized early preferences—disappears again soon after the birds have been separated.

IV. Conditions for the Establishment of Preferences

A. The Question of Reward

The fourth characteristic of imprinting—its completion at a time when the appropriate reaction is not yet performed—applies, as has also been mentioned by Lorenz from the beginning, *only* to sexual imprinting, for in filial imprinting the reaction itself, the following response, is more or less fully developed during the sensitive period. For sexual imprinting, however, this phenomenon really does exist. It has frequently been discussed in the literature, but different authors seem to have interpreted the original statement in different ways (cf. de Lannoy, 1967).

Perhaps the best way to discuss this phenomenon would be in relation to the question of reward. During many learning processes, especially during conventional conditioning, the reinforcement for the establishment of certain preferences is often provided by performing consummatory behavior (for detailed discussion, see Hinde, 1970, pp. 594 ff.). This does not exclude the importance of other forms of reward—for example, specific brain activity elicited by the stimulus situation (cf. Fabricius, 1962). The point here is that for sexual imprinting the classical type of external reward would be copulation. But, as mentioned above, most species of birds are not able to copulate and do not even show signs of copulatory behavior during the sensitive period. On the contrary, there is sometimes a considerable time interval between the end of that period and the appearance of the first copulations, which for the zebra finch is about 30 to 50 days, but for the greylag goose, for example, may be several months.

It follows that for the establishment of sexual preferences no *conventional* sexual reward is necessary. This does not exclude, however, the possibility that, as discussed above, some species may develop some sort of "early sexual motivation" and hence may get some "precopulatory sexual reward." The almost complete lack of any courtship behavior, however, also points to the possibility that reward may be completely nonsexual and that the reinforcement necessary for sexual imprinting is provided by another motivational system, and probably by the various factors connected with parent–infant relationships, like food, warmth, contact, and other classical reinforcers that have been discussed for filial imprinting (cf. Gray, 1963; Sluckin, 1965; Bateson, 1966; Salzen, 1966, 1968). In other words, during ordinary conditioning a particular reaction is reinforced and this is always similar to that for which the object preference is to be established. In sexual imprinting, reinforcement is probably not restricted to one particular reaction, and, if it is, this reaction may be quite different from the one for which the object preference is to be determined, and may be begging behavior or another infantile behavior pattern. As imprinting also involves "perceptual learning," however, it likewise appears to be possible that perhaps no particular response other than attentive responses need be involved ("non-reinforced learning"; cf. Sluckin, 1965).

In summary, therefore, the establishment of sexual preferences through imprinting seems to be independent of conventional sexual reward. Indeed sexual preferences established in this way cannot subsequently be altered even through subsequent reward through copulatory behavior.

This in turn raises the question of reward for the *maintenance* of sexual preferences. Schutz has found in ducks, and I have found in estrildine finches, that sexual preferences will be maintained even if—due to mechanical barriers or to avoidance reactions by the females—the male is never able to accomplish complete courtship and copulation with a female of the preferred species. If strange females do happen to react, this will increase the male's courtship activity. But for the maintenance of the actual preference such reactions are not necessary.

It may be concluded that in some groups of birds it has been proved that neither for the *establishment* nor for the *maintenance* of sexual preferences is any sexual reward necessary.

Returning to the characteristics of sexual imprinting given by Lorenz, it can be concluded, finally, that some evidence is available for all of them and that in some groups of birds, like estrildine finches, they are all fully realized.

Several further criteria for imprinting have been added subsequently by Hess and other authors. These are more special and in general refer only to, or have been proved only for, filial imprinting. Therefore, their discussion seems to be unnecessary in a brief review like this.

B. SPECIES-SPECIFIC PREFERENCES

Having discussed the external factors responsible for sexual imprinting, it is now worth while to mention its possible genetic background.

Two groups of facts indicate that genetic factors also may be involved in sexual imprinting. These are species-specific preferences for particular objects, and specific, sexual, and individual differences in imprintability.

As mentioned above, not all objects are equally suitable for imprinting, but it has been found that, as in filial imprinting (cf. Sluckin, 1965; Bateson, 1966), sexual preferences can be established more easily for some objects than for others. The evidence available indicates that most species imprint most easily on their *own* species. If no conspecifics are available, they imprint on similar species more easily than on dissimilar ones (cf. Gray, 1963; Guiton, 1966). According to Schutz (1965), for example, mallards are imprinted more easily on members of the family Anatidae than on birds of other groups. To explain the differences in the strength of attachments to different objects, Schein *et al.* (cited in Smith 1969, p. 77) have introduced the concept of "taxonomic proximity."

Three kinds of evidence show that zebra finches imprint most easily on their own species:

1. The clearest evidence comes from those males which had been reared by a *mixed* pair of foster parents (zebra male and Bengalese female, or vice versa). If tested in the usual free choice situation they nearly always prefer their own species, independently of the sex of the conspecific parent. This means that, if the birds are reared by two fosterers of which only one belongs to its own species, the latter is more effective for establishing sexual preferences. Similar results have been obtained for ducks by Schutz (1965).

2. Sexual preferences for the bird's own species are always more *rigid* than those for another one. A zebra finch raised by its own species will never court, in a free choice situation, a Bengalese finch female, but many zebra finches imprinted on Bengalese finches occasionally also court zebra finch females. Finally, hand-raised zebra finches preferred to court humans, but also showed some sexual behavior toward zebra finches, other estrildine finches, other species of birds, and even toward bumblebees flying past their cages: this means that, the more similar the imprinted object is to the bird's own species, the stronger the preference has proved to be.

3. *Reversal* of sexual preferences, which, as has been mentioned, is possible before the end of the sensitive period, can be achieved up to an age of about 40 days if the bird was foster-reared by another species, but only up to about 20 days if it was reared by its own species. It follows that a high degree of persistence is reached earlier if the imprinted object belongs to the bird's own species.

From the evidence given it becomes clear that imprinting on humans — that is, on a very dissimilar object — can be expected to be the least rigid of all cases of sexual imprinting. And this assumption is in accordance with the observations published about hand-raised birds: many of them have been reported to show only a slight preference for humans but to behave sexually also toward other objects (cf. Lorenz, 1935; Guiton, 1962; Gwinner, 1964; Hess and Hess, 1969; Smith, 1969). The same applies to birds imprinted on very unnatural dummies (cf. Guiton, 1961) as well as to hand-reared mammals which usually respond both to human beings and to receptive females of the proper species (Scott, 1964). Very rigid imprinting and complete irreversibility, on the other hand, have been found mostly in birds which had been imprinted on a closely related species.

Finally, there is still another source of evidence for such species-specific preferences. In several cases it has been shown that birds kept singly are more prone to imprinting on another species than are those raised with brood mates. And this raises the somewhat difficult question about the *influence of siblings* upon the determination of sexual preferences. Here, the data available are somewhat contradictory. In color imprinting of domestic pigeons, for example, Warriner et al. (1963) found that sibling color had no significant effect. Similar results have been obtained for domestic chicks by Lill and Wood-Gush (1965). In mallards, on the other hand, Schutz (1965) found that siblings do have an influence which, however, is smaller than that exerted by the mother (but see also Hess and Hess, 1969). And in bullfinches, Nicolai (1956) has suggested that siblings are of even greater importance for the subsequent choice of mate than are the parents.

These findings indicate that the influence of siblings may be different in different groups of birds. However, caution is necessary here, too, because the possible influence of siblings is not constant within a particular species but may depend on the way the birds have been raised — that is, on the kind of stimuli they have perceived. In zebra finches, for example, siblings are without any influence whatsoever if the young are cross-fostered by another species of estrildine finch (Immelmann, 1969a). But if zebra finches are raised by hand, siblings seem to be of crucial importance: thus, if these birds are raised alone, they imprint on humans, but if they are raised with siblings, they later prefer to court zebra finches. In other words, only if the parent object is extremely dissimilar from the bird's own species will the young imprint on each other: thus, imprinting to siblings seems to be merely a result of the absence of the normal imprinting object and does not permit conclusions about their influence under normal conditions (cf. Gray, 1963; Hess and Hess, 1969). The same may also apply, at least in some cases, to filial imprinting, for which evidence about the possible influence of brood mates is still somewhat confusing (Guiton, 1959; Hess, 1959a, 1964; Sluckin and Salzen, 1961; Fabricius, 1962; Taylor and Sluckin, 1964;

Polt and Hess, 1964; Lill and Wood-Gush, 1965; Bateson, 1966; Smith and Nott, 1970).

As a next step, one must consider the possible *mechanisms* for species-specific preferences. In this respect, quite a number of suggestions have been made, but, in contrast to filial imprinting, few definite data are available. One possible factor would be, as in filial imprinting, some sort of embryonic or postnatal experience leading to the formation of initial preferences that direct the young bird's attention preferentially to particular objects and finally result in long-lasting attachments (cf. Gottlieb, 1971). For sexual imprinting, however, this is only a hypothesis, and proof is still lacking.

A second mechanism could be that the birds simply react preferentially to objects similar to themselves (cf. Gottlieb, 1965; Bateson, 1966). This applies mainly to *acoustic* stimuli. In song-learning, for example, selective reactivity to certain sounds has been reported for many species of birds (cf. Thorpe, 1958; Nicolai, 1959; Immelmann, 1967; Marler, 1967). In the establishment of sexual preferences, on the other hand, the importance of such reactivity has not yet been worked out in detail. Some preliminary results are available for zebra finches. These birds have been found to respond to their species-specific calls even if they have never heard them before. But it is still unknown if this is the result of self-imprinting on their own calls which, as Güttinger (in preparation) has suggested from isolation experiments with many species of estrildine finches, seem to be innate, or if the ears of the birds are just particularly sensitive to certain frequencies, or if perhaps both reasons are combined.

In the *visual* sphere, we were not able to prove any species-specific preferences in zebra finches. Neither did males that had never before seen a conspecific female react to a female dummy more distinctly than to any other strange objects, nor did an increased opportunity for self-observation in a mirror-cage lead to a preference for the bird's own body color.

It seems possible, therefore, that in the zebra finch species-specific preferences are restricted to some of the calls, but that these preferences lead to an increased attention to conspecifics from the outset and thus support visual imprinting on the bird's own species. Here experimental investigations with deafened birds are urgently needed. Similar suggestions have been made, on the basis of similar experimental results, for filial imprinting in several species of precocial birds (cf. Gottlieb, 1965, 1968; Salzen and Cornell, 1968).

Apart from these more or less external factors—that is, factors that act via the sensory organs—the available evidence indicates that at least the *basis* for many species-specific preferences must be ultimately of genetic origin. In other words, in many species of birds there seems to be a preference for their own species which is largely independent of any intraspecific experience. In female domestic fowl, for example, Lill and Wood-Gush (1965) found a "truly innate preference" for wild-type males which was independent of the female's own body color, and in wild mallards Hess and Hess (1969) found a "specific innate knowledge of the visual characteristics of the species" (cf. also Guiton, 1962; Thorpe, 1963; p. 408; Gottlieb, 1965, 1968; Fox, 1969; Graves and Siegel, 1969).

To summarize this section, in many species of birds, some species-specific preferences facilitate imprinting on the bird's own species and thus make imprinting on another species more difficult. Under natural conditions, this probably helps to ensure that the birds are always imprinted on their own species even if they grow up, for example, in mixed breeding colonies. The nature of the species-specific preferences, however, seems to be variable and probably different in different groups of birds.

Another kind of evidence that points to the existence of a genetic basis for sexual imprinting is the large specific, sexual, and individual differences that have been found in imprintability.

Specific differences have been mentioned, for example, by Heinroth and Lorenz, who found that the effect of hand-rearing upon subsequent sexual attachments is quite different in different species. In estrildine finches, Goodwin (1971) has found differences in imprintability in two closely related species of blue-headed waxbills (*Uraeginthus bengalus* and *U. cyanocephalus*) (further examples: Schein *et al.,* 1962).

The most striking examples for *sexual differences* have been reported by Schutz (1964) for several species of sexually dimorphic ducks, where sexual imprinting occurs only in the male. In females, on the other hand, early experience with another species does not have any long-lasting effects. Instead they react to conspecific males even if they did not previously have any intraspecific experience. Here again, *specific* differences also become apparent, as in a monomorphic species of duck, the Chilean teal, *Anas flavirostris,* as well as in several monomorphic species of geese, the females are as easily imprinted as are the males.

Many similar results are available from other groups of birds. They indicate that in some species the male is more susceptible to imprinting than the female, whereas in others it is the other way round. The first possibility seems to be realized, for example, in bullfinches, zebra finches, and Bengalese finches, whereas the opposite has been reported to occur in house mice as well as in herring and lesser black-backed gulls.

Individual differences in imprintability finally have been reported, as for the following response, from quite a number of species. Schutz (1965) found that despite identical rearing conditions some cross-fostered male mallards paired with the foster species while others paired with their own species. The same situation has been reported by Goodwin (1971) for four female blue-headed waxbills (*Uraeginthus cyanocephalus*), three of which proved to be imprinted on the foster species while one proved not to be imprinted; and in the zebra finch, we have evidence that despite identical rearing conditions the end of the sensitive period does show a considerable amount of individual variation (further examples: Klopfer and Gottlieb, 1962; Lill and Wood-Gush, 1965; Sluckin, 1965; Schutz, 1968; Goodwin and Hess, 1969). This again points to the existence of some ultimately genetic basis for imprinting. In other words, how exclusively, how persistently, and at what age early experience can affect subsequent sexual preferences in a particular species, a particular sex, and a particular individual seems to be genetically determined. A possible biological significance of individual differences in sensitivity to early experience has been discussed by Klopfer and Gottlieb (1962).

V. Early Determination of Preferences Other Than Sexual

Sexual imprinting having been discussed in some detail, it is necessary to add a brief survey of some other contexts in which juvenile experience has been proved to exert a crucial influence on adult behavior.

It has been found that experience during the first days or weeks of life not only affects the subsequent choice of a mate, but may also have long-lasting effects on other object preferences, such as preferences for certain kinds of food (turtles, domestic chicks, gulls, birds of prey, zebra finches, flies, butterflies, etc.) (Burghardt, 1967; Cushing, 1944; Allen and Littleford, 1955; Hess, 1962; Hovanitz and Chang, 1962; Pimentel *et al.*, 1967; Rabinowitch, 1968, among others); for certain kinds of nesting material (zebra finches) (Sargent, 1965); for a certain kind of habitat (many birds, but also some species of amphibians and fish) (cf. Löhrl, 1959; Hasler, 1962; Hildén, 1965; Serventy, 1967, among others); or finally, in parasitic animals, for a particular species of host. The latter has been proved, for example, for parasitic insects by Thorpe and Jones (1937) and for the African viduine birds by Nicolai (1964), but it has also been supposed to occur in cuckoos and other parasitic birds (cf. Southern, 1954; Lack, 1963; Payne and Payne, 1967).

Many of these early acquisition processes clearly have some striking similarity to sexual imprinting. They are reported to be more or less restricted to periods very early in the individual's life, they often show a certain degree of generalization, and in many cases they are highly resistant to alteration through subsequent experience. Consequently, the term imprinting has frequently been used in this context, and terms like food imprinting, habitat imprinting, locality imprinting, environment imprinting, and host imprinting have been introduced.

Apart from these object preferences, early experience has likewise proved to exert a crucial influence on a variety of other phenomena of very different and sometimes rather comprehensive nature, such as the development of normal copulatory behavior (cf. Beach and Jaynes, 1954; Schein and Hale, 1959; Kruijt, 1962; Gruendel and Arnold, 1969); the development of contact behavior (Bauer, 1968; Brestowsky, 1968); the organization of maternal behavior (Scott, 1962; Harlow and Harlow, 1962); the level of aggressiveness (Beach and Jaynes, 1954; King and Gurney, 1954; King, 1957; Kruijt, 1962; Salzen, 1966; Sackett, 1967); the level of wildness, fearfulness, and tameness (Rasmussen, 1939; Beach and Jaynes, 1954; Seitz, 1959) and other integrations of opposed tendencies (cf. Kruijt, 1962; Salzen, 1966); or the degree of socialization and aggregative behavior (Collias, 1950; Beach and Jaynes, 1954; Weidmann, 1958; Denenberg, 1963; Waller and Waller, 1963; Poirier, 1968; Immelmann, 1969b; Evans, 1970). In the last-mentioned case there is a large amount of evidence mainly from various kinds of deprivation experiments. To mention only one example, Freedman *et al.* (1961) have found that in puppies the degree of socialization is definitely determined at an age of 2 to 13 weeks with a maximum of receptivity during the seventh week of age. A large number of further examples could be given for all the phenomena mentioned. And it has to be stressed that, even here, a sometimes well-circumscribed sensitive period and a subsequent persistence in the results of early experience point to some similarity to the main characters of imprinting and, therefore, the term imprinting or "imprinting-like process" has frequently been used in the literature. Finally, even the very early and rapid song-learning which is to be found in some species of passerine birds has repeatedly been compared to imprinting and by some authors has again been called imprinting or a "learning process akin to imprinting" (Thorpe, 1958, 1959; Mulligan, 1966).

Although the experimental data for many of these "imprinting-like processes" are still too few to permit definite conclusions about the *degree* of conformity with sexual imprinting, the few examples that could be mentioned clearly point to the fact that experience very early in life certainly does have a fundamental influence not only on the choice of a mate but also on a whole spectrum of other developmental processes.

VI. Context and Biological Significance of Imprinting

In a brief final discussion, I should like to raise two points: (1) the significance of the early determination of sexual preferences for the general concept of imprinting and (2) the biological function and possible evolutionary consequences of sexual imprinting.

1. The significance of the early determination of sexual preferences for the concept of imprinting can easily be seen if the four main criteria are compared for sexual and filial imprinting. The sensitive period usually is more obvious — that is, briefer and more rigid — in filial imprinting than in sexual imprinting, and in this respect the following response is really the classical type of imprinting. For *all* other criteria, on the other hand — and this has been emphasized by Lorenz from the beginning — sexual imprinting provides much more typical examples. In filial imprinting, irreversibility of a preference necessarily can be found only so long as the following reaction itself persists (which is usually only several weeks), whereas in sexual imprinting it has been proved, at least in some species, to be lifelong. The degree of generalization, as has been mentioned, is also greater in sexual imprinting, and the establishing of preferences before the appropriate reaction itself is fully developed applies *only* to sexual imprinting. It follows that any evaluation of the original concept is possible only if *both* processes and their characteristics are taken into account. It also becomes clear that in many respects sexual imprinting may even be *better* suited for the general understanding of the phenomenon of early fixation than filial imprinting (cf. Schutz, 1965), although several authors used to restrict the term imprinting to the following response and avoided it for sexual fixations.

This conclusion does not mean, however, that sexual and filial imprinting are two entirely different processes. There clearly are some striking parallels, the existence of which has been stressed by many authors. And this in turn does not imply that imprinting as a whole is entirely different from all other learning processes. Imprinting clearly is a kind of conditioning, but a kind that is characterized by several common criteria and hence deserves its own name. In my opinion, this is all that can be said at the moment, because for an exact evaluation of imprinting and its possible differences from other learning processes many more data are necessary than are at present available.

2. The most important function of sexual imprinting is to enable the birds to recognize members of their own species and thus to ensure that, under natural conditions, sexual behavior and pair-formation displays are restricted to conspecific mates. For this purpose, imprinting offers the combination of two distinct advantages which otherwise are distributed to *different* mechanisms of recognition. First, owing to its early sensitive period and subsequent stability, it ensures the availability of relevant information well before its first application and in this resembles genetically coded preferences. On the other hand, it may lead to a very *precise* recognition of the subsequent partner and is

quickly adaptable to any change in the species-specific characteristics; in this respect, it corresponds to other learning processes. It can be deduced that imprinting may be of special advantage in any rapidly evolving group, as well as wherever several closely related and similar species occur in the same region. Interestingly enough, both statements really do seem to apply to all groups of birds in which imprinting has been found to be a widespread phenomenon (ducks, gallinaceous birds, pigeons and doves, and estrildine finches).

In this connection is is worth while to consider again the sexual and species-specific differences that have been found in imprintability, because the discussion of biological functions may also lead to a better understanding of such differences. Sexual differences are frequently correlated with sexual *dimorphism* in appearance and behavior. We have seen that, in many dimorphic birds, sexual preferences of the female are much less affected by early experience than are those of the male.

a. In species where only the female cares for the young (for example, ducks and fowl) there may be a strong selection pressure against female imprintability, since it would result in homosexual pairing among adult females (cf. Bateson, 1966; Lill, 1968).

b. Another factor, which also applies to species where both parents care for the young, lies in the sexual dimorphism itself. In many birds where sexual differences in imprintability occur, the males are more colorful and/or possess the more elaborate courtship behavior, including distinctive calls (pigeons) or songs (passerine birds). This means that the males offer more distinct signals for species recognition, and it seems to be possible, therefore, that the females may rely to a certain extent on their unlearned preferences for some of the male characters. By contrast, owing to the fewer and less conspicuous distinguishing characters of the females, the males need more precise knowledge of the opposite sex. As a consequence, their natural preferences are completed to a greater extent through early experience. This possibility has been discussed for ducks and geese by Schutz (1964, 1965), but it seems to apply equally well to pigeons (Warriner *et al.*, 1963) and estrildine finches (cf. Goodwin, 1971).

In the few cases of sexual differences in imprintability of *monomorphic* species, the sex affected more strongly by early experience seems to be the one that plays the active role in pair formation and hence needs the more precise knowledge of the opposite sex (for gulls, see Harris, 1970).

Species-specific differences in imprintability can often be explained if the species-specific environment is taken into consideration—that is, apart from the number of sympatric species mentioned above, the breeding biology, or the methods of pair-formation.

Differences in *breeding biology*, for example, may result in different conditions for establishing long-lasting preferences. This applies to differences in participation of the sexes in parental duties, in the intensity of attachment between siblings, or in the duration of parental care. The latter, to give only one example, may have an influence upon the length of the sensitive period. By comparing ducks and geese, Schutz (1970) has found that sensitive periods for sexual imprinting closely correspond to the duration of parental care and, consequently, are much later and much more extended in geese than in ducks. The biological reason is quite obvious: while the young bird is still a member of the family group its opportunities to learn species-specific characteristics are greater than when it later has to live on its own or in much looser groups. Selection pressure, therefore, will certainly favor rapid and stable learning at that age.

Species-specific differences in *pair-formation* and in the nature of the pair-bond, on the other hand, may influence the speed of imprinting and the degree of irreversibility: for zebra finches and other estrildine finches, the remarkably early and rigid irreversibility is adaptive with regard to the breeding of several closely related species in mixed colonies and to early and prompt pair-formation, which in turn is an adaptation to the irregular breeding season. Similar suggestions have been made by Evans (1970) for the ring-billed gull (*Larus delawarensis*), which also breeds in mixed colonies. This species also shows an early termination of the sensitive period, ensuring attachment to parents and siblings prior to the onset of a degree of mobility sufficient to bring young chicks in close contact with another species.

In solitary nesters, on the other hand, or in species of birds in which, as with the bullfinch, pair-formation is a long-lasting process offering many opportunities for comparison with natural preferences, early irreversibility is perhaps not necessary, and in the particular species mentioned it is not attained before the second year of life. Similar views have been expressed with regard to the different lengths of sensitive periods for song-learning in different species of passerine birds (cf. Mulligan, 1966; Thorpe, 1965; Marler, 1967; Thielcke, 1969). From these considerations about the biological function of sexual imprinting, the following conclusions can be drawn.

Despite the many common characters of early learning processes, there are many differences in detail which are due to the different selection pressures affecting the conditions and adaptive requirements for the establishment of preferences. It clearly indicates that imprinting, like other learning processes, seems precisely designed to effect the result that the breeding structure of the species demands (cf. Thorpe, 1965). It becomes obvious, therefore, that in all investigations about imprinting the biology of the relevant species should be taken into close consideration.

Finally, it must be mentioned that, owing to its precise determination of subsequent mating preferences, sexual imprinting may also have some *evolutionary consequences,* as it may contribute to maintaining sexual isolation in sympatric species of birds. Under certain circumstances it may also lead to a reduction of intraspecific gene flow. If, for example, a mutation in some of the species-specific characters occurs within a population, the offspring of parents carrying the new signs will become imprinted on them and will subsequently pair preferentially with individuals that likewise possess these characters. As a consequence, a certain sexual isolation between the new form and the rest of the population may be developed, and this in turn—according to the strength of sexual imprinting or to the question of whether imprinting occurs in one or both sexes—may lead to different degrees of subdivision of gene pools and may thus be a first step in speciation or may contribute to the development and maintenance of a balanced polymorphism. A case of polymorphism based on imprinting has been found, in very extended investigations, by Cooch and his co-workers in the blue and white snow geese complex (*Anser caerulescens*) (cf. Cooch, 1961; Cooke and Cooch, 1968). Mathematical models of the influence of imprinting on population structure, and of its possible evolutionary consequence, have been developed by O'Donald (1960), Kalmus and Smith (1966), Mainardi *et al.* (1965), Scudo (1967), and Seiger (1967). They all lead to the conclusion that sexual imprinting certainly may be an important factor in the speciation of birds. This last conclusion not only applies to sexual imprinting; it has also been discussed for some other early fixations (Allee *et al.,* 1949; Goodwin and Hess, 1969) that I have mentioned, like host conditioning or habitat imprinting, and similar views have also been expressed with regard to early learning of song dialects in passerine birds (Nottebohm, 1969).

References

Allee, W. C., Emerson, A. E., Park, O., Park, Th., and Schmidt, K. P. 1949. "Principles of Animal Ecology." Saunders, Philadelphia.

Allen, J. F., and Littleford, R. A. 1955. Observations on the feeding habits and growth of immature diamondback terrapins. *Herpetologia* **11,** 77–80.

Andrew, R. J. 1964. The development of adult responses from responses given during imprinting by the domestic chick. *Anim. Behav.* **12,** 542–548.

Bateson, P. P. G. 1966. The characteristics and context of imprinting. *Biol. Rev.* **41,** 177–220.

Bateson, P. P. G., and Reese, E. P. 1969. The reinforcing properties of conspicuous stimuli in the imprinting situation. *Anim. Behav.* **17,** 692–699.

Bateson, P. P. G., Horn, G., and Rose, S. P. R. 1969. Effects of an imprinting procedure on regional incorporation of tritiated lysine into protein of chick brain. *Nature (London)* **223,** 534–535.

Bauer, J. 1968. Vergleichende Untersuchungen zum Kontaktverhalten verschiedener Arten der Gattung *Tilapia. Z. Tierpsychol.* **25,** 22–70.

Beach, F. A., and Jaynes, J. 1954. Effects of early experience upon the behaviour of animals. *Psychol. Bull.* **51**, 239–263.

Brestowsky, M. 1968. Vergleichende Untersuchungen zur Elternbindung von *Tilapia*-Jungfischen (Cichlidae, Pisces). *Z. Tierpsychol.* **25**, 761–828.

Burghardt, G. M. 1967. The primacy effect of the first feeding experience in the snapping turtle. *Psychonomic Sci.* **7**, 383–384.

Cheke, A. S. 1969. Mechanism and consequences of hybridization in sparrows *Passer, Nature (London)* **222**, 179–180.

Collias, N. E. 1950. Social life and the individual among vertebrate animals. *Ann. N.Y. Acad. Sci.* **51**, 1074–1092.

Cooch, F. G. 1961. Ecological aspects of the blue snow goose complex. *Auk* **78**, 72–89.

Cooke, F., and Cooch, F. G. 1968. The genetics of polymorphism in the goose *Anser caerulescens. Evolution* **22**, 289–300.

Craig, W. 1908. The voices of pigeons regarded as a means of social control. *Amer. J. Sociol.* **14**, 86–100.

Craig, W. 1914. Male doves reared in isolation. *J. Anim. Behav.* **4**, 121–133.

Cushing, J. E. 1944. The relation of non-heritable food habits to evolution. *Condor* **46**, 265–271.

Cushing, J. E., and Ramsey, A. O. 1949. The non-heritable aspects of family unity in birds. *Condor* **51**, 86–100.

de Lannoy, J. 1967. Zur Prägung von Instinkthandlungen. *Z. Tierpsychol.* **24**, 162–200.

Denenberg, V. H. 1963. Early experience and emotional development. *Sci. Amer.* **208**, 138–142.

Denenberg, V. H., Hudgens, G. A., and Zarrow, M. X. 1963. Mice reared with rats: Modification of behavior by early experience with another species. *Science* **143**, 380–381.

Evans, R. M. 1970. Imprinting and mobility in young ring-billed gulls, *Larus delawarensis. Anim. Behav. Monogr.* **3**, 193–248.

Fabricius, E. 1962. Some aspects of imprinting in birds. *Symp. Zool. Soc. London* No. 8, 139–148.

Fabricius, E. 1964. Crucial periods in the development of the following response in young nidifugous birds. *Z. Tierpsychol.* **21**, 326–337.

Fisher, E. A., and Hale, E. B. 1957. Stimulus determinants of sexual and aggressive behaviour in male domestic fowl. *Behaviour* **10**, 309–323.

Fox, M. W. 1969. Behavioral effects of rearing dogs with cats during the "critical period of socialization." *Behaviour* **35**, 273–280.

Freedman, D. G., King, J. A., and Elliot, O. 1961. Critical period in the social development of dogs. *Science* **133**, 1016–1017.

Fuller, J. L., and Waller, M. B. 1962. Is early experience different? *In* "Roots of Behavior" (E. L. Bliss, ed.), pp. 235–245. Harper, New York.

Goodwin, D. 1948. Some abnormal fixations in birds. *Ibis* **90**, 45–48.

Goodwin, D. 1958. The existence and causation of colour-preferences in the pairing of feral and domestic pigeons. *Bull. B.O.C.* **78**, 136–139.

Goodwin, D. 1971. Imprinting, or otherwise, in some cross-fostered red-cheeked and blue-headed cordon-bleus. *Avic. Mag.* **77**, 26–31.

Goodwin, E. B., and Hess, E. H. 1969. Innate visual form preferences in the imprinting behavior of hatchling chicks. *Behaviour* **34**, 238–254.

Gottlieb, G. 1965. Imprinting in relation to parental and species identification by avian neonates. *J. Comp. Physiol. Psychol.* **59**, 345–356.

Gottlieb, G. 1968. Species recognition in ground-nesting and hole-nesting ducklings. *Ecology* **49**, 87–95.

Gottlieb, G. 1971. "Development of Species Identification in Birds." University of Chicago Press, Chicago, Illinois.

Graves, H. B., and Siegel, P. B. 1969. Bidirectional selection for responses of *Gallus domesticus* chicks to an imprinting situation. *Anim. Behav.* **17**, 683–691.

Gray, P. H. 1963. The descriptive study of imprinting in birds from 1873–1953. *J. Gen. Psychol.* **68**, 333–346.

Gruendel, A. D., and Arnold, W. J. 1969. Effects of early social deprivation on reproductive behavior of male rats. *J. Comp. Physiol. Psychol.* **67**, 123–128.

Guiton, P. 1959. Socialisation and imprinting in brown leghorn chicks. *Anim. Behav.* **7**, 26–34.

Guiton, P. 1961. The influence of imprinting on the agonistic and courtship responses of the brown leghorn cock. *Anim. Behav.* **9**, 167–177.

Guiton, P. 1962. The development of sexual responses in the domestic fowl, in relation to the concept of imprinting. *Symp. Zool. Soc. London* **8**, 227–234.

Guiton, P. 1966. Early experience and sexual object-choice in the brown leghorn. *Anim. Behav.* **14**, 534–538.

Gwinner, E. 1964. Untersuchungen über das Ausdrucks- und Sozialverhalten des Kolkraben (*Corvus corax corax* L.). *Z. Tierpsychol.* **21**, 657–748.

Hamerstrom, F. 1970. "An Eagle to the Sky." Iowa State University Press, Ames, Iowa.

Harlow, H. F., and Harlow, M. K. 1962. Social deprivation in monkeys. *Sci. Amer.* **207**, 137–146.

Harris, M. P. 1970. Abnormal migration and hybridization of *Larus argentatus* and *L. fuscus* after interspecific fostering experiments. *Ibis* **112**, 488–498.

Hasler, A. D. 1962. Wegweiser für Zugfische. *Naturwiss. Rundsch.* **15**, 302–310.

Hediger, H. 1950. "Wild Animals in Captivity." Butterworths, London.

Heinroth, K. 1970. Über Handaufzuchten. *Zool. Gart.* **39**, 107–115.

Heinroth, O., and Heinroth, M. 1924–1933. "Die Vögel Mitteleuropas." Bermühler, Berlin.

Hess, E. H. 1959a. Imprinting. *Science* **130**, 133–141.

Hess, E. H. 1959b. The relationship between imprinting and motivation. *In* "Nebraska Symposium on Motivation" (M. R. Jones, ed.). Lincoln, Nebraska.

Hess, E. H. 1962. Imprinting and the "critical period" concept. *In* "Roots of Behavior" (E. L. Bliss, ed.), pp. 254–263. Harper, New York.

Hess, E. H. 1964. Imprinting in birds. *Science* **146**, 1128–1139.

Hess, E. H., and Hess, D. B. 1969. Innate factors in imprinting. *Psychonomic Sci.* **14**, 129–130.

Hildén, O. 1965. Habitat selection in birds. *Ann. Zool. Fenn.* **2**, 53–75.

Hinde, R. A. 1962. Some aspects of the imprinting problem. *Symp. Zool. Soc. London* **8**, 129–138.

Hinde, R. A. 1970. "Animal Behaviour," 2nd ed. McGraw-Hill, New York.

Hovanitz, W., and Chang, V. C. S. 1962. Three factors affecting larval choice of food plant. *J. Res. Lepidoptera* **1**, 51–61.

Immelmann, K. 1967. Zur ontogenetischen Gesangsentwicklung bei Prachtfinken. *Verh. Deut. Zool. Ges., Göttingen* **1966**, 320–332.

Immelmann, K. 1969a. Über den Einfluss frühkindlicher Erfahrungen auf die geschlechtliche Objektfixierung bei Estrildiden. *Z. Tierpsychol.* **26**, 677–691.

Immelmann, K. 1969b. Ökologische und stammesgeschichtliche Betrachtungen zum Prägungsphänomen. *Zool. Anz.* **183**, 1–12.

Immelmann, K. 1970. Zur ökologischen Bedeutung prägungsbedingter Isolationsmechanismen. *Verh. Zool. Ges., Köln* **1970**, 304–314.

Immelmann, K. 1972. The influence of early experience upon the development of social behaviour in estrildine finches. *Proc. XV. Int. Ornithol. Congr., Den Haag 1970* pp. 291–313.

Kalmus, H., and Smith, S. M. 1966. Some evolutionary consequences of pegmatypic mating systems (imprinting). *Amer. Natur.* **100**, 619–635.

Kear, J. 1960. Abnormal sexual behaviour of a hawfinch *Coccothraustes coccothraustes*. *Ibis* **102**, 614–616.

Kikkawa, J. 1969. Social behaviour and its evolution. *Aust. Natur. Hist.* **1969**, 200–204.

King, J. A. 1957. Relationships between early social experience and adult aggressive behavior in inbred mice. *J. Gen. Psychol.* **90**, 151–166.

King, J. A., and Gurney, N. L. 1954. Effect of early social experience on adult aggressive behavior in C57BL/10 mice. *J. Comp. Physiol. Psychol.* **47**, 326–330.

Klinghammer, E. 1967. Factors influencing choice of mate in altricial birds. *In* "Early Behavior: Comparative and Developmental Approaches" (H. W. Stevenson, ed.), pp. 5–42, Wiley, New York.

Klinghammer, E., and Hess, E. H. 1964. Imprinting in an altricial bird: The blond ring dove (*Streptopelia risoria*). *Science* **146**, 265–266.

Klopfer, P., and Gottlieb, G. 1962. Imprinting and behavioral polymorphism. *J. Comp. Physiol. Psychol.* **55**, 126–130.

Klopfer, P., Adams, D. K., and Klopfer, M. S. 1964. Maternal "imprinting" in goats. *Proc. Nat. Acad. Sci.* **52**, 911–914.

Kovach, J. K., Fabricius, E., and Fält, L. 1966. Relationships between imprinting and perceptual learning. *J. Comp. Physiol. Psychol.* **61**, 449–454.

Kruijt, J. P. 1962. Imprinting in relation to drive interactions in Burmese red jungle fowl. *Symp. Zool. Soc. London* **8**, 219–226.

Lack, D. 1963. Cuckoo hosts in England. *Bird Study* **10**, 185–201.

Lill, A. 1968. An analysis of sexual isolation in the domestic fowl. *Behaviour* **30**, 107–126.

Lill, A., and Wood-Gush, D. G. M. 1965. Potential ethological isolating mechanisms and assortative mating in the domestic fowl. *Behaviour* **30**, 16–44.

Löhrl, H. 1959. Zur Frage des Zeitpunktes einer Prägung auf die Heimatregion beim Halsbandschnäpper (*Ficedula albicollis*). *J. Ornithol.* **100**, 132–140.

Löhrl, H. 1961. Verhaltensweisen eines erfahrungslosen Weissen Storches. *Vogelwarte* **21**, 137–142.

Lorenz, K. 1935. Der Kumpan in der Umwelt des Vogels. *J. Ornithol.* **83**, 137–213, 289–413.

Lorenz, K. 1955. Morphology and behavior patterns in closely allied species. *In* "Group Processes" (B. Schaffner, ed.), pp. 168–220. Josiah Macy Foundation, Ithaca, New York.

Mainardi, M. 1968. Su alcuni fattori etologici determinanti accoppiamenti assortativi in *Drosophila melanogaster*. *Inst. Lombardo (Rend. Sci.)* **B102**, 160–169.

Mainardi, D., Marsan, M., and Pasquali, A. 1965. Causation of sexual preferences of the house mouse. The behaviour of mice reared by parents whose odour was artificially altered. *Atti. Soc. Ital. Sci. Natur. Museo Civ. Milano* **104**, 325–338.

Mainardi, D., Scudo, F. M., and Barbieri, D. 1965. Assortative mating based on early learning: population genetics. *Ateneo Parmense* **36**, 583–605.

Marler, P. 1967. Comparative study of song development in sparrows. *Proc. XIV Int. Ornithol. Congr., Oxford 1966*, 231–244.

Mohr, H. 1960. Über die Entwicklung einiger Verhaltensweisen bei handaufgezogenen Sperbern (*Accipiter n. nisus* L.) und Baumfalken (*Falco s. subbuteo* L.). *Z. Tierpsychol.* **17**, 700–727.

Moltz. H. 1963. Imprinting: an epigenetic approach. *Psychol. Rev.* **70**, 123–138.

Mueller, H. C. 1970. Courtship and copulation by a hand-reared broad-winged hawk. *Auk* **87**, 580.

Mulligan, J. A. 1966. Singing behavior and its development in the song sparrow. *Melospiza melodia. Univ. Calif. Publ. Zool.* **81**, 1–76.

Nice, M. M. 1965. Displays and songs of a hand-raised eastern meadowlark. *Living Bird* **4**, 161–172.

Nicolai, J. 1956. Zur Biologie und Ethologie des Gimpels (*Pyrrhula pyrrhula* L.). *Z. Tierpsychol.* **13**, 93–132.

Nicolai, J. 1959. Familientradition in der Gesangsentwicklung des Gimpels (*Pyrrhula pyrrhula* L.). *J. Ornithol.* **100**, 39–46.

Nicolai, J. 1964. Der Brutparasitismus der Viduinae als ethologisches Problem. *Z. Tierpsychol.* **21**, 129–204.

Nottebohm, F. 1969. The song of the chingolo, *Zonotrichia capensis*, in Argentina: description and evaluation of a system of dialects. *Condor* **71**, 299–315.

O'Donald, P. 1960. Inbreeding as a result of imprinting. *Heredity* **15**, 79–85.

Payne, R. B., and Payne, K. 1967. Cuckoo hosts in southern Africa. *Ostrich* **38**, 135–144.

Pimentel, D., Smith, G. J. C., and Soans, J. 1967. A population model of sympatric speciation. *Amer. Natur.* **101**, 493–504.

Poirier, F. E. 1968. The Nilgiri Langur (*Presbytis johnii*). Mother–infant relationships. M.S. Univ. of Florida.

Polt, J. M., and Hess, E. H. 1964. Following and imprinting: effects of light and social experience. *Science* **143**, 1185–1187.

Portielje, A. F. J. 1926. Zur Ethologie bzw. Psychologie von *Botaurus stellaris*. *Ardea* **15**, 1–15.

Rabinowitch, V. E. 1968. The role of experience in the development of food preferences in gull chicks. *Anim. Behav.* **16**, 425–428.

Räber, H. 1948. Analyse des Balzverhaltens eines domestizierten Truthahns (*Meleagris*). *Behaviour* **1**, 237–266.

Rasmussen, E. W. 1939. Wildness in rats. *Acta Psychol.* **4**, 295–304.

Richter, W. 1966. Mitotische Aktivität in den Matrixzonen des Tectum opticum von juvenilen und adulten *Lebistes reticulatus* (Peters 1859). *J. Hirnforsch.* **8**, 195–206.

Sackett, G. P. 1967. Some persistent effect of different rearing conditions on preadult social behavior in monkeys. *J. Comp. Physiol. Psychol.* **64**, 363–365.

Salzen, E. A. 1966. Imprinting in birds and primates. *Behaviour* **28**, 232–254.

Salzen, E. A. 1968. Contact and social attachment in domestic chicks. *Behaviour* **33**, 38–51.

Salzen, E. A., and Cornell, J. M. 1968. Self-perception and species recognition in birds. *Behaviour* **30**, 44–65.

Sargent, T. D. 1965. The role of experience in the nest building of the zebra finch. *Auk* **82**, 48–61.

Schein, M. W. 1963. On the irreversibility of imprinting. *Z. Tierpsychol.* **20**, 462–467.

Schein, M. W., and Hale, E. B. 1959. The effect of early social experience on male sexual behaviour of androgen injected turkeys. *Anim. Behav.* **7**, 189–200.

Schein, M. W., Fitch, R. J., and Hart, F. M. 1962. Sexual stimulus preferences of cross-species imprinted chickens and turkeys. *Amer. Zool.* **2**, 445.

Schutz, F. 1964. Über geschlechtlich unterschiedliche Objektfixierung sexueller Reaktionen bei Enten im Zusammenhang mit dem Prachtkleid des Männchens. *Verh. Deut. Zool. Ges., München* **1963**, 282–287.

Schutz, F. 1965. Sexuelle Prägung bei Anatiden. *Z. Tierpsychol.* **22**, 50–103.

Schutz, F. 1968. Sexuelle Prägungserscheinungen bei Tieren. *In* "Die Sexualität des Menschen, Handbuch der medizinischen Sexualforschung" (H. Giese, ed.), pp. 284–317. Ferdinand Enke, Stuttgart.

Schutz, F. 1969. Triebstrukturen und Fehlleitungen der Sexualität bei Tieren. *In* "Sexualität, Formen und Fehlentwicklungen" (A. Schelkopf, ed.), pp. 33–54. Vandenhoeck and Ruprecht, Göttingen, Germany.

Schutz, F. 1970. Zur sexuellen Prägbarkeit und sensiblen Phase von Gänsen und der Bedeutung der Farbe des Prägungsobjekts. *Verh. Zool. Ges., Würzburg* **1969**, 301–306.

Scott, J. P. 1962. Critical periods in behavioral development. *Science* **138**, 949–958.

Scott, J. P. 1964. The effects of early experience on social behavior and organization. *In*

"Social Behavior and Organization among Vertebrates" (W. Etkin, ed.), pp. 231–255. University of Chicago Press, Chicago, Illinois.

Scudo, F. M. 1967. L'accoppiamento assortativo basato sul fenotipo di parenti: Alcune conseguenze in popolazioni. *Inst. Lombardo (Rend. Sci.)* **B101**, 435–455.

Seiger, M. B. 1967. A computer simulation study of the influence of imprinting on population structure. *Amer. Natur.* **101**, 47–57.

Seitz, P. F. D. 1959. Infantile experience and adult behavior in animal subjects. *Psychosom. Med.* **21**, 353–378.

Serventy, D. L. 1967. Aspects of the population ecology of the short-tailed shearwater *Puffinus tenuirostris. Proc. XIV Int. Ornithol. Congr., Oxford 1966,* 165–190.

Sluckin, W. 1965. "Imprinting and Early Learning." Aldine, Chicago.

Sluckin, W., and Salzen, E. A. 1961. Imprinting and perceptual learning. *Exp. Psychol.* **13**, 65–77.

Smith, F. V. 1969. "Attachment of the Young. Imprinting and Other Developments." Oliver and Boyd, Edinburgh.

Smith, F. V., and Nott, K. H. 1970. The "critical period" in relation to the strength of the stimulus. *Z. Tierpsychol.* **27**, 108–115.

Smith, F. V., Nott, K. H., and Yarwood, A. 1970. Brain protein synthesis and the approach response of chicks to a visual stimulus. *Brain Res.* **21**, 79–90.

Southern, H. N. 1954. Mimicry in cuckoos' eggs. *In* "Evolution as a Process" (J. Huxley *et al.,* eds.), pp. 219–232. Allen and Unwin, London.

Steven, B. M. 1955. Transference of "imprinting" in a wild gosling. *Brit. J. Anim. Behav.* **3**, 14–16.

Storer, R. W. 1971. Classification of birds. *In* "Avian Biology" (D. S. Farner and J. R. King, eds.), pp. 1–18. Academic Press, New York.

Taylor, K. F., and Sluckin, W. 1964. Flocking of domestic chicks. *Nature* **201**, 108–109.

Thielcke, G. 1969. Geographic variation in bird vocalization. *In* "Bird Vocalization" (R. Hinde, ed.), pp. 311–339, Cambridge University Press, Cambridge.

Thielcke, H. 1966. Zum Verhalten eines menschengeprägten Blauflügelsonnenvogels (*Siva cyanouroptera*). *Vogelwelt* **87**, 117.

Thorpe, W. H. 1958. The learning of song patterns by birds, with special reference to the song of the chaffinch *Fringilla coelebs. Ibis* **100**, 535–570.

Thorpe, W. H. 1959. Learning. *Ibis* **101**, 337–353.

Thorpe, W. H. 1963. "Learning and Instinct in Animals," 2nd ed. Methuen, London.

Thorpe, W. H. 1965. The ontogeny of behavior. *In* "Ideas in Modern Biology" (J. A. Moore, ed.), pp. 485–518. Natural History Press, New York.

Thorpe, W. H., and Jones, F. G. W. 1937. Olfactory conditioning in a parasitic insect and its relation to the problem of host selection. *Proc. Roy. Soc.* **B124**, 56–81.

von Frisch, O. 1957. Mit einem Purpurreiher verheiratet. *Z. Tierpsychol.* **14**, 233–237.

von Frisch, O. 1966. Beitrag zur Ethologie der Blauracke (*Coracias garrulus*). *Z. Tierpsychol.* **23**, 44–51.

Waller, P. F., and Waller, M. B. 1963. Some relationships between early experience and later social behavior in ducklings. *Behaviour* **20**, 343–363.

Waller, R. 1942. Die erste geglückte Wanderfalkenzucht in der Gefangenschaft. *Dtsch. Falkenorden* **24.**

Walter, M. J. 1970. The effect of early experience on mate selection in the zebra finch (*Taeniopygia guttata castanotis* Gould). M.Sc. Thesis, Univ. of Queensland, Brisbane.

Warriner, C. V., Lemmon, W. B., and Ray, T. S. 1963. Early experience as a variable in mate selection. *Anim. Behav.* **11**, 221–224.

Weidmann, U. 1958. Verhaltensstudien an der Stockente. II. Versuche zur Auslösung und Prägung der Nachfolge- und Anschlussreaktion. *Z. Tierpsychol.* **15**, 277–300.

Whitman, C. O. 1919. "Orthogenetic Evolution in Pigeons. Vol. 3: The Behaviour of Pigeons." Carnegie Inst. Publ. no. 257, Washington.

Recognition Processes and Behavior, with Special Reference to Effects of Testosterone on Persistence

R. J. ANDREW

ETHOLOGY AND NEUROPHYSIOLOGY GROUP, SCHOOL OF BIOLOGICAL SCIENCES
UNIVERSITY OF SUSSEX
BRIGHTON, SUSSEX, ENGLAND

I. INTRODUCTION

The main purpose of this paper is to consider the general implications of recent findings that indicate a direct effect of testosterone, and perhaps other steroid hormones, on processes of attention and recognition. However, since the theoretical framework required for a proper presentation and evaluation of the results is, if not entirely novel, likely to be unfamiliar to many readers, it seems best to begin with a brief outline of the most basic findings from some recent studies of chick search behavior. All the changes induced by testosterone in these studies can be classed under one of three headings: increase in persistence of response to a particular type of stimulus, increase in persistence of response to stimuli in a particular place, and increase in resistance to distraction by irrelevant stimuli. In the following section, data demonstrating the first two types of change in the chick are summarized.

The main propositions advanced in the body of this paper are, first, that persistence of response to a stimulus, such as is involved in all three types of change listed above, depends not only on motivational factors and the organization of the environment, but also on independent processes which affect persistence directly. The second proposition is that testosterone increases such persistence.

There is evidence that human cognitive processes are affected by testosterone and probably also by glucocorticoids; the changes produced are suggestively similar to those described for the chick and give us some reason to suppose that we are dealing with processes of general importance in higher vertebrates.

II. Food Search Tests in Chicks

All the experiments considered in this section involved search by hungry chicks for food grains of the same type as were normally available in the home cage. Equal numbers of two colors (red and yellow) were available in each test. The preference of the chick for one or the other color was adjusted by the number of days for which each was available (by itself) in the home cage. The preferred and nonpreferred foods are referred to below as P and NP foods, respectively. Details of training and testing procedures may be found in Andrew and Rogers (in press; see also the Appendix). The test floor on which the food grains were presented might be free of all objects other than food ("plain") or covered with pebbles of the same general appearance, size, and color as the preferred food ("pebble" test). Such pebbles were firmly cemented down. Pebble tests provided a background over which careful search was necessary if the preferred food was to be obtained rapidly and accurately, without a large number of pecks made in error at pebbles. In some tests, food (and pebbles, if present) were distributed in roughly square clusters, which were separated one from another by bare floor, the minimum separation distance being 2 inches ("cluster" test). Moves from one area of search to another could thus be scored. In all tests each peck at red or yellow food or pebbles was recorded, so that the length of runs on each type of food could be studied. Search for one type of food clearly tended to exhaust it locally, even though sufficient of both types was present to ensure that both were always available somewhere on the floor. The resulting series of decision points, at which the animal might either shift to the second type of food or move to a new area of search, are very important in determining the pattern of choice of food.

Testosterone was given in oil as the oenanthate. Dosages are considered later, when it will be shown that effective levels correspond roughly to those for classical effects on copulation and attack. For the moment, all birds receiving testosterone will be distinguished as T's, and noninjected controls as C's (exact dosages, together with other details, are given in the Appendix).

The increase in persistence of search produced by testosterone shows itself both in more persistent choice of one type of food and in more persistent search in each area of search. The simplest data to interpret came from search over the pebble floor, when T's show much longer runs on P food than C's (Table I). Results from plain floor tests are more complicated. To discuss them, it is necessary to anticipate a later section and assume that the decision to peck a particular food grain depends on a comparison between centrally held specifications of the type of food sought and the characteristics shown by the grain. Pecking occurs if a criterion of match is met. The data to be presented suggest that this criterion may sometimes vary without any change in the type of food sought.

TABLE I
Duration of Runs on Different Backgrounds[a]

| | Before injection; pebble | | After injection | | | |
| | | | Pebble | | Plain | |
Test group	T	C	T	C	T	C
Mean run on:						
P food	11.0	12.5	36.7*	7.7	2.7*	16.5
NP food	2.1	3.4	0*	3.5	2.5*	1.0

[a] Injection followed immediately after the first test. During the 48 hours before the next test birds were maintained by force-feeding into the crop; no access to food grains was allowed during this period. All tests employed continuous floors.

Mean run lengths were calculated for each individual. The median value of each group of such means is tabulated above; the nonparametric tests which were employed were in all cases applied by ranking the individual means. The significance (Mann-Whitney) of the differences between T's and C's in each experiment is as follows: * $p < 0.001$. The changes in scores between the first and second pebble tests were not significant for C's, but were markedly so ($p < 0.001$, Wilcoxon) for mean runs on both P and NP food made by T's. One-tailed tests were used in both cases, since the differences were predicted.

If birds that have a strong preference for one type of food (usually that on which they have fed over the previous two or three days) are used in plain floor tests, then both T's and C's show long runs on P food. The only consistent difference is that T's rarely show runs on NP food longer than one or two pecks and, as a result, have shorter mean NP run lengths. A number of manipulations during training make pecks at NP food more likely in both T's and C's (for example, priming by presenting NP food alone immediately before test, or force-feeding with no access to normal food for two days before test). Following one or more of these, a quite new pattern of choices appears in T's. The insertion of one or sometimes two NP pecks just before moving to a new search area becomes so common that mean runs on P food become very much shortened in comparison with C's (Table I, force-feeding; Table II, priming and overnight exposure to NP) by these repeated interruptions.

TABLE II

Effects of Priming on Search[a]

Primed with:	Experiment 1				Experiment 2			
	P food		NP food		P food		NP food	
	T	C	T	C	T	C	T	C
P food (%)	94	96	89	79*	95	91.5	64†	75.5†
Mean run on:								
P food	13.7	33.5	13.3	10.2	21.0	21.0	4.8†	8.6
NP food	1.4	2.0	1.6	3.0	1.5	2.5	2.1†	3.5*
Mean longest run								
on NP food	2.0	2.0	2.0	4.0‡	2.0	3.5	4.0*	6.0*

[a] Tests were on plain clustered floors (see text) and were immediately preceded by priming, in which birds were allowed pecks at either preferred (P) or nonpreferred (NP) food. Birds that would not eat NP food during priming were excluded: as a result 13 T's and 11 C's were tested in experiment 1, and 15 T's and 14 C's in experiment 2, out of 17 T's and 17 C's. Experiment 1 was followed by overnight exposure to NP food, which explains the increased readiness to take NP food in experiment 2.

Significances of the differences between T's and C's for each experimental procedure are as follows: * $0.01 > p > 0.001$; † $p < 0.001$; ‡ $0.05 > p > 0.02$. Once again the median values of each group of individual means are tabulated. A one-tailed Wilcoxon test was used, since the differences were in the direction predicted from earlier experiments.

At first sight this appears to be evidence of lack of persistence, rather than persistence in search, in the same T's that were persistent in pebble tests. There is, however, evidence from cluster tests that the effect is produced by greater persistence in T's in search at a particular area. The model used here allows a clear distinction to be drawn between a choice of NP food made despite mismatch with P specifications, following a relaxation of the criteria of match, and such a choice made after NP specifications have come into use.

Relaxation of criteria of match is the most economical explanation for the way in which single NP pecks made just before a move are immediately replaced by P pecks in a new area of search. Consistent with this is the fact that, when chicks are maintained by force-feeding between injection and test (Table I), so that there has been minimal visual experience of food grains for two days before test, a great increase occurs (by comparison with any other training manipulation), both in the number of patterns of search at a particular cluster which end with NP pecks (P·NP patterns) and in the number of NP pecks emitted before moving (Table III). There is, however, no increase in the number of times that the first choice in a new area is of NP food. The birds thus search continuously for P food, but are usually ready to take NP food as second best. Protracted lack of visual experience of food might reasonably be expected to reduce the accuracy and/or detail of specifications of the visual characteristics of the two types of food grain and so make mismatch less effective in preventing acceptance.

TABLE III

PERCENTAGES OF EACH PATTERN OF SEARCH SHOWN BY T'S AND C'S[a]

Pattern of search	Force-fed		NP-primed		P-primed	
	T	C	T	C	T	C
P food only	35*	88	44†	63	83	87
NP food only	10	1	11	18	1	3
P·NP	35‡	9	22§	9	13	7
NP·P	4	0	12	7	2	1.5
Mixed	16‡	2	11†	3	1	1.5

[a]The patterns of search describe the order in which each type of food is taken during search at a single cluster of food. Thus, in P·NP search the birds take first P food, and then NP food, before finally moving to another cluster. In mixed search more than one shift occurs (for example, P·NP·P). The significances of differences between T's and C's are shown as follows: * $p < 0.001$; † $0.05 > p > 0.02$; ‡ $0.01 > p > 0.001$; § $0.02 > p > 0.01$ (Mann-Whitney comparisons of individual scores, two-tailed). The differences between the high ratio of P·NP to NP·P in the force-fed T's and the lower one in the priming groups are significant: $0.001 < p < 0.01$ P-primed; $0.025 < p < 0.05$ NP-primed (Mann-Whitney, one-tailed).

Priming with NP food, on the other hand, increases not only the number of P·NP patterns in T's, but also the number of NP·P and NP patterns (compare NP- and P-primed, Table III). Where a bird shows both P·NP and NP·P patterns in the same test, the patterns tend to occur in runs, so that the bird appears to search for the same type of food over a number of moves between clusters, taking the other only as second best just before moving (Rogers, personal communication, 1971). Priming with NP food thus may make more likely both relaxation of the criteria of match and full shifts to the use in search of specification for NP food.

In summary then, T's are more persistent in search at a particular area, in the sense that they are more likely to take food other than that for which they appear to be searching before they move; as a result, they do in fact emit more pecks between moves. Their resistance to shift to new specifications is perhaps clearest in the way in which they can repeatedly make single NP pecks just before moves without changing to search for NP.

The next step in understanding the changes responsible for this reduced likelihood of shifting to new search specifications in T's is clearly to examine the causation of shifts when they do occur. In general, any manipulation that forces the animal to choose or perhaps even to carefully inspect NP food grains tends to produce a shift to search for NP food. The most direct evidence for this comes from "priming" experiments, in which chicks are allowed a certain number of pecks (for example, 50) at food of only one color, immediately before proceeding to one of the standard search tests. It will be seen from Table II that priming with NP food markedly increases, in T's and C's alike, both the total amount of NP food taken during search and the length of runs on NP food. (This finding has now been replicated several times.)

These effects of priming suggest that inspection or choice of food of the type for which the chick is not at that time searching may produce similar changes during the search test itself. It will be remembered that C's shift readily between food types during search over a pebble background and show runs on NP food as well as on P food (Table I). The pebble background is likely to make chicks examine grains more carefully, since otherwise mistaken pecks at pebbles would be frequent. Search over it is also likely frequently to meet with a situation in which an NP food grain can be readily identified, but for the moment no P food can be localized. It will be seen that this would approximate to a very brief priming episode, which appears in C's to be sometimes sufficient to cause specifications for NP food to begin to be used in search.

Data for search over a clustered plain floor suggest that the number of inspections of the second type of food may be crucial (Rogers, 1971). It is not unusual in C's that (owing to prior training) do not have a strong preference for either type of food, and that have been primed with NP food, to take one or more grains just before they move to a new cluster (experiment 2B). Since the move follows at once, it seems likely that both it, and the acceptance of NP food, are caused by the lack of immediately localizable P food (which may indeed all have been eaten in that cluster). If only one NP grain has been taken, the animal is very likely ($p < 0.01$) to return at once to P food in the new cluster, just as is typical for T's in such a search situation. However, if two or more have been taken, the bird continues to eat NP food in the new cluster ($0.01 < P < 0.05$). Clearly, such data can also be explained in terms of a hypothetical increase in preference for NP food which precedes any choice of NP food and causes both the taking of two or more grains before the move and the continued choice of NP food in the new cluster. However, the resemblances of the effect to the consequences of priming make such an explanation less likely.

It is important finally to establish that the changes described do not simply reflect a change sensitivity to food deprivation in T's. In the experiments so far discussed, chicks were deprived of food for 3 hours before testing. This period was selected because Andrew and Rogers (1972) had found that little or no difference was produced in the patterns of search characteristic of either T's or C's by deprivation periods of 1, 3, or 5½ hours (Table IV). The independence of these patterns from effects of food deprivation is made even clearer by the fact that they were very largely unchanged at zero deprivation, following crop-loading with glucose solution. Feeding ceased, but chicks continued to peck intermittently with closed bill. The group of C's showed no significant change in the pattern of pecking under these conditions, while T's showed only a slight (although significant) lengthening of runs on NP food.

TABLE IV
LEVELS OF DEPRIVATION AND SEARCH[a]

| | Mean run | | | |
| | P food | | NP food | |
Hours of deprivation	T	C	T	C
0	4.1*	15.3	3.1	3.0
1	4.5†	27.4	2.0‡	3.2
3	4.6†	26.9	2.1‡	1.5
5 ½	4.9†	16.5	2.1	1.5

[a] Tests employed plain continuous floors throughout. The scores for 0 hour are derived from pecks with the closed bill, which did not result in swallowing. Significances, given for differences between T's and C's, are as follows: * $0.01 > p > 0.001$; † $p < 0.001$; ‡ $0.02 > p > 0.01$. Median values of the groups of means are tabulated. Mann-Whitney tests (one-tailed) were used for runs on P food, and Moses tests for runs on NP food, since control scores were markedly bimodal, lying on either side of T scores.

The only significant change with deprivation level was between 0- and 1-hour deprivation in T's: $0.01 > p > 0.001$ for mean NP runs.

There is thus evidence that testosterone makes chicks more persistent in their search for a particular type of food object, and that this is accompanied by, and probably depends on an increased resistance to shifts following inspection and choice of a nonpreferred object. Testosterone also increases the persistence of search in a particular area. These changes produced by testosterone are independent of level of food deprivation and thus appear to involve relatively direct effects on persistence.

At this point, it will be necessary to consider in more detail the kinds of processes that might underlie recognition and search, and in particular the form that specifications of a search object might take. Once this has been done, it will be possible to use further chick data to decide more exactly what process might be changed by testosterone.

III. THEORIES OF RECOGNITION

Throughout this paper it is argued that the most accurate description of the change produced by testosterone in search and related behavior is an increased persistence in use of the specifications used in recognizing the search object; this persistence is to some extent independent of variables like physiological deficit or length of prior training. In view of the continuing controversy over the value of theoretical approaches that employ concepts such as specifications, models, or images, it is necessary to discuss some past theories of this kind. It will be best to begin by defining some of the terms and concepts that have been used.

First, the experimental procedures employed in the past can be classified as follows:

1. Habituation. The repeated presentation of a stimulus at short intervals (usually of a few seconds or at most minutes) may lead to a progressive reduction or disappearance of the response initially evoked by the stimulus. Commonly the response considered is a component of the orientation reflex, or an escape or defense response. The interpolation in the series of presentations of a changed stimulus shows that the reduction is more or less specific to the first stimulus. The induction of changes in the home environment (that is, in stimuli that have been continuously present) could be regarded as a variant of this method.

2. Recognition of Novelty or Familiarity. A stimulus is presented usually, but not necessarily repeatedly. After a relatively long period (hours or days) a range of stimuli are presented and the subject shows to what extent they are considered to resemble or to differ from the first stimuli. Behavior used for this purpose includes the filial responses of chicks and ducklings, fleeing responses, and smiling and attending visually (that is, an orientation response) in the human infant.

It will be seen that there is no absolute distinction between this technique and the first, since an arbitrary division has been drawn between a period of minutes and a period of hours between training and test. Hinde (1970) has emphasized that there is no reason to suppose that changes set up by a habituation procedure (as here defined) should not persist for very long periods. However, recognition procedures do offer a possible means of selecting for study such very persistent changes, since they exclude a variety of ephemeral change which may be involved in habituation.

3. Recognition of Conditioned and Unconditioned Stimuli. Here responses such as lever operation are commonly measured, although orientation responses have once again been studied, as in (1) and (2). Choice is usually between only two stimuli, and these differ in one or, at the most, two or three parameters. As a result, many of the processes that are obvious and important in search situations are obscured or excluded. These include, for example, the wide and to some extent simultaneous scanning of a range of stimuli, followed by the choice of one for more extended examination. Equally important is the fact that the probability of rejection of a stimulus object that is not identical with the CS is likely to be very different in a search situation (where a variety of other possible stimuli are simultaneously and freely available) and in a discrimination learning situation. In the latter, for example, a strategy may have been elaborated which determines that only two stimulus objects should be examined and that one is likely or certain to yield reinforcement. Nevertheless, any process found to be of importance in search is likely also to operate in discrimination learning, even though it may be obscured and difficult to study, and evidence from discrimination learning will therefore, be considered in the succeeding discussion.

In a search situation, a subject picks out a particular stimulus, whose characteristics have been learned during earlier presentation, from among an array of stimuli which include ones differing from that sought. The chick experiments already described provide a typical example. The most extensive and important body of data comes from studies of human selective attention. Here the subject is instructed to attend only to stimuli that have certain characteristics, which may be apparently simple (for example, only sounds presented to the left ear) or complex (for example, only words spoken by a female voice). Both the identification of such stimuli and the rejection of others involve a variety of recognition processes. Search tests more closely resembling the animal ones have also been used widely in work on human cognition (Section VII).

4. Pattern Learning: Short-Term and Permanent Storage. Pattern learning is clearly involved in the early training involved in (1) and (3). However, studies of human memory can use the more direct procedure of asking for rehearsal of the pattern that has been presented, when this consists in a series of words, for example. Short-term storage of a stimulus pattern, both when permanent storage results and when it does not, could involve processes that are also important in the test phases of (2) and (3).

Central "models" of stimuli have been postulated to explain results obtained with all the above procedures. The more neutral term "specifications" will be used here. A formal model of the way in which such specifications might be used in recognition will be presented in a moment. First, however, it should be noted that the use of a term of this type implies that the following characteristics of the process of recognition might be independently manipulable by the experimenter, and might also be important in normal behavior:

(a) The retrieval of previously stored specifications which are appropriate to the perceptual input that is to be recognized.

(b) The persistence in an activated state (that is, available for use) of the specifications, once they are retrieved, or, in the case of procedure (4), elaborated from input.

(c) A comparison between input and activated specifications, which involves a criterion of match, that can be varied.

(d) The accuracy and detail of the activated specifications.

(e) The stability of the activated specifications: that is, the readiness with which they change, if at all, as a result of presentation of stimuli resembling the stimulus which they describe.

(f) The readiness with which recognition (that is, a judgment of match) is followed by a particular response.

The theoretical approach taken here (which will be termed a "recognition–response" theory, where convenience requires a brief means of reference) regards all these processes as capable of independent variation. A more detailed presentation of one possible model of the processes of recognition may be helpful at this point. It will simplify discussion to assume, as is customary, that perceptual analysis of a stimulus pattern results in a description in terms of parameters $A, B \ldots N$. The nature of such parameters cannot be rigorously defined, but in human perception they would certainly have to include types of shape, for example. Stored specifications would then use the same parameters. Retrieval could potentially occur as follows. When a presented stimulus is about to be recognized, the values of one or more of its parameters, after analysis, could be used to retrieve through an index central specifications which have approximately similar values for the same parameters.

These specifications are likely to include values for parameters other than those used in retrieval, since they are based on past experience of stimulus objects; recognition will then require comparison between specified values of all parameters and the corresponding values presented by the stimulus. This is a basic difference between the hypothetical mechanism of recognition presented here, and evocation of a response by any parameter for which an appropriate S–R connection has been established. In search situations it is possible that specifications for the search object may be retrieved as a result of presentation of appropriate discriminating stimuli (for example, signals that indicate that food is likely to be available).

The specifications, once retrieved, can be held activated and used in comparison against the parameter values present in perceptual input. A separate comparator circuit for each parameter would be one way of representing this process. Mismatch would then result in comparator output. It is assumed that this will also occur when there is inadequate information in perceptual input about the parameter specified centrally; on this view, the recognition of a complex stimulus with corresponding detailed and accurate central specifications is likely to be accompanied by some comparator output, even though a perfect match is finally obtained.

An output from the comparator for A (for example) can have three types of consequences: (1) perceptual processes may be affected specifically (for example, visual scanning to obtain more information about A may result), or generally by the development or exaggeration of receptor reflexes which bring all the major sense organs to bear ("alert response"). (2) Certain particular responses, which are characteristically evoked by "interesting stimuli," may be produced; chick calls and smiling in the human infant are considered later as possible examples. (3) If there is a response appropriate to recognition (for example, pecking food), this will be delayed until output falls to some critical level (see Sokolov, 1963, p. 293). Evidence has already been presented which suggests that in the chick the criterion of match that must be met before the response is emitted can change temporarily without any change in specifications.

A most important feature of the model is that specifications may persist and remain available over one or more subsequent comparisons. (One explanation of the results discussed here is that testosterone makes such persistence more likely.) A clearing input delivered after recognition is complete or after a response, to the mechanism holding the specifications currently in use is one process that might control change of specifications, but a variety of other possibilities exist. Thus specifications might tend to be degraded in the course of comparison itself.

It is now possible to consider the way in which theories of this type have been used in the past to explain results obtained by the procedures listed earlier.

A. HABITUATION

Sokolov (1963) discussed habituation in a highly influential paper from which are derived some of the features of the approach taken here. Some of his postulates need only be mentioned briefly, since they would not form part of any general theoretical framework. Thus Sokolov suggests that comparison is cortical in habituation in a mammal. Second, he postulates that mismatch results in the removal or reduction of gating on afferent pathways which lead to an "amplifying system," whose output gives rise to orientation responses. Clearly there is no reason why the operations initiated by mismatch should involve or be confined to changes in transmission of perceptual information.

The crucial part of the theory is that habituation depends on the progressive elaboration of a central model for the repeatedly presented stimulus, and that it is complete when the presentation of the stimulus is followed by its comparison with a fully matching model. Horn (1967) has argued that this is a more complicated process than is required to explain the facts and has suggested two alternative explanations. One is a self-generated depression of sensitivity which is peculiar to the input channel appropriate to the repeated stimulus. Another, which is better suited to the explanation of the general depression of responsiveness which may result from repetitive stimulation, postulates a second channel, also activated by the stimulus, which slowly leads to the activation of an inhibitory mechanism. This then tends to block the specific input channel, rather as postulated by Sokolov (1963). The first hypothesis is both an adequate and a likely explanation of many instances of habituation, although it must be borne in mind when evaluating the physiological evidence, that repeated presentation (for example) of exactly the same stimulus on exactly the same part of the retina of a completely immobilized eye may well lead to depression of single unit activity by processes unlike those present in a normal animal.

However, even where a model that postulates depressed transmissivity of a specific input channel is reasonable, it is not necessarily the most helpful one. Such changes in transmissivity have at least two properties involved in the establishment of central specifications: storage of varying permanency, and comparison to the extent that a similar but not identical stimulus employs a similar or overlapping channel. As soon as questions of degree of channel overlap are considered, it may be more convenient to turn to Sokolov's formulation.

In one instance (the loss of habituation following a change in the temporal patterning of the stimulus, such as the omission of a component), Horn himself postulates a unit or circuit with memory properties (for example, "cell K," Horn, 1967) and a comparison between it and input. Here, the basic features of Sokolov's theory are retained. In terms of recognition–response theory, the process of retrieval is involved, in the sense that the presentation of part of the stimulus has evidently brought into play information relating to the rest of it. The same could be true also of inspection of part of a topographically complex stimuli, although a simple habituation procedure is not well suited to demonstrate this.

B. RECOGNITION OF NOVELTY OR FAMILIARITY

When we consider the recognition of novelty or familiarity, the situation proves to be quite different. Almost all authors have used terms equivalent to central specifications, despite the hostility of psychologists to a concept so obviously descended through the "schemata" of Bartlett and Piaget from the philosophical "idea." A legitimate criticism of such an approach is that it leads to formulations that are too vague to allow any concrete predictions, and it is here a main concern to show that a recognition–response theory can lead to clear and novel predictions.

A convenient first example is provided by the argument, which was advanced by Hebb (1946), that fleeing and avoidance of a strange stimulus can occur only after accurate central representations of familiar stimuli have been stored. Salzen (1962) took a similar position when he postulated that "neuronal models" (a term taken from Sokolov) of the imprinting object and of other features of the environment are established by chicks early in life. Once this has occurred, new objects can evoke fleeing because comparison with central specifications shows that they have not been encountered before.

Quantitative data of a comparable kind are provided by Kagan (1970), who reviews his own and earlier work on the responses of human infants to visual patterns that deviate in various ways from any previously encountered. Two responses measured were duration of gaze and smiling. Both showed an inverted-U relationship with size of deviation, being maximally evoked by moderate rather than small or large deviations, which both tend to be ignored. Kagan postulates that deviations are measured by comparison between perceptual input and an appropriate central "schema" set up during earlier presentations. (The term "schema" is derived from Piaget, but here is confined to specifications of a stimulus pattern, rather than also including form of response.) Clearly these findings, and to some extent the qualitative observations of Hebb and Salzen, do suggest central specifications which are stored, retrieved, and compared with input. In addition, criteria of match are applied in the sense that the type and intensity of response evoked are related to the degree of match. Kagan's work also raises questions that center around the accuracy and the likelihood of retrieval for use in comparison of specifications. He explains the fact that large deviations produce much lower fixation times than do moderate deviations by postulating that the infant does not perceive stimuli that deviate widely from previously presented patterns as transformations of such patterns. A mechanism that might produce an effect of this type is as follows: If retrieval is based on some of the characteristics of the stimulus pattern presented, then a large enough change in the pattern will mean that specifications for the training pattern will not be retrieved and used in comparison. Since there has been no opportunity to elaborate precise specifications of a type suitable to be retrieved, retrieval activates instead generalized specifications resulting from a variety of ill-remembered but broadly comparable experiences in the past. (Alternatively, retrieval may be of specifications for component parts of the pattern only.) Comparison is brief because parameters are specified within such broad limits that match is quickly computed. Clearly, if animals with precisely controlled prior experience were used, a wide variety of experiments could be designed to test the value of such a hypothesis.

C. SEARCH AND DISCRIMINATION

The suggestion that central specifications are used in search originates with von Uexküll and Kriszat (1934), who introduced the term "search image." They pointed out that, unless a pattern was expected (and so by their theory a search image for its was in use), it might be completely missed, even though components of it were perceived as conspicuous cues. Tinbergen (1960) adapted the concept to explain the way in which predators appear to search for only one type of prey at a time. Croze (1970) showed that carrion crows can be trained to "match to sample" — that is, look for a shell of the type pointed out to them against the extremely varied visual background provided by a shingle beach. Two or three experiences were enough to initiate such behavior, and the search was very specific, with no response being made to the vast majority of available objects. Color, texture, and shape were all shown to be employed in different searches, and it seems certain that in any particular search a number of parameters are required to pick out the type of object sought. An explanation of such findings in terms of comparison between central specifications and input is straightforward and appealing.

However, it is clearly necessary to examine possible alternative explanations of search data. Dawkins (1969a,b,c) has discussed in detail sequences of choices between two stimuli, both of which are acceptable (either because both are a competent UCS for the response, or because choice of either is rewarded). As has already been noted, such a situation does not test the full range of abilities involved in a search test. However, Dawkins' theoretical model does provide what at first sight appear to be alternative explanations of some aspects of the chick search data, which are particularly relevant here, since his own data are drawn from chicks.

Dawkins' model assumes that there is a fixed hierarchy of parameters (for example, color < shape < position in chick), and that whenever possible choice is made on the first parameter in the hierarchy. Choices made on color, for example, are controlled by central changes such that, when the likelihood of pecking is low, only the most preferred color will be pecked, but (and this is crucial) when the likelihood is high, one or more other colors will be taken with equal readiness. At such times choice on color is not possible, even though the available stimuli differ in color, and the next parameter is used; in the last resort a parameter like position is used, on which choice of a preferred value (for example, "nearest") is always possible.

This model does, in fact, postulate central specifications, which take the form of the order in which parameters are tested, and the values of each parameter that are preferred. It is essentially applicable only to data from search in which the same central specifications remain continuously in use. (Thus shifts to runs on NP food after NP priming would require changes in order of use of parameters or of preferred values of parameters, on this model also.) The acceptance of NP food just before a move to a new search area, after which P food is again taken as soon as it is available, could be explained if it were supposed that the likelihood of pecking rises when P food momentarily cannot be located in the area of search. On Dawkins' model this might allow choice to be made on position or some other parameter by which NP food is acceptable.

The most important specific feature of the model, to which it owes its success in quantitative predictions of the relative distribution of choices between two stimuli, is the assumption that any particular choice is made on one parameter only, even though preferred values for several parameters are specified. A comparable assumption underlies a great deal of S-R theorizing, and it is therefore an important point to examine further. A strategy of this type is forced on the animal in many tests by the fact that the paired stimuli presented for choice differ only in one parameter. In a transfer experiment, for example, a rat that has learned that a white square is positive may be forced to choose between a white triangle and a black square.

However, where multiple cues are available, there is no reason to assume that animals do not use in choice central specifications that include all of them. Warren and McGonigle (1969) review evidence favoring this hypothesis. First, a discrimination in which two cues are available and used is not more resistant to extinction than one in which there is

only one relevant cue. This suggests, contrary to the theory of Sutherland *et al.* (1965), that analysts for each cue do not condition and extinguish independently. Second, preference tests following discrimination learning show that animals treat a stimulus changed in any
parameter as novel (and commonly show this by choosing it in preference
to the other unchanged stimulus). This suggests that all parameters of
each stimulus may be examined during choice, even in a discrimination
situation. Finally, more recent work on the recognition of patterns in
which complex relationships between components are crucial has led to
the introduction of central specifications as an explanatory concept.
Sutherland (1969) presents a theory of such recognition, involving the
matching of input to a stored description, which he has applied to discrimination experiments.

Instances where search or choice appear to depend on a single parameter are thus probably best treated as a limiting and special case.

D. SELECTIVE ATTENTION

It is well known that, if a range of stimuli are presented while a human
being has his attention occupied in some way, only significant stimuli
such as his own name are likely to be noticed (that is, be later recollected,
or evoke orientation when presented). Moray (1969) has reviewed a wide
variety of experiments of a type originally introduced by Broadbent, in
which two auditory inputs or "channels" (for example, right and left
ears) are used. Attention is sustained on one of the channels by asking
the subject to repeat the words as he hears them. Moray argues that his
own data can be explained only if it is postulated that, for attention to
shift to the second channel, two criteria must be met. First (to summarize a complex theoretical position) for the moment no recognition
must be in progress in the first channel, and second, some sort of
change must occur in the second channel. If, after such a shift, the input
on the second channel appears to correspond to (that is, retrieve) an
"important recognizer" or "dictionary unit," attention is sustained for
long enough to allow comparison and judgment of match; otherwise, it
switches back without continuing comparison further.

This theory involves comparison of central specifications with input
in two potentially separate processes. Both deserve further discussion.
The first is involved in the restriction of attention to a single channel
during the task. The properties which now have to be ascribed to a
"channel," have become exceedingly complex in human studies. (Thus
a subject may attend to one voice out of several, or to French but not
English.) In effect, the recognition procedures that have to be applied
to incoming stimuli in order to reject them or process them further are
equivalent to the use of elaborate search specifications. The retention of

the original term "channel" may indeed now be unfortunate, since it makes it likely that the properties of the channel that make it specifically available to certain stimuli only will be taken for granted. (The explanations of habituation, which have already been discussed, and S–R theory involve the same drawback.)

Secondly, the recognition and rejection of irrelevant stimuli are of special importance in search situations. Moray's theory, if developed further, suggests that two steps may determine the effect of an irrelevant or distracting stimulus. The first, which appears not to have previously been suggested, is that efficiency of retrieval may be crucial. If the time available for recognition of an irrelevant stimulus is very limited, as Moray's data and theory suggest, then the only stimuli likely to be recognized are those that correspond to specifications that are easy to retrieve. What properties make a set of specifications easy or difficult to retrieve remain to be defined by future work. Repeated presentations of exactly the same stimulus might be expected to establish stable and exact specifications, whereas absence of experience of any similar stimuli would presumably make retrieval of these specifications, rather than any other, more likely.

The second step which determines what, if any, change in behavior will occur depends on the results of comparison between input and specifications. The decision that there is match may affect overt behavior, if an appropriate and high-priority response is called for. On the other hand, mismatch is likely to result in receptor reflexes (for example, shift of gaze), which also will tend to interfere with the previously dominant behavior.

It is clearly important to know to what extent human selective attention theory is applicable to animals. Studies of hippocampal function provide some relevant evidence. Removal of the hippocampus is known to make it more difficult for a mammal to inhibit responses to one out of two alternative stimuli (for example, during extinction of discrimination, Webster and Voneida, 1964). However, inhibition is probably not the primary process affected: hippocampectomized rhesus learn as quickly as normals to avoid pressing a nonreinforced key. What they never do is cease to inspect the key briefly when it is illuminated (Douglas and Pribram, 1969). Such a stimulus may be regarded (in selective attention terms) as an input along the channel predominantly in use. A very different stimulus such as a sound, attention to which would require a shift to another channel, is less likely to distract hippocampectomized animals (e.g., Douglas, 1967). Many of the large number of studies of the hippocampus can, in fact, be explained if it is assumed to make easier the rapid recognition of new stimuli, during periods when a particular set of central specifications are in use. Without it, a stimulus resembling that sought will be fully examined, even though rapid recognition might have enabled its immediate rejection. On the other hand, the same recognition processes would make it far easier to pick out, identify, and respond to motivating stimuli, different from that to which the animal had begun to respond. Karmos and Grastyan (1961) describe how hippocampectomized cats would respond at once to an auditory CS by approaching the loudspeaker through which it was played, but would then have great difficulty in turning away and moving to the food source, which was placed at a little distance.

The most important point for the present argument, however, is not the approach to hippocampal function which is suggested by recognition–response theory. Douglas (1967) has already remarked on the probability that the hippocampus is concerned with attention shift. It is rather that processes similar to human selective attention must be considered in animal studies.

E. ATTENTION SHIFT AND NONREINFORCEMENT

McFarland (1966) has presented a theory of attention shift which postulates comparison between an "output copy," which is a central representation of the expected consequences of the animal's behavior, and the actual consequences. If there is a mismatch ("feedback discrepancy"), then attention is switched. He considers only the special case where such a switch is to stimuli appropriate to evoke appetitive behavior of a new type, but a switch to examine any conspicuous stimuli would probably be quite consistent with his formulation.

Two points deserve stressing. Firstly, although the theory postulates a comparison between centrally held information and sensory input, this is of a special type. Comparison of an output copy with sensory input may or may not be equivalent to a series of recognitions of stimuli, using specifications that are activated in relation to the behavior that has just been performed; it seems premature to discuss this further here.

Secondly, whatever the underlying mechanism, McFarland's theory and data both would predict attention shift following nonreinforcement. In a search situation, mismatch is likely to lead to moving to a new area of search. This could be adequately explained by assuming that scanning continues until match occurs; if this involves a distant stimulus, then the animal may move to it. On the other hand, repeated mismatches might be equivalent to a period of nonreinforcement. In the chick experiments, for example, feeding pecks are evidently often checked or inhibited during such periods. McFarland's hypothesis thus makes it necessary to consider whether differences in the effectiveness of nonreinforcement (such as might be induced by testosterone, for example) might not be important in affecting shifts between one set of specifications and another.

IV. Processes Responsible for Persistence in the Chick

The main changes that might explain increased persistence in the food search situation would appear from the data and arguments so far presented, to be:

1. Decreased likelihood of prolonged examination of stimuli other than those sought. This could depend on increased efficiency of rejection after brief examination.

2. Decreased sensitivity to mismatch (nonreinforcement), or to consequences of mismatch.

3. Increased likelihood of retrieving specifications for preferred food at the beginning of search, or at any point during search when specifications are cleared or lost. If this possibility is to be clearly different from (4), it must depend on a change in retrieval processes, and not on a period of increased availability or "activation" of the specifications.

4. Increased persistence of activation or availability of search specifications, once they have come into use.

The potential interactions between such changes and their consequences are very complex. Nevertheless it is possible to show that the last is most likely to be the primary site of action of testosterone.

A decrease in examination of stimuli other than the type being sought (1) could increase persistence by reducing the number of those prolonged examinations that might retrieve NP specifications, and so make possible a change of specifications. Evidence has already been presented that T's are more likely than C's to take an NP grain before moving to a new area of search (at least when prior training has not made preference for P too great). Evidence that inspection, as well as choice of NP food in priming, affects subsequent search at least as markedly in T's as in C's will be described and discussed below. There is thus no reason to suppose that T's examine NP food less frequently or more briefly.

Marked changes in sensitivity to mismatch or nonreinforcement (2) are also not very probable in T's. No difference in extinction rate between T's and C's have been found in studies of lever-pecking for a food reward (P. Messent, personal communication). The same was true of an extinction situation in which a wider range of behavior patterns was measured (extinction experiment, see Appendix); the study was in fact the one in which the testosterone effect was first detected. Chicks (both T's and C's), were trained daily to run to and feed from a food dish at one end of a rectangular chamber. On three successive test days the food dish was empty. Both T's and C's ceased to look in the dish at about the same rate. However, there was a marked and significant ($p < 0.001$) difference in the amount of time each spent searching over the floor of the test chamber. Initially, both T's and C's spent about half their time looking at the floor, usually before or after visits to the food dish. The C's continued to search over the whole chamber, even after inhibiting looking in the dish, whereas T's spent progressively less and less time in such behavior. Instead they began to show a significant ($p < 0.001$) increase in periods of standing still. These rarely lasted more than a few seconds and resembled periods of immobility shown by both C's and T's while staring into the empty food dish. (Other experiments showed that T's are not more likely to become drowsy than C's, but rather the reverse.) The T's would seem thus to remain longer under the control of stimuli associated with feeding from the food dish, but nevertheless to inhibit actual approach to the food dish as readily as C's.

Even if T's and C's do not differ in their sensitivity to continuous non-reinforcement, T's might be less affected by a few mismatches. This could explain the greater likelihood that T's will resist priming with NP food, if preference for P food is high (Table II). However, a more careful examination of the results of such priming suggests that T's are far from unaffected. If individual scores following P and NP priming are compared under such conditions, T's show a decrease in the amount of NP food taken after NP priming, whereas C's show a slight increase. The changes are small, but the difference is significant ($0.025 > p > 0.01$) and has been replicated several times (Andrew, unpublished observations). Such "negative priming" in T's, which commonly involves the complete avoidance of the occasional single or double NP pecks that otherwise occur, indicate that T's are not only examining NP food, but are also responding to the resulting mismatch by a more precise or careful use of search specifications. A similar consequence of the presence of quite unacceptable grains has already been postulated to explain the search shown by T's over a pebble background (see Section II). Finally, when preferences for P and NP food are relatively balanced, T's increase their choice of NP food following NP priming just as readily as do C's (see Table II, and below).

An increase in the likelihood of retrieval of the specifications for P food (3) could be due, as already discussed, to the properties of the specifications themselves. These are unlikely to differ between T's and C's in the experiment (Table I) in which all birds were maintained over the 48 hours between injection and test by force-feeding into the crop, since specifications were established before injection in both groups. The usual differences in pattern of search were nevertheless present (and in fact were unusually marked). The consequences of changes in the retrieval process itself are difficult to predict and probably could not be distinguished at present from (4).

Increased persistence of search specifications in T's in an activated or available state (4) would not be subject to any of the above objections. The hypothesis that search specifications can remain activated for periods of several minutes, once retrieved, is further supported by recent experiments on the after-effects of priming (decay of priming experiment, see Appendix). Birds were trained to shift readily between P and NP food by a regime in which the type of food available in the home cage was changed several times. The T's and C's that showed a replicable and clear effect of NP priming were chosen. The effects of priming following delays of 0, 10, 20, and 30 minutes were then compared; each bird was given separate tests at each delay, the order of testing being randomly different in different individuals. Decay to the state characteristic of the individual in the absence of priming was obvious in all cases and took 20 to 30 minutes. The C's tended to show more rapid and variable decay; this difference promises to allow direct study of the nature of the persistence effect (Rogers, 1971).

In both T's and C's the effects of NP priming could be abolished by external disturbance. Two methods were used, both of which were effective. The chick might be removed from the home cage and dropped, so that it fluttered to the ground, or another chick might be introduced briefly into the home cage. It will be seen that a temporary and unstable effect of this kind agrees well with the various distinctions drawn here between the stable, learned specification for P food (and NP food) and the more variable strategy determining which specifications should be used at any particular time.

The conclusion reached earlier—that place of search is more persistently specified in T's—also suggests that persistence of specifications is in an activated state, since such specifications of place must change repeatedly in the course of a test. Each successive temporary specification would thus seem to be more persistent, once set up.

V.   PERSISTENCE IN SITUATIONS OTHER THAN FOOD SEARCH

If the explanation of the effects of testosterone on food search advanced here is true, changes in persistence and distractibility would be expected in a wide variety of experimental situations. Differences explicable by increased persistence and reduced distractibility of T's have in fact been found in a number of different chick studies now in progress, only two of which will be mentioned here. These have been deliberately chosen as examples of very different results potentially explicable by the present hypothesis, rather than as results that are susceptible of no other explanation.

First, Messent (personal communication) has shown that T's are much more likely to show again a pecking response to an internally illuminated glass bead, once this has been evoked by the bead, than are C's. Two different procedures were followed. In the first, the bead was coated with methyl anthranilate (which is repellent to chicks) at its first presentation; both T's and C's showed an equally great reduction in likelihood of pecking in the test presentation, which followed after several hours. In the second, the first presentation was of an untreated bead, which was pecked readily by both T's and C's. Here the anthranilate presentation which followed depressed the final test scores as much as in the first procedure for C's, but had very little effect on T's, which continued to peck readily at test ($p < 0.001$).

A second line of evidence comes from the effect of testosterone on the peeps ("distress calls") given by chicks when placed for 5 minutes in a strange cage at 5°C. Testosterone markedly depresses the rate of peeping in male chicks in such a test (Andrew, 1963). It is also known to cause the appearance of a number of new calls, some of which (waning bouts, cackles) can be evoked by changes in stimulation (Andrew, 1963, 1972a). One cause of the reduction in the rate of peeping might thus be competition from alternative responses. Since the same calls appear in both sexes after testosterone, such competition may explain the low rates of peeping shown at the beginning of the test by injected males and females alike at all three dosages (5, 12.5, and 25 mg) (Fig. 1). The scores for control males and females are identical over the same period, as would be expected on this hypothesis, and both show lower frequencies of short calls given in bouts (such as might be facilitated by testosterone) than do the testosterone-treated groups.

However, it is difficult to explain the marked differences in the levels of peep scores over the main part of the test in this way. Calls that might be facilitated by testosterone are rare in all groups at this time, and all female groups, whether injected or not, show similar scores. Direct observation of other behavior of the chicks suggests that greater persistence of attention to particular localizable stimuli in males treated with testosterone may explain their much lower rate of peeping in comparison with male controls. During such attention all chicks, whether injected or not, tend to cease peeps and may become completely silent. Such an interpretation is consistent with increased persistence of central specifications, once retrieved for recognition. It could also be explained, if viewed in isolation, by a variety of other reasons. Thus a rise in threshold of fleeing following testosterone would be an adequate explanation, if peeps could be regarded as in some way a response associated with fleeing. (In fact, even low-intensity fleeing responses were very rare in all groups.) Alternatively, if peeps are caused by perceived discrep-

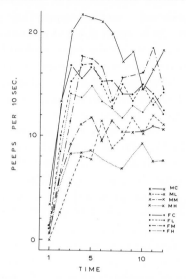

FIG. 1. The mean numbers of peeps given by each group in consecutive 10-second periods are shown for a session of 2 minutes in a cold chamber held at 5°C (C = control; $L = 5$, $M = 12.5$, and $H = 25$ mg of oenanthate). The difference between control and injected birds is significant in the second interval for males ($p < 0.014$) and in the first and second for females ($p < 0.001$). Scores lumped over intervals 3 through 12 showed no significant differences between female groups, but MC were significantly higher than MH ($p < 0.001$) and ML + MM ($0.001 < p < 0.01$); the other differences between male groups were not significant. Corresponding male and female groups all differed significantly (all at $0.02 < p < 0.05$); the difference between male and female controls probably depends on attentional differences which will be discussed elsewhere. Significances are one-tailed for males, since they were predicted from earlier studies, and two-tailed for females.

ancies between test chamber and home cage, it could be argued that greater persistence of home cage specifications should prolong the period of high peeping in T's. This is not incompatible with the results actually obtained for rates of peeping during a short exposure to the cold chamber; the length of time for which peeping would persist was not measured. Further discussion, however, is inappropriate here. Enough has been said to show that the present theoretical structure could potentially explain some effects on calls. Demonstration that this is so will have to wait on further experiment and a much more extensive discussion.

Finally, it is also possible that increased persistence of attention to a particular stimulus or type of stimulus is one of the effects leading to the facilitation of responses like copulation and attack by testosterone. Such an increase might improve summation of the motivating effects of an appropriate stimulus. It might also make the animal more likely to persist in responding, despite minor obstacles and distractions. An effect of the latter type would explain some puzzling differences between scores obtained in a test in which copulation was made as easy as possible, and one in which it was necessary to make determined efforts to scramble on top of the copulation object. Briefly, these differences would be explained if copulation in the difficult test required both direct facilitation of copulation and increased persistence, and if the first effect appeared at lower doses and more rapidly than the second.

VI. IS THE EFFECT OF TESTOSTERONE ON SEARCH A PHYSIOLOGICAL ONE?

Up to this point we have been concerned with the changes induced by testosterone in the chick chiefly as a means of examining the processes involved in recognition and persistence. It is clearly important to know whether physiological levels of androgen produce changes of this sort in normal adult males. At present only indirect evidence is available from a comparison of the dosage dependencies of the facilitation of copulation and attack with that of the effect on search. In the experiments on persistence in chicks, single doses of 25 mg and 12.5 mg of testosterone oenanthate were administered; 12.5 mg of testosterone is approximately the dosage found effective in inducing marked facilitation of copulation and other behavior in previous studies (Noble and Zitrin, 1941; Andrew, 1966). The most accurate estimate of lowest effective dose was obtained by Collias (1950), who found a daily dose of 0.7 mg of testosterone propionate (14 mg over 20 days) to be clearly effective in facilitating crowing and mating attempts, whereas 0.5 mg (10 mg over 20 days) produced little change.

However, although it thus seems likely that very roughly comparable dosages are effective in producing both types of change, so many factors are likely to affect dosage dependency that it is clearly necessary to study this for both changes under identical conditions. This was therefore done, testing the same chicks for changes in persistence and for the other behavioral effects of testosterone. Single doses of 25 mg, 12.5 mg, and 5 mg of testosterone oenanthate were given. A plain floor was used in the search test. The main effect of testosterone was a marked shortening of the mean run length on NP food (Table V). It will be seen that in male chicks the two highest dosage groups had very similar means, whereas the value for the 5-mg group was intermediate between that for the controls and those of the 12.5- and 25-mg groups. The same is true of copulation scores (which were obtained on the days before and after that on which the search tests was administered; see also below). It is also worthy of note that the females showed no effects on either search or copulation at any dosage, even though their comb growth

TABLE V

DOSAGE DEPENDENCY OF CHANGES IN PERSISTENCE AND IN COPULATION[a]

Testosterone dose (mg)	Mean run on NP food	Copulation score
Males		
25	1.33*	7.13*
12.5	1.20*	7.20*
5	2.00†	6.30†
C	3.67	4.05
Females		
25	1.67	1.95
12.5	2.00	1.50
5	1.00	1.67
C	1.00	1.50

[a] Individual copulation scores used a ranking scale from 0 (ignores copulation object) to 11 (full intense copulation on two immediately consecutive tests). The medians of scores for the days immediately before and immediately after the day on which the food search test was given were used, since no copulation test was administered on the latter. Significances of differences from control values (one-tailed Mann-Whitney) are as follows: * $0.01 > p > 0.001$; † $0.05 > p > 0.02$. Medians of each group of scores are tabulated. Females show no effect of testosterone on any score, but it should be noted that the control and low-dose group already show the very low NP runs characteristic of the high-dose males; the significant sex differences in uninjected animals will be discussed elsewhere. The male 5-mg group had scores differing significantly from those of the two higher dose groups in the direction of control scores, for both copulation and runs on NP food (Andrew, 1972b).

showed that circulating levels of androgen were comparable with those in males. It could, however, be argued that the control female scores for mean run on NP food were already so close to those of the higher-dose males that no further change could be expected.

In conclusion, the results are sufficient to show that the dosage dependency of the effect on copulation is broadly similar to that of the effect on search. The present argument does not require that it should be identical, since it is not postulated that the same androgen-sensitive structures are involved.

It should finally be noted that the effects of androgens on human cognition which are about to be discussed were obtained both when physiological dosages of exogenous testosterone were given and also when high and low levels of endogenous androgens were compared.

It is relevant in this connection that the dosage required to initiate behavioral changes in young chicks falls within the range of values given in the literature for various peripheral changes in mammals. Thus Collias' daily dose of 0.7 mg of testosterone propionate is approximately 10 mg/kg, allowing 70 gm as the mean weight of a growing chick. If 300 gm is taken as the weight of a castrated male rat, daily doses of testosterone propionate required to restore function range from approximately 65 mg/kg (spontaneous activity, Pederson-Bjergaard and Tonnesen, 1954) to approximately 17 mg/kg (seminal vesicle weight, Rudolph and Starnes, 1954). It seems likely that maintenance doses may prove to be considerably lower than the initiating dose in the chick, since Schleidt (1970) has found 15 mg/kg to be necessary to induce copulation in the turkey poult, whereas 0.1 mg/kg was enough in adult castrates; this should be borne in mind in future comparisons.

VIII. Effects of Steroids on Human Cognition

It has already been noted that most of the processes considered in recognition–response theories are also postulated by theories of selective attention in man. This is also true of human theories of attention: retrieval of specifications through an index at the start of recognition, followed by a judgment of identity by a process effectively equivalent to comparison, is discussed, for example, by Norman (1968). It thus seems justifiable to examine possible explanations of recent data on direct effects of androgens on human cognition (Broverman et al., 1968) in terms of recognition–response theory.

Scores on two types of tests have been shown to correlate highly with indices of androgen levels. First, young adult males, who by their thickset physique (for example, greater shoulder and chest width in relation to height), more extensive body hair (Broverman et al., 1964), and above-average 17-ketosteroid excretion (Klaiber et al., 1967) showed themselves to have high levels of endogenous androgens, were also unusually good at "tasks requiring sustained rapid volleys of the same responses to a limited set of stimuli" (Broverman et al., 1964). The test that was most obviously of this type (and on which high-androgen males performed unusually well) was "speed of naming repeated objects," in which three very different figures had to be named as quickly as possible in a long sequence in which they were repeated at random. The ability to persist in rapid recognition of the same very limited number of figures is crucial to the good performance of high-androgen males on this test, since they did not do any better in the "speed of recognition test" than would be expected from their general performance on all tests. In this second test, figures of similar complexity were presented in exactly the same way, but they depicted a wide variety of objects, and the subject had to scan them as rapidly as possible, making sure only that they depicted something familiar, until he reached a nonsense figure.

The first test is in some ways comparable with search over a pebble background, since ability to resist attention shift and distraction is likely to be crucial in maintaining speed at so repetitive a task. In other terms, the situation is one in which increased persistence of central specifications would improve performance. This is not necessarily true of the second task, where such increased persistence would be likely to cause interference between successive recognitions, since any time spent using specifications previously in use would, by the nature of the test, be time wasted.

A similar explanation may hold for a more recent experiment (Klaiber *et al.*, 1972) in which testosterone, infused to bring plasma levels to somewhat above normal, increased performance when subjects were asked to subtract mentally the same number repeatedly from an initial large number as many times as possible without making a mistake. Here any inability to maintain the current result of subtraction (due to distraction or inattention) will terminate the process or introduce an error.

Subjects who score high on such tests as "speed of naming repeated objects" (and who tend to have high androgen levels) characteristically score low on tests requiring "perceptual restructuring." Well-known and much used tests of this type are the Thurstone-Gottschaldt or Witkin-Gottschaldt embedded-figure tests, in which an initially presented pattern has to be found within a larger pattern, of which it is now part. Unfortunately the literature contains what appear to be two opposed interpretations of poor performance on such tests.

Witkin *et al.* (1962) have shown that subjects with low ability at embedded-figure tests tend to have their judgments of the verticality of a rod affected more markedly than is usual by the tilting of the frame in which the rod is presented. A variety of other tests show that such subjects ("field-dependent") are less able to maintain a previously established standard or estimate against contradictory perceptual inputs. Broverman, on the other hand, explains the poor performance of his high-androgen "strong automatizers" on embedded-figure tests as due to inability to inhibit "or delay initial response tendencies to obvious stimulus attributes in favour of responses to less obvious stimulus attributes" (Broverman *et al.*, 1968). The two explanations appear roughly to correspond, in terms of the recognition–response theory, to two possible extremes. In the Witkin explanation, subjects who are unable to maintain search specifications for the hidden figure continuously available or with complete accuracy are likely to be handicapped. The alternative condition, which may be that shown by strong automatizers, is that of unusual persistence in each examination of successive parts of the main pattern: this would tend to delay final identification, since the first part examined is unlikely to be the correct one.[1] The first condition

---

[1] Note that a similar argument could hold for poor performance of strong automatizers on the Wechsler blocks and Porteus mazes (Broverman, 1964).

may be compared to that of control chicks searching over pebbles, and the second to testosterone-treated chicks, when they show more persistent search at each discrete search area on the test floor. If, as is possible, the two effects both exist but in different subjects, an inverted-U relationship would be predicted between persistence of specification and performance on embedded-figure tests. Women showing poor performance may well do so because they show the first condition. Broverman et al. (1968) argue (on the basis of such performance) that they too should be regarded as, in the main, strong automatizers, and that this indicated that estrogens have in this respect an effect similar to that of androgens, but greater. However, other tests show women to perform on the average better then men, when it is an advantage to replace specifications rapidly and completely by new specifications that have just been retrieved. This is well shown by their high scores on tests that load heavily[2] on "factor II" of Goodenough and Kays (1961). Many of these are tests of rapidity of recognition of a pattern whose nature could not have been predicted in advance, either because it had not been presented previously (for example, ease of recognition of an out-of-focus picture presented once) or because there were a large number of alternatives which might have been presented. Others are tests of immediate memory (Tyler, 1956); however, here also rapidity and accuracy of coding perceptual inputs in terms of previously stored central specification are likely to improve performance.

In summary, then, there is suggestive evidence that increased ability in men to maintain the same search specifications in use over a great many consecutive examinations is promoted by high but physiological levels of testosterone. This effect of testosterone resembles in many respects that described earlier in this paper for chicks. It is far from clear how such ability affects scores on embedded-figure tests or whether women, on the average, resemble high-androgen males. However, it is possible to explain the wide range of data presented above by postulating that women, on the average, do poorly on embedded-figure tests, but well on a number of others, because they change specifications readily.

It is possible that other steroids may be involved in rather similar effects on human cognition. Henkin (1970) has shown that low glucocorticoid levels in man are associated with remarkable lowering of the detection thresholds for gustatory, olfactory, and auditory stimuli, accompanied by a marked elevation of the recognition threshold when the subject is asked to decide, not whether a stimulus is present or ab-

[2] The correlations between scores obtained on a battery of cognitive tests are commonly described after factor analysis as though they were caused by a number of hypothetical causal variables or "factors." Groups of tests that correlate highly are then said to load chiefly in one common factor.

sent, but what it is. Correction of the glucocorticoid deficiency restores normal performance, and (in the case of taste thresholds, at least) the diurnal cycle of glucocorticoid secretion produces comparable smaller effects in normal subjects. A variety of explanations are clearly possible, but an effect of some sort on recognition processes is strongly suggested. A deficit in retrieval or persistence of activation of specifications might interfere with identification. The simultaneous drop in detection threshold is a difficulty in almost any theory. It may represent a difference in strategy on the part of subjects who are accustomed to an inability to recognize stimuli, so that they are more likely to report detection of a stimulus that an ordinary subject might detect but reject as not identifiable.

VIII. Conclusions: Motivational Implications

A. Causation of the Orientation Reflex

Sokolov (1960, p. 230) notes that the orienting reflex appears both as a result (in our present terms) of a mismatch between central specifications and sensory input and as a result of "lack of information" about the stimulus. This may be compared with the suggestion advanced here (see Section II) that the orientation reflex appears during recognition and continues to develop until the criterion of match is met. The shorter time spent in recognition of the CS when the CR is fully established can reasonably be attributed to an immediate shift of attention to the source of reinforcement.

Three types of situation in which the orientation reflex is likely to develop may conveniently be distinguished:

1. Comparison during recognition, which ends in a judgment of match.
2. Comparison that ends in mismatch.
3. Judgment of match, but under circumstances that prevent an appropriate response from being emitted. This last situation is complex, since it may give rise to repeated examination of the stimulus, presumably with repeated recognition, whereas inability to perform the response is itself likely to depend on a judgment of mismatch (cf. McFarland's "feedback discrepancy," Section III, E).

The motivational implications of this theoretical approach are due to the fact that it may apply to a wide range of responses. The orientation reflex itself, as usually defined, is heterogeneous, involving cardiovascular changes as well as alert responses. Other responses which are evoked both by novel and by familiar but significant stimuli, include increased postural tonus, locomotory responses, some vocalizations (Andrew, 1964, 1969), and preparations for exertion, which may involve cooling responses, as well as increased blood supply to skeletal muscles (Hilton, 1966). Andrew (1972b) has recently stressed the importance of such responses in animal communication.

Analysis in terms of recognition processes has proved particularly helpful in the case of chick calls (Andrew, unpublished observations). One example must suffice here. Chicks often give a brief, characteristic trill when unexpectedly tapped, or when they themselves stumble or wake suddenly from a doze. The T's commonly give the same call as they look down at food to begin a fresh bout of feeding. This indication that the sight of food after a brief attention elsewhere may be in some sense startling is difficult to explain without reference to attention and recognition. The present theory would explain the trills in both situations as associated with a period in which recognition processes have begun, but have not yet reached a judgment of match.

An approach of this sort may also be useful in studies of attack and fleeing. As has already been noted, the conditions that determine whether a novel pattern should elicit prolonged attention, be ignored or, on the other hand, provoke fleeing or defensive attack remain ill-defined.

B. Changes in the Persistence in Use of Central Specifications

It has already been noted that increased persistence might make the evocation of certain responses more likely, either by allowing summation of the motivating effects of a particular type of stimulus over a longer period of time, or by making approach and other necessary preliminary behavior more likely to continue in the face of obstacles. Increased persistence could also extend the duration of phases of behavior. If stimuli of types other than that being responded to are only cursorily examined (as is likely to be the case while one set of specifications remain in use), shifts to new responses will be made less likely.

It is interesting that changes in the time for which successive phases of behavior last have been picked out as a fundamental effect in a number of recent studies of brain function. De Ruiter and Wiepkema (1969) for example, argue that lesions of the ventromedial hypothalamic nucleus not only produce "finickiness" in feeding but reduce the persistence of other phases of behavior, such as attack and copulation.

It is also worth noting that attentional changes of this kind are likely to affect behavior characteristic of transition from one major phase to another. The marked increase in head shaking produced by testosterone in chicks in an extinction situation is one possible example of such an effect (Andrew, unpublished observations).

If the effect of testosterone on persistence proves to be physiological, it is thus likely to produce global changes in behavior. It is interesting that these are such as would be likely to be adaptive if they were to appear in males at the onset of breeding. At this time, increased persistence in response to particular stimuli would make more likely the successful acquisition and retention of territory, mate, breeding place, and other important resources. Since increased aggressivity is adaptive only in that it tends to attain the same ends, increased persistence would seem, if anything, more adaptive than a direct facilitation of attack on rival conspecifics. In young animals, on the other hand, marked persistence may be disadvantageous, both when learning which stimuli to respond to (for example, in feeding), and in situations where ready flight and avoidance are the best strategy, even if they involve the interruption of a sequence of behavior.

Acknowledgments

It is a pleasure to acknowledge the contribution of Dr. L. Rogers to the work reported here, and to thank Professor R. A. Hinde and Dr. P. J. B. Slater for their comments on earlier manuscripts. Support was received from the Medical Research Council and Science Research Council for much of the experimental work on chicks.

APPENDIX

The chicks were Warren sex-link (Southdown Hatcheries, Uckfield, Sussex) and were male, except where otherwise stated. The color of the food available in the home cage is shown below by a sequence of capital letters (R = red, Y = yellow), one for each day from day 2 on. A zero indicates tube feeding, and hyphenation indicates that a change was made during a day. The day of injection is enclosed in parentheses. Numbers identify the relevant test, which was performed on the day whose capital letter it follows. Hours of deprivation before test are shown.

(a) TABLE I: R R R Y Y (R) R R-Y Y1, Y2.   25 mg.
      Tests 1 and 2: 3 hours.

(b) TABLES II AND III: R R R R R R R (R1) 0, 012, 03.   25 mg.
      Tests 1, 2, and 3: 5 hours.

(c) TABLE IV: R R R Y-R (R) Y R Y1 Y1.   25 mg.

Test 1 was administered over 2 consecutive days. All individuals received tests at all four deprivation levels (0, 1, 3, and 5½ hours, two per day), the order of administration being randomized between individuals, and balanced overall.

(d) *Extinction Experiment:* Food Y throughout. Training in test chamber on days 2 through 7 and day 9. Tests on days 10 through 12 at 1 hour, 3 hours, and 1 hour, respectively. 25 mg.

(e) *Decay of Priming Experiment:* R R R (R) Y R Y1, R or Y2, Y or R3, R or Y4.

Tests 1 through 4 employed the different delays (see text) in an order randomized and balanced between individuals. Half had R Y R and half had Y R Y on the last 3 days.

(f) TABLE V: R (R) R Y Y Y Y R R1 R2. 0, 5, 12.5, 25 mg. 3 hours.

Copulation tests on days before and after search test (test 1). Test 2: Peeping in cold chamber.

References

Andrew, R. J. 1963. Effect of testosterone on the behaviour of the domestic chick. *J. Comp. Physiol. Psychol.* **56**, 933–940.

Andrew, R. J. 1964. Vocalization in chicks and the concept of stimulus contrast. *Anim. Behav.* **12**, 64–76.

Andrew, R. J. 1966. Precocious adult behaviour in the young chick. *Anim. Behav.* **14**, 485–500.

Andrew, R. J. 1969. The effect of testosterone on avian vocalizations. *In* "Bird Vocalizations" (R. A. Hinde, ed.), pp. 97–130. Cambridge Univ. Press, London and New York.

Andrew, R. J. 1972a. The information potentially available in animal displays. *In* "Non-Verbal Communication" (R. A. Hinde, ed.), pp. 179–206. Cambridge Univ. Press, London and New York.

Andrew, R. J. 1972b. Changes in search behavior in male and female chicks, following different doses of testosterone. *Anim. Behav.* In press.

Andrew, R. J., and Rogers, L. 1972. Testosterone, search behaviour and persistence. *Nature* **237**, 343–346.

Broverman, D. M. 1964. Generality and behavioral correlates of cognitive styles. *J. Consult. Psychol.* **28**, 487–500.

Broverman, D. M., Broverman, I. K., Vogel, W., Palmer, R. D., and Klaiber, E. L. 1964. The automatization cognitive style and physical development. *Child Develop.* **35**, 1343–1359.

Broverman, D. M., Klaiber, E. L., Kobayashi, Y., and Vogel, W. 1968. Roles of activation and inhibition in sex differences in cognitive abilities. *Psychol. Rev.* **75**, 23–50.

Collias, N. E. 1950. Hormones and behavior, with special reference to birds and the mechanisms of hormonal action. *Symp. Steroid Horm.* [*Proc.*], *Madison, Wis. 1949* pp. 277–329.

Croze, H. 1970. Searching image in carrion crows. *Z. Tierpsychol. Beih.* **5**, pp. 1–85.

Dawkins, R. 1969a. A threshold model of choice behaviour. *Anim. Behav.* **17**, 120–133.

Dawkins, R. 1969b. The attention threshold model. *Anim. Behav.* **17**, 134–141.

Dawkins, R. 1969c. The "peck-no peck decision-maker" in the Black-headed Gull chick. *Anim. Behav.* **17**, 243–251.

De Ruiter, L., and Wiepkema, P. R. 1969. The goldthioglucose (GTG) syndrome in mice. *Psychiat. Neurol. Neurochir.* **72**, 455–480.

Douglas, R. J. 1967. The hippocampus and behavior. *Psychol. Bull.* **67**, 416–442.

Douglas, R. J., and Pribram, K. H. 1969. Distraction and inhibition in monkeys with limbic lesions. *J. Comp. Physiol. Psychol.* **69**, 473–480.

Goodenough, D. R., and Kays, S. A. 1961. Field dependence and intellectual functioning. *J. Abnorm. Soc. Psychol.* **63**, 241–246.

Hebb, D. O. 1946. On the nature of fear. *Psychol. Rev.* **53**, 259–276.

Henkin, R. I. 1970. The neuroendocrine control of perception. *In* "Perception and Its Disorders" (D. Hamburg, ed.), pp. 54–107. Williams & Wilkins, Baltimore, Maryland.

Hilton, S. M. 1966. Hypothalamic regulation of the cardiovascular system. *Brit. Med. Bull.* **22**, 243–248.

Hinde, R. A. 1970. Behavioural habituation. *In* "Short-Term Changes in Neural Activity and Behaviour" (G. Horn and R. A. Hinde, eds.), pp. 3–40. Cambridge Univ. Press, London and New York.

Horn, G. 1967. Neuronal mechanisms of habituation. *Nature (London)* **215**, 707–711.

Horn, G., and Hinde, R. A., eds. 1970. "Short-Term Changes in Neural Activity and Behaviour." Cambridge Univ. Press, London and New York.

Kagan, J. 1970. Attention and psychological change in the young child. *Science* **170**, 826–832.

Karmos, G., and Grastyan, E. 1961. Influence of hippocampal lesions on simple and delayed conditional reflexes. *Acta Physiol.* **21**, 215–224.

Klaiber, E. L., Broverman, D. L., and Kobayashi, Y. 1967. The automatization cognitive style, androgens and monoamine oxidase. *Psychopharmacologia* **11**, 320–336.

Klaiber, E. L., Broverman, D. M., Vogel, W., Abraham, G. E., and Cone, F. L. 1972. *J. Clin. Endocrinol. Metab.* In press.

McFarland, D. J. 1966. The role of attention in the disinhibition of displacement activity. *Quart. J. Exp. Psychol.* **18**, 19–30.

Moray, N. 1969. "Attention: Selective Processes in Vision and Hearing." Hutchinson, London.

Noble, G. K., and Zitrin, A. 1941. Induction of mating behavior in male and female chicks following injection of sex hormones. *Endocrinology* **30**, 327–334.

Norman, D. A. 1968. Toward a theory of memory and attention. *Psychol. Rev.* **75**, 522–536.

Pederson-Bjergaard, K., and Tonnesen, M. 1954. The effects of steroid hormones on muscular activity in rats. *Acta Endocrinol. (Copenhagen)* **17**, 329–337.

Rogers, L. 1971. Testosterone, isthmo-optic lesions and visual search in chickens. Ph.D. Thesis, Univ. of Sussex, Sussex.

Rudolph, G. G., and Starnes, W. R. 1954. Effect of castration and testosterone administration on seminal vesicles and prostrate of rats. *Amer. J. Physiol.* **179**, 415–418.

Salzen, E. A. 1962. Imprinting and fear. *Symp. Zool. Soc. London* **8**, 199–217.

Schleidt, W. M. 1970. Precocial sexual behaviour in turkeys (*Meleagris gallopavo* L.) *Anim. Behav.* **18**, 760–761.

Sokolov, E. N. 1960. Neuronal models and the orienting reflex. *In* "The Central Nervous System and Behaviour" (M. A. B. Brazier, ed.), pp. 187–276. Josiah Macy, New York

Sokolov, E. N. 1963. "Perception and the Conditioned Reflex." Pergamon, London.

Sutherland, N. S. 1968. Outlines of a theory of pattern recognition in animals and man. *Proc. Roy. Soc. (London), Ser. B* **171**, 297–317.

Sutherland, N. S., Mackintosh, N. J., and Wolfe, J. B. 1965. Extinction as a function of the order of partial and consistent re-inforcement. *J. Exp. Psychol.* **69**, 56–59.

Tinbergen, L. 1960. The natural control of insects in pine woods. *Arch. Neer. Zool.* **13**, 265–379.

Tyler, L. E. 1956. "The Psychology of Human Differences." Appleton, New York.

von Uexküll, J., and Kriszat, G. 1934. "Streifzüge durch die Umwelten von Tieren und Menschen." Springer-Verlag, Berlin and New York.

Warren, J. M., and McGonigle, B. 1969. Attention theory and discrimination learning. In "Animal Discrimination Learning" (R. M. Gilbert and N. S. Sutherland, eds.), pp. 113–136. Academic Press, New York.

Webster, D. B., and Voneida, T. J. 1964. Learning deficits following hippocampal lesions in split-brain cats. *Exp. Neurol.* **10,** 170–182.

Witkin, H. A., Dyk, R. B., Faterson, H. F., Goodenough, D. R., and Karp, S. A. 1962. "Psychological Differentiation." Wiley, New York.

Author Index

209

Subject Index